SOLVING PROBLEMS USING

ELEMENTARY MATHEMATICS

WITH LAB MANUAL

DAVID GAY

University of Arizona, Tuscon

CUSTOM EDITION FOR
MONMOUTH UNIVERSITY

Houghton Mifflin Company
Boston New York

Custom Publishing Editor: Dan Luciano
Custom Publishing Production Manager: Kathleen McCourt
Custom Publishing Project Coordinator: Kayla Whittet

Technical illustrations and drawings by Barbara Barnett Illustrations and Associates. Cartoons by Tom Barnett. Computer generated illustrations by Alexander Productions.

Printed in the United States of America.

ISBN: 0-618-28022-7
N01418

1 2 3 4 5 6 7 8 9 - CCI - 04 03 02

 Houghton Mifflin
Custom Publishing

222 Berkeley Street • Boston, MA 02116

Address all correspondence and order information to the above address.

CONTENTS

CHAPTER 6   DIVISION OF WHOLE NUMBERS   237

FOREWORD

Mathematics is something that is meant to be done and enjoyed. It is a way to solve interesting problems that could not otherwise be solved, or to solve problems much more efficiently than they could otherwise be solved. It is not a spectator sport, nor is it a way to provide dreary, boring activities to keep children busy.

Unfortunately, much of school mathematics gives the impression that we teach it to keep children occupied so they won't have time to get into trouble: a sort of replacement for the nineteenth century practice of making samplers, except in the case of samplers the final product was beautiful and worth saving. A major goal of the National Council of Teachers of Mathematics *Standards for Teaching Mathematics*, and other similar reports, is to help students see that mathematics is exciting and useful by allowing them to actually do mathematics.

In this book David Gay makes the learner an active participant in doing mathematics. He helps the reader discover how mathematical thinking can be used to analyze and solve varied problems, some of which should be of interest to almost anybody, no matter what his or her previous background. He brings his extensive knowledge and creative imagination to elementary school mathematics and provides motivated and intellectually honest development of topics that should be taught to young children.

Prospective teachers who study this material and who do a reasonable number of the many problems and laboratory activities suggested in this book and its companion laboratory manual will derive a much better understanding of what mathematics is, why we teach it, and how they can teach it so children will learn and enjoy mathematics. Their pupils will think of mathematics as something to be done and enjoyed—as something they can figure out themselves (without memorizing formulas or procedures), and as something that is useful in solving problems that they wish to solve for their own benefit and for the benefit of others.

Stephen S. Willoughby

PREFACE

TO THE READER A compelling reason why mathematics holds a central position in our educational system is that it can be useful in solving problems. Everybody, at one time or another, solves problems using mathematics. The more skill you have at solving problems with mathematics, the more options are open to you. The success of an engineer or scientist depends heavily on an ability to solve problems with mathematics. Although not everyone becomes an engineer or scientist, the recent proliferation of high-speed, electronic computers means that there are fewer jobs available to those without mathematical problem-solving skills.

"Skill" does not refer here to a tool to be used routinely or mechanically, without thinking. In the real world, routine problems such as "multiply these two numbers" or "simplify this algebraic expression" do not often appear. A real problem usually must be carried through a number of stages before it can be solved by activities such as "divide this fraction by that one." Problem-solving skills for the real world involve thinking and active involvement. These are skills of survival, and their use is very human.

The purpose of this book is to get you actively involved in solving problems with mathematics. This will be done in several ways. First, you will be introduced to some useful problem-solving strategies and given the opportunity to work with them. Secondly, you will encounter problems that are not routine, but realistic problems, which I hope you will perceive as really needing solutions. Thirdly, solutions to several of these problems will appear in the text, demonstrating to you (in an informal way) processes that lead to a solution, including the meanderings and dead-ends characteristic of any real problem-solving situation. Finally, you will see how mathematical ideas and techniques develop out of this process: a new idea is usually a consequence of solving a problem (or several problems), a new technique comes about because there is a need for it.

You intend to teach mathematics in an elementary or middle school; the mathematics of this text is closely related to the mathematics taught in such a school. However, you will have seen much of this before opening this book. How do you become involved when the problems are easy (to you) and the mathematical idea or technique is one that you already know? How do you think about a technique whose use has become routine? How do you think about an idea you may not have been encouraged to think about? When you become a teacher, you will want to be able to put yourself in your students' shoes; you will want to know what it is like to solve problems with limited knowledge. To turn the difficulty of thinking about something routine into an advantage, the text will ask you to solve a "simple" problem as if you were a person with a certain limited knowledge. For example, to introduce multiplication of several-digit whole numbers, a problem will appear that (you and I know) can be solved by the usual method. You will be asked to assume that you don't know the method and then to solve the problem using only other skills of arithmetic (addition, subtraction, single-digit multiplication, . . .).

Solving a problem using limited knowledge has positive consequences. First, you will learn directly that there are many ways to solve a problem, that there may be "unsophisticated" yet successful ways of solving a problem, and that deciding on the best way to solve a problem may depend on the person solving it. Secondly, it should make you aware of things you already know but haven't thought about lately. Thirdly, it should give you an understanding of how one piece of mathematics follows from another. This approach also makes sense to a future teacher: to nurture a mathematical idea in the mind of a fourth grader, it might be good if it first thrived in the mind of her teacher.

Here is what I want from your use of this book. I want you to begin to own, personally, the mathematical ideas that you once knew unthinkingly or only peripherally (and sometimes anxiously). I want you to begin to believe that mathematics is useful and use it. I want you to become competent and confident using mathematical ideas and techniques. I want you to be ready to learn how to get other persons actively involved in problem solving. I want you to have a blast solving problems.

Learning to solve problems can be frustrating, like learning to swim. Until you get that stroke down, you feel awkward and out of place. But when you grasp it, it's as if you and the water are one machine working together. Until you get the hang of solving problems, you can feel pretty inept. But when you finally succeed in solving a problem you haven't solved before, you will have a wonderful feeling of satisfaction. I hope that you will experience the joy of discovering mathematical facts you never knew before and of understanding for the first time how certain mathematical ideas and techniques fit together. As you solve more problems and gain more confidence in your mathematical abilities, you will have these good experiences more and more often.

Good luck and happy problem solving!

HOW EACH CHAPTER IS ORGANIZED

First Part of the Chapter Each chapter develops ideas and techniques that are related by a common theme. The first part of the chapter develops these in the following format: statement of a problem, solution of the problem, mathematical idea springing from the solution, exercises to try out the new idea. This format may repeat itself several times during a chapter. Each problem is chosen because it needs to be solved and because the techniques acquired up to that point for solving it are clumsy or inefficient. The solution to one problem will typically build on previous solutions and mathematical ideas.

The first part of the chapter is its core. Its style is informal, allowing ideas to germinate and evolve naturally.

Second Part of the Chapter The second part of the chapter embellishes the first. Its style is less leisurely and more condensed. It contains one or more sections of the following types. (Many chapters contain all types.)

- *Looking back* This section looks at the ideas of the first part of the chapter in a more rigorous or formal way than the first part does. It should provide you with a different perspective on the earlier material.

- *Looking ahead* This section relates the ideas of the first part to themes developed later in the text.

- *Extending ideas* This section carries some of the ideas of the first part further and puts them in a larger mathematical context. The ideas developed here will probably not be encountered later in the book.

■ *Calculators and computers* This section discusses how calculators or computers (or both) can illustrate an idea, carry out a technique, or solve a problem. Chapter 1 has an introduction to calculators as well as to programming a computer in BASIC. (I encourage you to use calculators and computers to help you solve all the problems in this book, especially those that require a lot of computation.)

END-OF-CHAPTER FEATURES

■ *Important ideas and techniques* This is a summary of the main concepts and techniques of the chapter. This should be useful for study and review.

■ *Problem set* This is a collection of problems to solve to test your understanding and hone your problem-solving skills. The ideas and techniques of the chapter should be useful here. The problem set has two parts. Most of the problems in **Practicing Skills** are routine, needing only one or two steps to solve. A problem here may be like a problem solved in the chapter itself—in order to solve, you mimic the solution given in the text. The problems in the Using Ideas sections are more involved and may require you to use the ideas and techniques of the chapter in new ways. Or, you may need to develop a new, related idea or technique.

■ *Three-chapter review* This is a set of problems for use as a "Sample Test" over the material of the previous three chapters. Solutions to the problems in these Reviews are in the back of the book.

OTHER FEATURES OF THE TEXT

STOP (Try this yourself) The stop sign occurs in the text after a statement of a problem, followed by an exhortation to try the problem before reading the text's solution. This is an important message! You need to get actively involved in solving problems in order to get the most out of this text.

Italics Key words appear in italics.

Boxes Boxed material highlights important definitions, ideas, and techniques. This should be useful for reference and review.

Boldface Color When a problem-solving strategy is used to solve a problem, its name will be printed in colored, boldface type. A list of all problem-solving strategies announced in this book is printed in the index under "Strategies for solving problems."

Exercises These occur throughout the text so that you can test your understanding immediately after an idea or technique has been presented. The answers to these exercises are in the back of the book.

Hands-on Activities Throughout the text you are encouraged to use objects to solve problems and enhance your understanding. Use these also to become acquainted with materials for teaching mathematics. Some of these items are readily available—stones, rulers, compasses, protractors. I may suggest that you trace others, cut them out, and tape them together.

Historical Comments These boxed items are meant to add human interest to the text's development and enlighten its ideas, without interrupting its flow.

STUDENT LAB MANUAL   The *Lab Manual* is a workbook-sized paperback containing laboratory activities to accompany specific topics in the text. The activities are designed especially to be used with hands-on materials.

The manual also contains things to cut out and assemble. Some of these can be used to accompany the text; others can be used to carry out the laboratory activities. The pages are perforated for easy removal.

Three of the lab activities involve the use of a computer spreadsheet.

STUDENT SOLUTIONS MANUAL   The *Solutions Manual* contains worked-out solutions to all exercises interspersed throughout the text and to many of the problems in the chapters' problem sets. This will provide you with more examples of problem solutions.

TO THE INSTRUCTOR   **This Book and the NCTM Standards**   My selection of topics and My approach follow the recommendations made by the National Council of Teachers of Mathematics in its *Curriculum and Evaluation Standards for School Mathematics* (1989), commonly referred to as "The NCTM Standards." I feel that this text reinforces the goals of the Standards in the following particularly strong ways:

1. *Learning to value mathematics.* A strong attempt is made to connect the mathematics of this text with its uses in the real world. Real problems are presented that need to be solved. The mathematical ideas and techniques evolve from the need to create efficient solutions to these problems.

2. *Becoming confident in one's own ability.* To keep from overwhelming the reader with unnecessary terminology and symbolism, I try to introduce just those concepts and techniques that are needed and that emerge naturally from problem situations. I try to make the material appropriate for the reader's background and for how the reader will use it. The writing style is friendly and conversational; it is meant to help the reader become a participant in the development.

3. *Becoming a mathematical problem solver.* Problem solving is the heart of this book. The text integrates problem solving in its development: concepts emerge from problems and their solutions. I make every attempt to engage the reader in problem-solving activities and to provide all the aids I can for the reader to be successful in them.

4. *Learning to communicate mathematically.* Readers are encouraged to use certain strategies not only to solve problems but also to communicate ideas: draw a picture, make a model (use hands-on items), organize data in a table, make a graph, draw a histogram, and so on. These form part of a common language for users of this text. In part of each chapter's problem set (Using Ideas), the reader is asked to communicate his or her solution to each problem in the form of a written essay. In the *Lab Manual* are activities for several readers to work together solving problems and learning to communicate their ideas with each other.

5. *Learning to reason mathematically.* I make every effort to have the material make sense and hang together. Not only are there connections between the mathematics of the text and its real world uses, but also there are connections between mathematical ideas developed in the text itself. Making connections is an important aspect of reasoning. I provide arguments appropriate to the reader, plausible arguments that may not always be rigorous to a mathematician. I ask the readers to make similar connections and arguments in writing out the solutions to their problems.

Additional Themes Woven into the Text Several topics occur in several chapters as subsidiary themes.

■ *Number line* This device is for visualizing the operations and the order relationships of numbers. Its use appears in chapters 3 through 11.

■ *Algebra* This topic occurs in chapters 4 through 11 to show the connections between elementary mathematics and algebra.

■ *Graphing* This theme is introduced in chapter 14 and is developed thereafter as a subtopic in the chapters on geometry, chapters 15 to 20.

■ *Computational tools* The use of calculators and computers is introduced in chapter 1 and recurs throughout the text. Which tool is appropriate for which problem is frequently discussed.

The use of computers is integrated in the text in a variety of ways. Just enough BASIC commands are introduced in chapter 1 to solve some of the problems there. Additional BASIC commands are introduced as needed in later chapters. A section on *Logo* occurs in chapter 16, an early geometry chapter. The *Lab Manual* contains several activities using a computer spreadsheet. One of these can be used as an alternative to BASIC in chapter 12; this same activity may also be adapted for earlier use with the text. Another can be used with the sections on graphing. A third can be used with chapter 22, which deals with organization of data.

Possible Courses Using This Book You can use this text to design several different courses. There are two features of the book that can be particularly helpful to you in doing this.

First of all, the book contains material on a variety of topics, from chapters on whole number numeration and fractions to those on geometry and measurement, from chapters on estimation and graphing to those on probability and statistics.

Secondly, each chapter is designed so that you can choose the degree of informality or formality for treating the covered topics. The essential part of each chapter is the first part in which the main ideas are developed through solving many problems. In the second part there are many options for covering additional material. Some sections of this second part present the earlier material from a more formal or abstract viewpoint. Others present enrichment material. Still others present material that is developed through the themes mentioned above. Of course, you can select as many of these additional sections as you wish. If you want a more informal course, you may want to supplement the first part of the chapter with only one or two sections (or even none) of the second part. If you want a more formal course, you may want to supplement the first part with several sections of the second.

Here are some possible courses in which the first part of each chapter is covered plus an occasional section from the second part:

One semester (three hours per week) or one quarter (five hours per week) courses.

■ Problem solving, whole numbers, fractions, and number theory: chapters 1–10.

■ Problem solving, whole numbers, fractions, and probability: chapters 1–6, 8–10, 21.

■ Problem solving, estimating, graphing, and geometry: chapters 1, 12–20.

Two semester (three hours each per week) or two quarter course (five hours each per week).

- First semester/quarter: problem solving, whole numbers, fractions, and integers: chapters 1–6, 8–11.
- Second semester/quarter: estimating, geometry, probability, and data presentation: chapters 12–13, 15–22.

Intense one semester course (four hours per week).

- Problem solving, whole numbers, fractions, and geometry: chapters 1–6, 8–10, 13, 15–20.

There are, of course, many other possibilities.

Instructor's Handbook   This is a paperback that contains answers to all exercises and problems in the text that do not already appear at the end of the book.

ACKNOWLEDGMENTS   This book is the result of twelve years of development. There were two stages. The first consisted of a lot of experimentation with materials for a mathematics course for prospective elementary school teachers at the University of Arizona. During this time, I can't remember having an inkling that a book might evolve from these materials. In the second stage, the text was prepared; it has been used in classes for four years and completely revised three times.

During both stages several persons made contributions to the final outcome of the project. My own students unwittingly encouraged me to experiment with new materials in the first place. I am particularly grateful to those who began their studies with me saying "I don't like mathematics and I was never any good at it" and left with "Hey! I *can* do it; math is neat!" Thanks also to the students who used the first versions of the text and put up with the misprints, omissions, and obscure explanations.

A second group to which I am indebted is the group of teaching assistants at the University of Arizona who worked with me in the experimental first stage or taught with the manuscript in the second stage. These persons were not only willing to try new ideas but also forced me to articulate mine better: Debi Anderson, Fernando Avila-Murillo, Teri Bennett, Jim Cain, Mirian Cuesta, Mark Dougan, Sil diGregorio, Steve Hammel, Gary Hudson, Steve Hughes, Grace Ikanaga, Jill Keller, Donna Krawczyk, Erich Kuball, Harry Miller, Burr Munsell, Diane Riggs, Steve Slonaker, Susan Taylor, Jon Thomsen, Steve Wheaton, and Mary Wheeler. I especially appreciate the assistance of Deborah Yoklic and James Abolt who are part of this group and who wrote new problems.

I am also grateful to those colleagues in the Mathematics Department of the University of Arizona who taught the course with me, who tolerated my sometimes outrageous ideas, and who in the end supported this project wholeheartedly: Fred Stevenson, Gail Konkle, Virginia Horak, and Rich Friedlander. I want to give special thanks to Art Steinbrenner, from whom I learned what teaching mathematics to future elementary school teachers is all about.

It may not be traditional to thank one's competitors. However, I have found that several good books have helped me to find out what works for me and what are the important ideas. These are *From Sticks and Stones* by Paul Johnson, *Mathematics for Elementary Teachers* by Eugene Krause, and *Mathematics, an Informal Approach* by Albert Bennett and Leonard Nelson.

A book on solving problems needs good problems to solve. Rich sources of these I have used are *The Math Workshop: Algebra* by Deborah Hughes Hallett, *Using Algebra* by Ethan Bolker, *Make It Simpler* by Carol Meyer and Tom Sallee, *Sourcebook of Applications of School Mathematics* by Donald Bushaw et al., and *When Are We Ever Gonna Have to Use This?* by Hal Saunders. A book that was invaluable to me in the development of chapter 3 is *Number Words and Number Symbols* by Karl Menninger.

I am grateful to these reviewers for their helpful comments:

Mary K. Alter, University of Maryland
Elton E. Beougher, Fort Hays State University
James R. Boone, Texas A & M University
Douglas K. Brumbach, University of Central Florida
Donald Buckeye, Eastern Michigan University
Jane Carr, McNeese State University
Helen Coulson, California State University Northridge
Georgia K. Eddy, student at University of Arizona
Adelaide T. Harmon-Elliott, California Polytechnic State University, San Luis Obispo
Patricia Henry, Weber State College
Diana Jordan, Cleveland State University
Martha C. Jordan, Okaloosa-Walton Jr. College
Alice J. Kelly, University of Santa Clara
Ben Lane, Eastern Kentucky University
Stanley M. Lukawecki, Clemson University
Robert Matulis, Millersville University
Curtis McKnight, University of Oklahoma
Ruth Ann Meyer. Western Michigan University
Philip Montgomery, University of Kansas
Barbara Moses, Bowling Green State University
Charles Nelson, University of Florida
Bernadette Perham, Ball State University
James Riley, Western Michigan University
Lee Saunders, Miami University
Ned Schillow, Lehigh County Community College
Tammy Sewell, student at University of Arizona
Lisa M. Stark, student at University of Arizona
Diane Thiessen, University of Northern Iowa
Barbara Wilmot, Illinois State University
James N. Younglove, University of Houston, University Park

and especially to Lawrence Feldman, University of Pennsylvania, Ben Lane, Eastern Kentucky University, and Steve Willoughby, University of Arizona, who read the entire manuscript.

I want to give a special thanks to Alice Kelly, who reviewed the manuscript at several stages, wrote some original problems, solved all of the exercises, and put together the Student's and Instructor's Manuals.

Finally, many persons at Dellen/Macmillan have given a lot of tender loving care to this project. I want to express my gratitude to them, especially to Janet Bollow, designer and production coordinator, and to Don Dellen, the boss of it all. It has been a pleasure and a privilege to work with you!

David Gay

PROBLEM-SOLVING STRATEGIES

CHAPTER

In this chapter we will discuss several strategies for solving problems. To introduce each one, we will pose a problem, solve it, and then discuss the strategy (or strategies) we used. To benefit from our solutions, you must try the problem yourself. The aim is for you to become a better problem solver, and you learn from doing. When each problem is stated in the text, take pencil and paper and try to solve it. Spend time on it. Then, whether you solve the problem or not, read our solution. Incidentally, a solution includes an "answer" as well as the method of obtaining the answer. Method and answer are both important. Following our solution is a discussion of the strategies used.

When you solve one of these problems, compare your solution with ours. If your solution differs from ours, don't be surprised or dismayed. A given problem may have many different acceptable solutions. Compare your friends' solutions with yours as well. To give you a realistic idea of what is involved in solving a problem, some of our solutions may contain false starts, dead ends, or seemingly aimless wanderings, all normal occurrences when problems are being solved. Sometimes our solution won't be particularly polished or clever or even the shortest possible. Don't let the length of a solution scare you. Solving a problem can take a while.

So, get yourself lots of blank paper, a bunch of sharpened pencils, a cool drink, and dig in. Work the problems and the exercises as you read along. You are on your way to becoming a good problem solver!

THE DITCH
DIGGING PROBLEM

Be sure to try this
problem yourself before
looking at our solution!

A Solution to the Ditch
Digging Problem

You have just landed a job working on a ranch. Your first assignment is to help dig a ditch 720 ft long, which will be used to bring water to the ranch animals. You and two other people, Jack and Sarah, will be digging the ditch. The ranch foreman claims that if all of you keep digging steadily, the job can be completed in 3 days. You are now at the end of the first day. Sarah has hurt her back and will not be able to continue with the digging. Nevertheless, the foreman is in a hurry to get the ditch dug. You want to know how much longer it will take you and Jack to complete the job. You have noticed that all three of you seemed to dig at about the same rate.

You think "Let me draw a picture of the ditch. That will give me a feeling for what the problem is about.

"We were supposed to have finished the ditch in 3 days. Let me mark each day's part of the ditch on my picture.

Day 1	Day 2	Day 3

There were three of us digging. I can divide the part of the ditch for each day into three equal pieces; I'll mark one of them M for me; another, J for Jack, and the third, S for Sarah.

Day 1			Day 2			Day 3		
M	J	S	M	J	S	M	J	S

That describes what we *were going* to do. Now to describe what we *will be* doing: The first day is the same, since we've completed it. Sarah won't be with us for the next 2 days. Let me cross out what she would have done.

Day 1			Day 2			Day 3		
M	J	S	M	J	S	M	J	S

If I do one of the parts that Sarah won't be able to do and Jack does the other, then we could finish the job in 1 extra day! Here's how the digging would go.

DAY 1			DAY 2		DAY 3		DAY 4	
M	J	S	M	J	J	M	J	M

"It will take us 4 days in all. You know, I never used the fact that the ditch is 720 feet long. . . ."

Our solution to the ditch digging problem uses a device that will be useful in solving other problems. That device is *drawing a picture*. As we solve more and more problems in this book, you will see the sorts of pictures we use and the ways they are used, sometimes as an important part of a solution and sometimes just as a way to get a feeling for what the problem is about. You will also see how an initial picture can be made more useful by adding details (such as labels) or by altering it. Sometimes the first picture will be discarded in favor of a more appropriate one.

Another solution to the ditch digging problem might be quicker. Our solution involved drawing a picture, fiddling with it, looking at it this way and that—all activities that take time. Solving problems *will* take time.

1.2 PROBLEM SOLVING IN THIS BOOK

Practically every idea or technique discussed in this book will come about as the result of solving some problem or another; thus, the strategies we develop are an important feature of the book. You will see them used many times in this and later chapters. To emphasize their use as well as to point out where a given strategy is used, we will indicate its occurrence by printing its name in color, like this:

Draw a picture.

In later chapters, not only will we use the strategies developed in chapter 1 but we will also introduce new ones. We will announce each new strategy when it is first used and flag each use afterward by using color. Inside the back cover you will find a list of all the problem-solving strategies announced in this book with the page number on which the strategy is first used.

EXERCISES

1. Four bricklayers are laying the cement block for a new house. They all work at the same rate, and it is estimated that it will take them 5 days to do the job. At the end of 2 days on the job, two of the bricklayers become sick. With just the two workers, how many more days will it take to complete the job?

2. With the increased use of economy cars, parking lots find that they can reduce the size of their spaces and use the resulting area for other things. Downtown Parking Lot plans to take advantage of this to comply with a recent greenery ordinance for downtown establishments. Each row of Downtown Parking Lot consists of six spaces for parking cars side by side (versus front to back). Each space is 12 ft long and 7 ft wide. The lot owner wants to use one end of each row for greenery that she plans to plant. She wants this garden area to be 12 ft long and 8 ft wide. She wants to know how many inches each parking space will have to be reduced to allow room for the same number of spaces in each row and for the planting. Help her solve this problem.

THE PROBLEM OF WHERE TO CATCH THE BUS

You live on a bus line 21 mi from your work. In the morning you plan to leave your home, walk along the bus line to a bus stop, and get on a bus that will drop you off at work an hour later. Your walk to the bus is an important part of your day's exercise and you would like your walk to the bus to give you as lengthy an exercise period as possible. You also don't want to be late for work; you want to get there within an hour of leaving your home. Where along the line should you catch the bus? Some clues that may help:

Try the problem
yourself first!

- You walk at the rate of 4 mph.
- The buses on this route average 30 mph and pass by every 5 min.
- It is possible to catch a bus anywhere along the way.

What is your solution to this problem?

A Solution to the Problem of Where to Catch the Bus

You might solve the problem this way: "Let me draw a picture of the bus line.

Then let me label one end Home and the other end Work.

The point to catch the bus is between Home and Work.

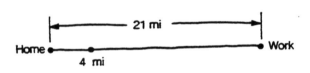

Let me guess where the point is. I walk at the rate of 4 mph. Let me try a point 4 miles from Home.

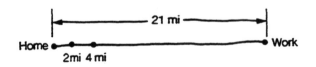

If I got on the bus there, I'd use up the whole hour walking! That guess is not the right answer, but it tells me that I would have to get on the bus somewhere between Home and the 4-mile point. Let me try the 2-mile point.

It would take me half an hour to walk that, plus another 5 minutes to wait for the bus. How long would it take the bus to go the rest of the way? The bus has to go 19 miles at 30 miles per hour. If the bus goes 30 miles in an hour, it would go 10 miles in 19 minutes. So it would take more than half an hour to go 19 miles. That's too long. But now I know that the point to get on the bus is between Home and the 2-mile point. Let me try 1 mile from home.

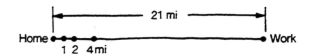

How long will it take me to walk that 1 mile? I walk 4 miles in 60 minutes, so I walk 1 mile in 15 minutes. Allowing 5 minutes to wait for the bus would leave 40 minutes for riding on the bus. The bus can go 10 miles in 20 minutes and 20 miles in 40 minutes. I'd be traveling on the bus for 20 miles. That's just right!"

Strategy 2: Make a Guess

Our solution to the problem of where to catch the bus used several devices. We used one of these before, drawing a picture. The picture in the bus problem helped to keep us focused on the heart of the problem: to find the best *point* for boarding the bus.

Another device used is called **making a guess**. Students in mathematics classes are frequently discouraged from guessing. But there are many advantages to this approach. First of all, permitting yourself (the problem solver) to make a guess frees you from any hesitation you might have in getting started. You are allowed to jump in and try something. Second of all, making a guess will tell you something about the problem. If your initial guess doesn't work, maybe you'll learn something from your mistake and try another guess that will be better. The solver of the bus problem learned a lot about the first guess: "If I were to get on the bus at the 4-mile point, then I would use up a whole hour. There would be no time for the bus trip and I'd be late for work." Not only does the solver learn that 4 miles is *not* the answer, but also he learns that the true answer has to be a distance between 0 and 4 miles. The answer cannot be 12 miles or 20 miles or even 100 miles. The possibilities for the answer have been narrowed down. After the initial guess, more guesses were made. After each guess, the search was narrowed even more: The second guess was 2 miles; the consequences of this guess narrowed the search to distances between 0 and 2 miles. The third guess was right on target.

As with drawing a picture, you notice that making a guess (and following through on its implications) can take time. But frequently, this strategy is just what you need to solve a problem.

The problems we have dealt with so far have neat, whole number solutions. Not all problems are like this. Watch for problems with "messier" (and more interesting) solutions.

EXERCISE

3. You live on a bus line 30 mi from work. You want to take 1 hour to go to work, and you want to combine walking with riding the bus. The bus travels at 45 mph, and comes by every 5 min; your walking rate is 3 mph. Where along the route should you get on the bus in order to spend the least amount of time on the bus? (This problem may not come out "even" as in the problems above. Find the answer to the nearest half mile. But don't be late to work!)

THE PROBLEM OF THE MISSING TIME

You just read the results of the 200-yd backstroke event in the local paper, but one of the times was missing. It said that the three swimmers from State had times of

Don't forget to try
the problem yourself.

2:12.43, 2:14.09, and 2:19.66, while from your school, Garcia had a time of 2:11.93 and Hersch a time of 2:17.59. You know that Pepper also swam, but her time was not mentioned. The article did say that your team scored a total of 9 points in the event (in which first place gets 6 points, second gets 4 points, third gets 3 points, fourth gets 2 points, and fifth gets 1 point). You want to know where Pepper finished.*

A Solution to the Problem of the Missing Time

You feel that it might be useful to organize the information you read in the paper. You decide to arrange the times in order of finish together with the names of the swimmers having those times.

2:11.93 Garcia
2:12.43 A
2:14.09 B
2:17.59 Hersch
2:19.66 C

(You call the unknown State swimmers A, B, and C.) You think: "I need to figure out where Pepper fits in. It might be useful to know that our team got 9 points. Let me write down the point system.

PLACE	POINTS
1st	6
2d	4
3d	3
4th	2
5th	1
6th	0

Pepper finished in one of the six places. Let me make a guess: Suppose that Pepper finished in first place. That would mean the following finishing order.

Pepper •
2:11.93 Garcia
2:12.43 A
2:14.09 B
2:17.59 Hersch
2:19.66 C

With this finishing order, our team would have gotten these points.

PLACE	POINTS	
1st	6	×
2d	4	×
3d	3	
4th	2	
5th	1	×
6th	0	
Total points: >11		

---

* Adapted from Carol Meyer and Tom Sallee, *Make It Simpler*, Addison-Wesley, Reading, MA, 1983, p. 276. (All further references to this work indicate adaptations from it.)

"Eleven points is too many. Let me make another guess: Suppose Pepper finished in second place. Again our team would get more points than the newspaper article claimed. I should try Pepper in third place. Before doing that, let me extend my chart to keep track of the information I'm gathering. Then I can figure out the total number of points for Pepper's finishing in fourth, fifth, and sixth place, too.

		PEPPER'S POSITION					
Place	Points	1st	2d	3d	4th	5th	6th
1st	6	×	×	×	×	×	×
2d	4	×	×				
3d	3			×			
4th	2				×	×	×
5th	1	×	×	×	×	×	
6th	0						×
Total points for us: →		11	11	10	9	9	8

The only way we can get 9 points for the event is if Pepper finishes in fourth or fifth position! So, the finishing times look like this.

2:11.93 Garcia
2:12.43 A
2:14.09 B
2:17.59 Hersch ⟵ Pepper
2:19.66 C

"When I see her again, I'll have to ask Pepper which position it was exactly. One thing is for certain: State got only 7 points in the backstroke event."

Strategy 3: Organizing the Data

One feature of the solution of the missing time problem is how it handled all the bits of information given in the statement of the problem. There were several times and names and a point scoring scheme. To use all of this, you *organize the data*. Since it is not always clear how to do this, you jump in and try. You start with the obvious. What kinds of data are there? For this problem there are times, names, and scoring points. You start with the times and make a list, fastest to slowest. To handle the names, you tack them on to the first list. For the points, you make a chart from the scoring scheme. The list and chart help you to focus on the problem; they help you think of possible positions for Pepper. You are ready for a guess. You make one and several more. It is the last bit of information—the total score for your team—that tells you which guesses work.

Another interesting feature of our solution to the missing time problem is that there are two correct answers. Some problems are like that.

EXERCISE 4. Our volleyball team had just finished playing in a tournament, and the 20 of us decided to go to the yogurt shop across the street for a snack before heading home. Each of us ordered either a small cone (for $ .50), a large cone (for $ .70), or a large dish with nuts and carob chips (for $1.30). After everyone had ordered, the bill came to exactly $19.00. On the way home, I was trying to remember what people had ordered, but I finally had to give up. I decided to figure out how many people might have ordered large dishes. Help me.*

THE BIRDSEED PROBLEM

Don't forget, try this yourself.

The zoo is ordering birdseed. The keeper of the bird cages knows that two crested cockatoos will eat 2 lb of birdseed every 2 wk; that three Peruvian parrots will eat 3 lb of birdseed every 3 wk; and that four Mexican macaws will eat 4 lb of birdseed every 4 wk. How much birdseed should the zoo order for its twelve crested cockatoos, twelve Peruvian parrots, and twelve Mexican macaws for 12 wk?[†]

A Solution to the Birdseed Problem

You decide that this problem calls for some organization of data.

These birds	eat this amount	in this time
2 CC	2 lb	2 wk
3 PP	3 lb	3 wk
4 MM	4 lb	4 wk

"I want to find out what 12 crested cockatoos, 12 Peruvian parrots, and 12 Mexican macaws will eat in 12 weeks. Let me fit those questions into my chart.

These birds	eat this amount	in this time
2 CC	2 lb	2 wk
3 PP	3 lb	3 wk
4 MM	4 lb	4 wk
12 CC	?	12 wk
12 PP	?	12 wk
12 MM	?	12 wk

It looks like a lot to figure out all at once. But I don't have to do it all at once. Let me figure out what the 12 cockatoos need first. Then I can figure out what the 12 parrots need; and after that, I can deal with the 12 macaws. Those are smaller problems. After solving them, I can add the three answers together to get the solution to the big problem.
"Here is the beginning of my chart again.

These birds	eat this amount	in this time
2 CC	2 lb	2 wk

I want to know about birdseed for 12 cockatoos for 12 weeks. A simpler problem would be 12 cockatoos in 2 weeks. If 2 cockatoos eat 2 pounds in 2 weeks, 1 cockatoo would eat 1 pound in 2 weeks.

These birds	eat this amount	in this time
2 CC	2 lb	2 wk
1 CC	1 lb	2 wk

* *Make It Simpler*, p. 361.
† *Make It Simpler*, p. 37.

It follows that 12 cockatoos would eat 12 times as much in the same amount of time.

These birds	eat this amount	in this time
2 CC	2 lb	2 wk
1 CC	1 lb	2 wk
12 CC	12 lb	2 wk

If they eat that much in 2 weeks, then they'd eat 6 times that much in 12 weeks.

These birds	eat this amount	in this time
2 CC	2 lb	2 wk
1 CC	1 lb	2 wk
12 CC	12 lb	2 wk
12 CC	*72 lb*	12 wk

That solves the problem with the cockatoos. I can use the same procedure with the parrots.

These birds	eat this amount	in this time
3 PP	3 lb	3 wk
1 PP	1 lb	3 wk
12 PP	12 lb	3 wk

If 12 parrots eat 12 pounds in 3 weeks, they'd eat 4 times that much in 12 weeks.

These birds	eat this amount	in this time
3 PP	3 lb	3 wk
1 PP	1 lb	3 wk
12 PP	12 lb	3 wk
12 PP	*48 lb*	12 wk

"Now let's deal with the macaws.

These birds	eat this amount	in this time
4 MM	4 lb	4 wk
1 MM	1 lb	4 wk
12 MM	12 lb	4 wk
12 MM	*36 lb*	12 wk

"I've solved the three smaller problems: 12 crested cockatoos eat 72 pounds in 12 weeks, 12 Peruvian parrots eat 48 pounds in 12 weeks, and 12 Mexican macaws eat 36 pounds in 12 weeks. The solution to the big problem is the sum of the three amounts of birdseed: 72 lb + 48 lb + 36 lb = 156 lb. The zoo should order 156 pounds of birdseed."

Strategy 4: Break the Problem Up into Smaller Problems

Strategy 5: Solve a Simpler, Similar Problem

Being overwhelmed by a large amount of data and a large number of anticipated steps for solving the problem can put you on a road to failure. The person who solved the birdseed problem above used several devices to avoid this. We have already discussed one of these, organizing the data.

The person solving the birdseed problem discovered that the whole problem could be solved by solving three smaller problems: find the amount of birdseed needed for (1) the cockatoos, (2) the parrots, and (3) the macaws. This device is called *breaking the big problem up into smaller problems.*

A third device was introduced in trying to figure out how much birdseed would be needed for 12 cockatoos in 12 wk. The solver might have asked: "Is there a simpler, similar problem I can solve? Maybe solving such a problem will give me a clue." He then went on to solve these simpler problems: (1) How much birdseed is needed for 1 cockatoo in 2 wk? (2) How much birdseed is needed for 12 cockatoos in 2 wk? From there he went on to complete a solution to the problem of the cockatoos; he attacked the problems for the parrots and the macaws similarly. This is called *solving simpler, similar problems.*

EXERCISE
5. Two women were complaining about their teenagers' preoccupation with clean hair. One moaned, "My four boys will use up 3 bottles of shampoo in 2 weeks." The other replied, "My five girls will use up 4 bottles of shampoo in 3 weeks." Who uses the most shampoo in a week, one of the boys or one of the girls? How much more?*

1.3

THE SWITCHING
PROBLEM

GETTING OUT OF A RUT

You are the engineer of a switching locomotive in a railroad yard. Your job today is to interchange the positions of the two coal cars shown below, a Santa Fe car and a Southern Pacific car, and return the locomotive to its original position.

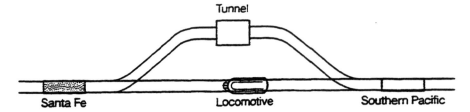

The cars and the locomotive can hook together in any combination, and the locomotive can push or pull either car or both cars simultaneously. You can use the side track with the tunnel. However, although the tunnel is big enough to allow each car to pass through, it is not big enough for the locomotive. Each car is longer than the tunnel so that when it is in the tunnel it can be accessible to the locomotive from either end. How can you manage to exchange the positions of the two coal cars?[†]

Try it, please.

---

* *Make It Simpler,* p. 163.

[†] From Bonnie Averbach and Orin Chein, *Mathematics: problem solving through recreational mathematics,* W. H. Freeman, San Francisco, 1980, p. 3, problem 1.6.

You draw a large picture of the track, switches, and tunnel, and you select a penny, a dime, and a nickel to play the roles of the two cars and engine. You can move these objects around on your picture using the restrictions described in the problem. After moving the "engine" and these two "cars" around a bit without success, you stop and ask, "Is there a simpler problem?"

You think: "If there were fewer objects to move around, the problem would be simpler. Is there a problem I can solve with just the locomotive and *one* car? Let me take the locomotive and the Santa Fe car and try to exchange their positions.

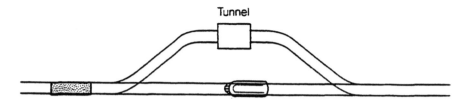

"The locomotive pulls the Santa Fe car to the right.

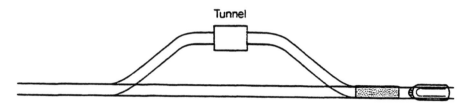

"The locomotive pushes the Santa Fe car into the tunnel.

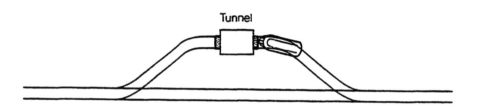

"The locomotive returns to the main track, then moves left.

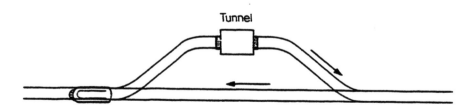

"The locomotive picks up the Santa Fe car at the tunnel and pulls it back to the main track.

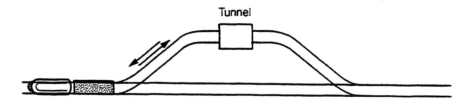

"The locomotive pushes the Santa Fe car to the right, then returns to where the Santa Fe car started.

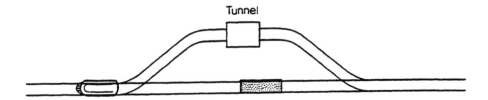

"That solves a problem with one coal car. Will this help me?"

You move the "cars" around some more. You exchange the positions of L (locomotive) and SF (Santa Fe car). You try shunting SF, then exchanging the positions of L and SP (Southern Pacific car). You are frustrated: SF gets in the way. You think: "So far, no success. One thing I haven't done is to hitch all three together. Can I use this capability and the solution to the simpler problem to solve the big problem?

"Here's an idea. Hook up SP and L together and treat the two in combination as if they were just the locomotive. If the locomotive can't get through the tunnel, neither can the combination of the two together. I'd have only two things to switch: SF and the combination. I could use the solution to the simpler problem to exchange the positions of the combination and the SF. We start out as before.

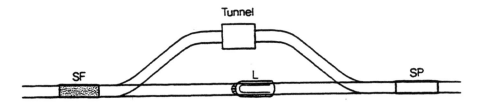

Then hook up L with SP to make the combination. Exchange the combination with SF to get this.

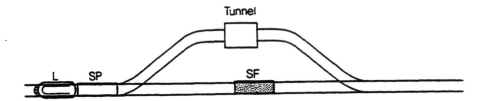

Now all I have to do is push SF to the right, dismantle the combination, and exchange the positions of SP and L. That's the simpler problem again, only in reverse. It should work.

"Combination pushes SF to the right.

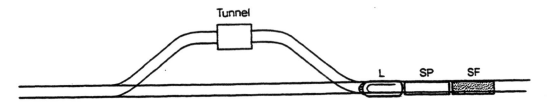

"To exchange positions of L and SP, L pulls SP to the left, then pushes it into the tunnel.

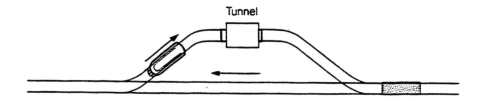

"L returns to the main track and moves right.

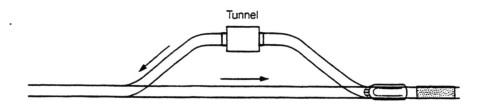

"L picks up SP in the tunnel at right and moves back to the main track.

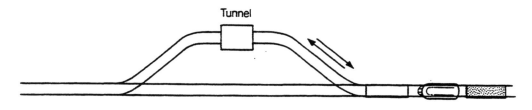

"That does it!"

Strategy 6: Building a Model

Strategy 7: Getting Out of a Rut

In the solution just presented, the solver did more than draw a picture; she *built a model* of the tracks, switches, cars, and locomotive. It was crude but useful.

Another feature of the solution is a strategy discussed before: Solve a simpler problem. In the solution to the switching problem, the simpler problem was switching one of the cars with the locomotive. The solution to the simpler problem turned out to be an important ingredient in the final solution. Things do not always work out as nicely as this. The solution to a simpler problem may simply get you started and give you insight. It's a valuable investment of time in any case.

A third feature of the solution is finding a new way to look at a problem after you are frustrated in your original approach. Finding a radically new way to look at a problem is called *getting out of a rut*, and it means breaking out of set ways of thinking. In the solution to the switching problem, the solver tried everything involving exchanging positions of a pair—a locomotive with a car, a car with a car—and got nowhere. The rut was in thinking that this was the only way. The insight that broke down this mental block—and eventually led to a solution—was the idea that a locomotive hitched to a car could be treated as *one thing* to exchange positions with the remaining car.

Incidentally, not everybody experiences the rut that occurred in our solution to the switching problem. As a person solves more and more problems, many mental blocks disappear.

6. Below is a picture of the same railroad yard that appeared in the switching problem.

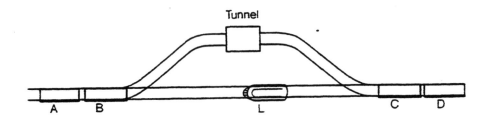

This time there are four railroad cars, A, B, C, and D, in addition to L, the locomotive. They are arranged in the order A B L C D. Using the side track and the conditions given in the switching problem, rearrange the cars in this order: C D L A B, as shown in the next figure.

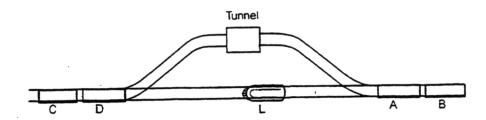

7. Starting again with order A B L C D, rearrange the cars in this order: D C L B A.

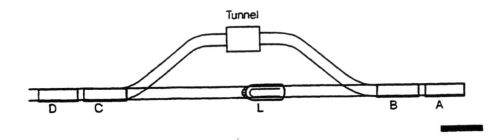

1.4   THE "12 MATH MYTHS"

In case you feel frustrated or anxious or angry while you are working on the problems in the text or at the end of this chapter, you might want to take a peek at what Stanley Kogelman and Joseph Warren call the "12 math myths."

1. Men are better in math than women.

2. Math requires logic, not intuition.

3. You must always know how you got the answer.
4. Math is not creative.
5. There is a best way to do a math problem.
6. It's always important to get the answer exactly right.
7. It's bad to count on your fingers.
8. Mathematicians do problems quickly, in their heads.
9. Math requires a good memory.
10. Math is done by working intensely until the problem is solved.
11. Some people have a "math mind" and some don't.
12. There is a magic key to doing math.*

Perhaps a better name for these "myths" would be the "12 Math Misconceptions"!

1.5   USING SEVERAL STRATEGIES

In the remainder of the chapter we will solve problems using the strategies we've introduced in new ways. Some strategies combined will be so useful that we will identify the combination as a new strategy. Organizing guesses in a chart is a good example of one of these useful combinations.

The solutions to the remaining problems are long and involve the use of many strategies. You will not always know this in advance, but it is helpful to make an initial plan of attack with the idea that you can revise it when necessary. Being in the middle of a lengthy solution is like trying to find a path through a jungle without having any idea of where you are going. Making a plan is one way to deal with unknown territory. Sometimes when you are in a jungle, unexpected things come up; you find that your original plan is not working and you must alter it. Unexpected things may come up in solving a problem. You may have to revise your original plan.

THE COFFEE BLEND PROBLEM

Have you tried the problem yet?

Max's Coffee Mill sells coffee by the pound. At the moment, Max sells inexpensive Costa Rican coffee for $4.50/lb and expensive mocha coffee for $7.00/lb. Because of the expense, most customers avoid the mocha. Max feels that his customers would be interested in a blend of Costa Rican and mocha that is richer in flavor than the Costa Rican but not as expensive as the mocha. He thinks that a blend costing $5.20/lb would be priced just about right. To try out the new blend, he plans to have 50 lb of it on hand to sell. He needs to know how many pounds of Costa Rican and how many pounds of mocha he will need to do this.

A Solution to the Coffee Blend Problem

Max decides to make a guess: "Suppose I were to try 30 pounds of Costa Rican in the blend. That would mean 50 − 30 = 20 pounds of mocha. Thirty pounds of Costa Rican would cost 30 × $4.50 = $135, and 20 pounds of mocha would cost 20 × $7 = $140. The total cost would be $135 + $140 = $275. How does that figure compare with what I *want* the blend to cost? A blend of 50 pounds at $5.20/lb would cost 50 × $5.20 = $260. That is my target cost. My guess would result in a blend that is too expensive ($275). It looks as if I should have more of the inexpensive Costa

---

* From Stanley Kogelman and Joseph Warren, *Mind over Math*, Dial, New York, 1978, pp. 31ff.

Rican in my blend and less mocha. I should make another guess. Let me organize what I've got.

COSTA RICAN (POUNDS)	MOCHA (POUNDS)	COST— COSTA RICAN	COST—MOCHA	TOTAL COST	TARGET COST OF BLEND
30	20	$135	$140	$275	$260

"Let me try a guess of 40 pounds of Costa Rican. Here is what would happen.

COSTA RICAN (POUNDS)	MOCHA (POUNDS)	COST— COSTA RICAN	COST—MOCHA	TOTAL COST	TARGET COST OF BLEND
30	20	$135	$140	$275	$260
40	10	$180	$70	$250	
35	15	$157.50	$105	$262.50	
36	14	$162	$98	$260	

This amount is too small. Try something between 30 and 40.

This is closer but still too high. Try a bit more Costa Rican in the blend.

Just right!

The blend I want will consist of 36 pounds of Costa Rican and 14 pounds of mocha."

Strategy 8: Organize Your Guesses in a Chart

The method of solving the coffee blend problem involves a combination of two strategies we have seen before. One strategy is guessing; the other is organizing the data. In our solution, Max began with a guess and then calculated the consequences of this guess. On the basis of those consequences, he made his next guess, hoping by that to zero in on the target cost: the cost of the desired blend. To help him make subsequent guesses, he decided to use another strategy we've seen, organization of data. Strictly speaking, the data he organized were not data contained in the original problem but data generated by the guesses he made. We call this combination of strategies *organize your guesses in a chart*. It is so useful that we will illustrate its use in a solution to the next problem.

You might be tempted to solve the following problem using algebra. (You might have been tempted that way with the coffee blend problem too!) Organizing guesses in a chart is a problem-solving tool accessible to people with few or no algebra skills. It is a tool that helps you focus on the problem and gain an understanding of it; it may lead to success where algebra fails. It may also help you figure out how to solve it with algebra. If you like, try solving the problems both ways—using algebra and by organizing guesses in a chart. Then compare the solutions.

THE SUITCASE PROBLEM

No peeking at the solution until you try it!

Half an hour ago Susan left town on a business trip. Her husband, Robert, has just discovered that she left her packed suitcase behind. He decides to get in his car with the suitcase and overtake her. She is driving her own car, and Robert figures that she will be traveling at an average of 50 mph. He also figures that he can travel at an average of 60 mph. As he pulls away from the curb, he looks nervously at his watch and starts to figure out how long it will take him to reach her. Help him to figure out how long.

A Solution to the Suitcase Problem

To get started with the problem, let's *make a guess* of 1 hr as the time it will take for Robert to reach Susan. We need to figure out some consequences of this guess.

One hour after Robert leaves, Susan will have been traveling for $1\frac{1}{2}$ hr. At 50 mph, that puts her 75 mi from town. Robert will have been traveling for 1 hr at 60 mph. That puts him 60 mi from town. At this point, we make a chart to organize these and subsequent data.

	TIME FROM ROBERT'S DEPARTURE	SUSAN'S DISTANCE FROM TOWN	ROBERT'S DISTANCE FROM TOWN
Guess 1	1 hr	75 mi	60 mi
Guess 2	2 hr	125 mi	120 mi
Guess 3	3 hr	175 mi	180 mi
Guess 4	$2\frac{1}{2}$ hr	150 mi	150 mi

Robert has passed Susan!

This is it!

EXERCISES

8. You want to prepare a 70-lb mixture of peanuts and cashews that will cost $1.95/lb. Here is what you know:
   ■ Peanuts cost $1.37/lb.
   ■ Cashews cost $3.13/lb.
   You want to know how many pounds of each nut should go into the mixture. Solve this problem by making guesses and organizing the consequences in a chart.

9. To entice customers, a department store advertises black and white television sets on sale at a price that causes them a loss of $18 per set. When the customers come in, the store hopes they will buy color instead, on which the profit is $81 per set. In a typical day, 30 TVs are sold. How many of these must be color sets for the store to show a net profit? (Solve this problem by making guesses and organizing the consequences in a chart.)

10. At 8:17 P.M. a known criminal is seen passing the city limits of Winslow in a car going 70 mph. At 8:32 P.M., a policeman in pursuit of the criminal is seen passing

the same point going in the same direction at 80 mph. Assuming that they both continue in the same direction and at the same speed, find the time that the policeman overtakes the criminal. (Make guesses and organize them in a chart.)

1.6   MAKING A PLAN

THE MOUNTAIN CLIMB PROBLEM

Tomorrow you are going to climb to the top of Mt. Massive, leaving from your home in Half Moon Gulch. A profile of the trail you will follow, as seen from a nearby valley, is shown in the picture.

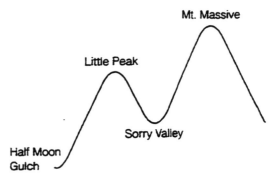

You have a dinner date tomorrow night at 7 P.M. in Half Moon Gulch. You want to know what's the latest time tomorrow morning you can leave on the hike and still make your date on time. To help you determine this, you have made the following list:

■ From past experience in climbing mountains, you know that your climbing rate averages 1000 ft of altitude gain each hour.

■ Also from past experience, you know that your descending rate is a steady 1500 ft of altitude loss each hour.

■ The altitude of Mt. Massive is 14,420 ft.

■ The altitude of Half Moon Gulch is 10,050 ft.

■ There is an altitude loss of 315 ft from Little Peak to Sorry Valley; otherwise, the climb is steadily upward.

■ When you reach the top of Mt. Massive, you will spend an hour resting.

■ When you get back home from the climb, you will need an hour to get cleaned up and dressed for dinner.

Don't forget to try the problem first.

What time should you leave in the morning?

A Solution to the Mountain Climb Problem

To get some feeling for the problem, you decide to draw a time line, a picture of how time will pass tomorrow.

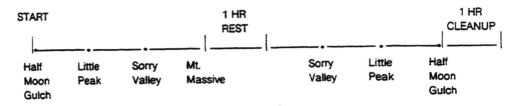

To this picture you decide to add information about altitudes and altitude gains and losses:

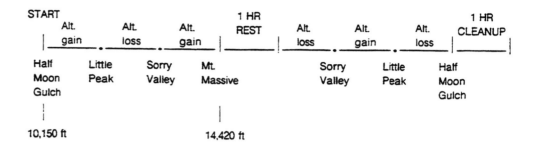

You figure that if you knew how long each of the little stretches would take, you could add all these times up. You know about two of those times already: the 1-hr rest at the top and the 1-hr cleanup. To figure the times for altitude gains and losses, you plan first to determine the altitude gain for each stretch; from that you will calculate the time for that stretch using the rate for climbing or the rate for descending.

When you start off to determine the altitude gain for the first stretch, you notice that the altitude of Little Peak is not given. You realize that there is no way to figure out the altitude of Little Peak with the information given. So much for your first plan.

You look at your time line again. You think: "There is a simpler problem to solve. If there were no Little Peak, figuring out the altitude gain would be easy. Putting Little Peak back would introduce some altitude loss and some altitude gain. I know how much the loss is. But how much is the gain? Here's a picture.

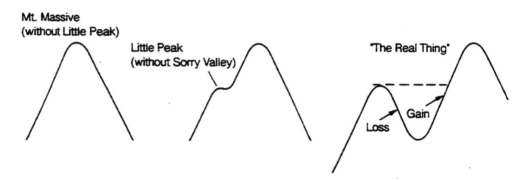

"The altitude gain added by Little Peak is the same as the altitude loss added. Now I can figure out the total amount of altitude gain on my ascent. In fact, why not figure out the *total* amount of altitude gain in the ascent *and* descent. Here is my plan for solving the problem.

PLAN

1. Figure total amount of altitude gain.
   Trip up:
   Trip down:
   Total:

2. Figure total amount of altitude loss.
   Trip up:
   Trip down:
   Total:

3. Figure time for total altitude gain.

4. Figure time for total altitude loss.

5. Add up the following times:
   Time for altitude gain:
   Time for altitude loss:
   Time for rest at top: 1 hr
   Time for cleanup at bottom: 1 hr
   _____
   Total time:

6. Figure out when I should leave in the morning.

"The plan breaks the big problem into a lot of smaller problems. What's more, my total altitude gain must be equal to my total altitude loss.

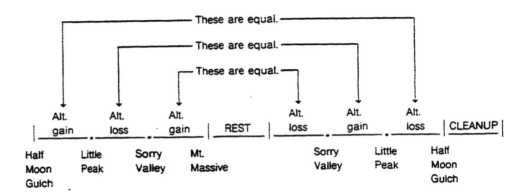

"Solving part 1 of my plan would solve part 2!
"Let me solve part 1. The altitude gain on trip up is this much.

Gain for these two pieces is:

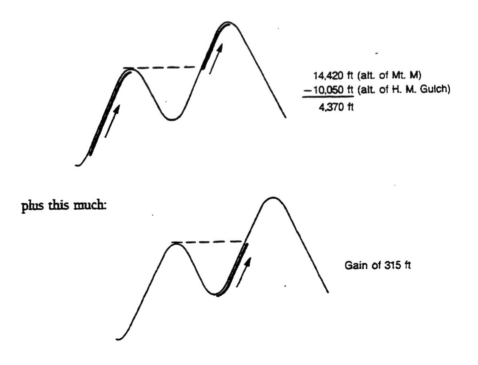

14,420 ft (alt. of Mt. M)
−10,050 ft (alt. of H. M. Gulch)
_____
4,370 ft

plus this much:

Gain of 315 ft

On the trip down, the only altitude gain is this:

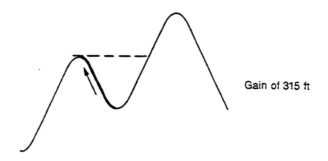

Gain of 315 ft

"Adding up these amounts, I get:

1. Altitude gain on trip up: 4370 ft

                                     +315 ft

   Altitude gain on trip down: 315 ft

   Total altitude gain: 5000 ft

2. Total altitude loss: 5000 ft

"Since I gain altitude at the rate of 1000 feet per hour, I have this:

3. Time spent in gaining altitude is 5 hours.

"That takes care of parts 1, 2, and 3 of my plan. Since the total amount of altitude loss is also 5000 feet, I should be able to figure out the total amount of time spent losing altitude. The rate at which I lose altitude is 1500 feet per hour. In 3 hours I'd lose 3×1500 feet = 4500 feet in altitude. How long would it take me to lose 500 feet? It would take a third of an hour, or 20 minutes. So I can conclude:

4. Time spent in losing altitude is 3 hours, 20 minutes.

"That takes care of part 4. Now for part 5 of the plan:

5. Add up the following times:
    Time for altitude gain: 5 hr
    Time for altitude loss: 3 hr, 20 min
    Time for rest at top: 1 hr
    Time for cleanup at bottom: 1 hr

      Total time: 10 hr, 20 min

"Finally, to figure out when I leave in the morning, I know that I leave 10 hours and 20 minutes before dinner time at 7 P.M. That's 3 hours and 20 minutes before noon or 20 minutes before 9 A.M. or

6. I leave on my hike at 8:40 A.M."

Strategy 9: Making a Plan

The solution to the mountain climb problem involved the use of several strategies: drawing pictures, organizing data, and solving simpler problems. Furthermore, the solution has a feature that appeared before but is more evident this time. We call this feature *making a plan*. This feature should be more prominent when a problem contains a variety of data and when it appears that a variety of strategies will be used. Let's see how this device was used in your solution to the mountain climb problem.

1. You drew a time line and labeled it using given information. This *initial plan* uses the strategies drawing a picture and organizing data.

2. You decide to figure out times for the individual stretches, then add them up. This *second plan* for the remainder of the solution uses the strategy break the problem up into small problems.

3. Since the second plan wouldn't work, you needed to revise it. You figured out the effect of Little Peak on altitude gain and replaced the second plan with a *third plan* by breaking the problem up into small problems in a different way.

In the coffee blend problem, the strategy making a plan was used in the following way:

1. Your initial plan was to make a guess, calculate its consequences, and make a second plan based on what happened.

2. Your second plan was to make more guesses, organize the consequences in a chart, and zero in on a solution.

The mountain climb problem also illustrates the need for *revising the plan* if the previous one doesn't work. In the coffee blend problem, there was no need to revise the second plan.

Knowing that you can revise an initial plan may help you to jump into a problem without knowing the eventual outcome at the start. It enables you to keep going in the middle of a problem when you still don't know where and when and what the end will be. Beginning to solve a problem is like entering uncharted territory. The strategies help you to explore this territory; organizing these strategies into a plan of action keeps you focused on finding what you are looking for.

EXERCISE

11. Just behind Mt. Massive is a ridge that leads to Big Peak, at the same elevation as Mt. Massive. Suppose that in addition to hiking to Mt. Massive you decide to include the hike along the ridge to the top of Big Peak and back. When should you leave in the morning for this trip? (Again, you want to be back in time for your date.) A silhouette of the ridge is shown.

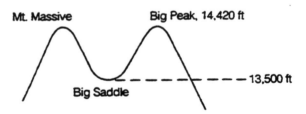

1.7   LOOKING FOR A PATTERN

THE PROBLEM OF THE EMPTY ENVELOPE

A secretary was sending out promotional brochures to the firm's prospective clients. After counting out eight brochures, typing addresses on eight envelopes, and stuffing the brochures into the envelopes and sealing them, the secretary discovered one brochure on the floor. Since he did not want to retype all the envelopes, he decided to use a pan balance scale (shown) to determine which envelope was missing a brochure. How can he use the balance scale to do this?

Lighter envelope

A Solution to the Empty Envelope Problem

All eight sealed envelopes weigh the same, except for the one with the missing brochure. The problem is to identify the lighter envelope. One way to solve it is to take one of the envelopes and put it in the left-hand pan. Then, keeping that envelope in the left-hand pan, place each of the other envelopes in turn in the right-hand pan until the empty envelope is found. The empty envelope can be found in at most seven weighings.

A Second Solution to the Empty Envelope Problem

The secretary says, "I've got a better solution than that. Divide the envelopes up into pairs.

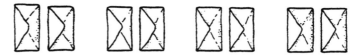

The empty envelope will be in one of the pairs. Take the envelopes in the first pair and compare them using the pan balance, one in one pan, the other in the other pan. If the pans don't balance, I have located the empty envelope: It's on the upper pan. Then I'm finished. If the pans do balance, I haven't located the empty envelope, so I move to the next pair and try the same thing. After, at most, four weighings, I locate the empty envelope. That's better than seven weighings."

THE SECOND EMPTY ENVELOPE PROBLEM

Is there a method that guarantees finding the empty envelope in fewer than four moves? In fact, what is the SMALLEST number of moves?

A Solution to the Second Empty Envelope Problem

Place four envelopes on one pan and the remaining four in the other. The empty envelope must be on the pan that is higher.

Remove the four envelopes from the lower pan. Of the four envelopes in the higher pan place two on one pan and two in the other. Again, the empty envelope is in the higher pan.

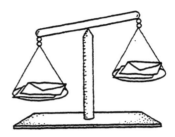

Finally, compare the weights of the last two envelopes using the pan balance. You have found the empty envelope in three moves.

Is this the best we can do? Is there a method for weighing the envelopes that will identify the empty envelope in no more than two weighings? Let's see if we can find simpler, similar problems whose solutions could give us some clues. How about if there are seven envelopes equal in weight except for one empty envelope, which we want to find? Or six envelopes, one of them empty? Or the very simple problem of two envelopes, one of them empty? There is a whole collection of simpler problems:

- Two envelopes of which one is empty. Find it.
- Three envelopes equal in weight except an empty one. Find it.
- Four envelopes equal in weight except an empty one. Find it.
- Five envelopes equal in weight except an empty one. Find it.
- Six envelopes equal in weight except an empty one. Find it.
- Seven envelopes equal in weight except an empty one. Find it.

Let's solve these. Maybe we'll notice a pattern.

2 *envelopes, labeled A and B:* Weigh A against B. The lighter one is the one you're looking for. *One* weighing is sufficient.

3 *envelopes labeled A, B and, C:* Weigh A against B. If one is lighter, that's the empty one; if they are the same weight, the empty one must be C. At most, *one* weighing is necessary.

4 *envelopes labeled A, B, C, and D:* Weigh A and B against C and D. The lighter pair must contain the empty envelope. Using the lighter pair, follow the same procedure as with the two-envelope procedure. At most, *two* weighings are necessary.

5 *envelopes labeled A, B, C, D, and E:* Weigh A and B against C and D, as with four envelopes. If the empty one is not among A, B, C, and D, then it must be E. At most, *two* weighings are necessary.

6 *envelopes labeled A, B, C, D, E, and F:* Weigh A, B, and C against D, E, and F. The lighter of the two groups must contain the empty envelope. Using the lighter group, proceed as with the three-envelope procedure. At most, *two* weighings are necessary.

7 *envelopes labeled A, B, C, D, E, F, and G:* Weigh A, B, and C against D, E, and F as with six envelopes. If the empty one is not among A, B, C, D, E, and F, it must be G. At most, *two* weighings are necessary.

Now let's look at the problem with eight envelopes and consider what the choices are for the first weighing:

FOUR against four
THREE against three
TWO against two
ONE against one

We used the first choice earlier. Our first weighing in the six- and seven-envelope procedures consisted of weighing three envelopes against three envelopes. For both of those, we needed at most two weighings. Let's try this choice for the first weighing in the eight envelopes problem.

8 *envelopes labeled A, B, C, D, E, F, G, and H:* Weigh A, B, and C against D, E, and F as with the six-envelope procedure.

If the empty envelope were in neither pan, then the empty envelope would be among G and H. To identify the empty one in this case requires one more weighing for a total of two weighings. If the empty envelope were in one of the pans, then according to the six-envelope procedure, it would take two weighings in all to identify the empty one. Two weighings for eight envelopes is sufficient.

EXERCISES

12. What is the fewest number of weighings you will need for nine envelopes, and what is your method?

13. What is the fewest number of weighings you will need for ten envelopes and what is your method?

Strategy 10: Looking for a Pattern

In solving the second empty envelope problem, we thought of a natural line-up of simpler and similar problems, from the simplest (two envelopes) to the most complex (seven envelopes). We had a feeling that solving all of them in that order might reveal a pattern giving us strong clues about what to do with eight envelopes. This strategy is called *looking for a pattern*.

14. Suppose this time you have eighteen envelopes equal in weight except for one empty one. What is the fewest number of weighings you will need to find the empty one? What is your method?

THE BEST-PRICE PROBLEM

A gift shop chain in the Southwest presently sells miniature cactus gardens for $20 each. It costs the chain $10 per garden for materials, assembling, and packaging. The chain's management is considering changing the price per garden to improve total profits from the gardens. At the present price the chain sells 200/wk. Marketing consultants have told the chain that for each decrease of $1 in the present selling price, the chain can sell 5 additional gardens above the 200. Similarly, for each $1 increase in the selling price, the chain will sell 5 gardens fewer than the 200. (For example, at a price of $21 each, the chain will sell 195; at a price of $22 each, the chain will sell 190; and so on.) Management wants to know whether it should raise or lower the selling price and by how much in order that its total income from the gardens be as large as possible.

Try it!

A Solution to the Best-Price Problem

Management suggests: "Let's make a guess. What would happen if we were to lower the price by $1? The price of each garden would be $19, we would sell 205 of them, and we would have a total profit of 205 × $9 = $1845.

"How does that compare with what we're doing now? Right now we sell 200 gardens at $20 each with a total profit of 200 × $10 = $2000. Lowering the price $1 won't do us any good! Let's look at this a little more closely and try some more numbers. First, let's get organized and make a chart.

PRICE EACH	NUMBER SOLD	TOTAL DOLLAR PROFITS
20	200	2000
19	205	1845

What would happen if we were to lower the price to $18?

PRICE EACH	NUMBER SOLD	TOTAL DOLLAR PROFITS
20	200	2000
19	205	1845
18	210	1680

This is even worse.
"Let's try a price increase.

PRICE EACH	NUMBER SOLD	TOTAL DOLLAR PROFITS
20	200	2000
21	195	2145

That looks promising. Let's try more figures.

PRICE EACH	NUMBER SOLD	TOTAL DOLLAR PROFITS
20	200	2000
21	195	2145
22	190	2280
23	185	2405
24	180	2520
25	175	2625
26	170	2720

Profits keep going up. Let's try $30, $40, and $50.

PRICE EACH	NUMBER SOLD	TOTAL DOLLAR PROFITS
20	200	2000
21	195	2145
22	190	2280
23	185	2405
24	180	2520
25	175	2625
26	170	2720
⋮		
30	150	3000
⋮		
40	100	3000
⋮		
50	50	2000

"At a price of $50, we make just what we're making now. Both $30 and $40 are the best prices so far. Let's check the total profits for a price between $30 and $40.

PRICE EACH	NUMBER SOLD	TOTAL DOLLAR PROFITS
20	200	2000
21	195	2145
22	190	2280
23	185	2405
24	180	2520
25	175	2625
26	170	2720
⋮		
30	150	3000
⋮		
35	125	3125
⋮		
40	100	3000
⋮		
50	50	2000

The best price is $35 so far. Let's check prices on either side of $35.

PRICE EACH	NUMBER SOLD	TOTAL DOLLAR PROFITS
20	200	2000
21	195	2145
22	190	2280
23	185	2405
24	180	2520
25	175	2625
26	170	2720
⋮		
30	150	3000
⋮		
34	130	3120
35	125	3125
36	120	3120
⋮		
40	100	3000
⋮		
50	50	2000

It looks as if total profits go up as the price increases from $20 to $35 and go down as the price increases from $35. Total profits seem to peak at $35."

1.8 COMBINING STRATEGIES ONCE AGAIN: GUESSES, CHARTS, AND PATTERNS

The solution to the best-price problem involved making guesses, organizing their consequences in a chart, and observing a pattern in the chart. Management observed that total profits increase from $2000 to $3125 as the price increases from $20 to $35 and total profits *decrease* from $3125 to $2000 as the price *increases* from $35 to $50. Observing this pattern enabled management to solve the problem.

EXERCISES

15. Is it possible that if the price in the best-price problem were increased to some figure in excess of $50, the total profits might increase again—to some figure above $3125? Is it possible that if the price were lowered *enough*, the total profits might get bigger?

16. The chain will be opening a branch in the Northeast, where the market for cactus gardens is different. There, a marketing consultant estimates that at a price of $26 the branch can sell 60/wk, that each $1 increase in price will decrease sales by 10 gardens/wk, and that each $1 decrease in price will increase sales by 10 gardens/wk. Because of shipping costs, the cost per garden to the chain has increased to $14. What should the price per garden be so that the chain's profits for the branch is greatest?

1.9 LOOKING BACK: POLYA AND THE ART OF SOLVING PROBLEMS

George Polya (1887–1985), perhaps more than anyone else, was responsible for the present concern among mathematics educators with problem solving. It was his belief that we should be spending time in school solving nonroutine problems and that we should be teaching ways to approach such problems. Polya was born in Hungary and came to this country in 1940. He was a research mathematician and a university professor at Stanford and at the Swiss Technical Institute in Zurich. As a teacher, he wanted to convey to his students what is involved in solving problems. In 1945, he wrote his first of several books on problem solving, *How to Solve It*. In that book, his outline for "how to solve it" has the following main parts:

> Understanding the problem
> Devising a plan
> Carrying out the plan
> Looking back*

All of the strategies we have been discussing fit somewhere into this comprehensive scheme:

■ Understanding the Problem
  Draw a picture
  Organize the data
  Make a guess
  Make a model

■ Devising a plan
  Break the problem down into simpler problems
  Solve a similar problem
  Organize your guesses in a chart
  Look for a pattern

■ Carrying out the plan
  Revise your plan if necessary
  Get out of a rut

■ Looking back

Here is a paraphrase of what Polya has to say about looking back:

> Can you *check your answer to the problem*? Can you check the steps you took in coming up with the answer? Can you get your answer by another method, another series of steps? Is your answer to the problem now clear and obvious to you? Can you use your answer or the method of solution for some other problem?

Polya is interested in having us learn something about our solution to a problem not only so that we can be ready for the next problem that comes up but also so that we can think of new problems while we're waiting. Posing problems is almost as important as solving them. Solving a problem frequently involves changing course and solving a related one that you pose. Besides, a problem that you've posed yourself is more exciting to solve—you've got more at stake!

---

* George Polya, *How to Solve It*, 2d ed., Doubleday, Garden City, N.Y., pp. xvi–xvii.

1.10 USING CALCULATORS TO SOLVE PROBLEMS

Many of the problems in this book are easier to solve with a calculator than without. This is especially true for a solution involving a lot of arithmetical calculations. For example, in the coffee blend problem, we made a lot of guesses, determined consequences for each guess, and organized guesses and consequences in a chart. To figure out the consequences for each guess, we had to make some calculations. While it turns out that we made only four guesses, other problems may have solutions that require more. The amount of arithmetic would get to be too much, unless, of course, you use a calculator.

Following are some tips on how to use a calculator. There are two parts to the discussion: keying in numbers and the order of operations; and the constant feature. We will elaborate on these in later chapters.

Keying in Numbers and the Order of Operations

No doubt you have already used a calculator and are familiar with the four keys of the calculator that perform the operations of arithmetic:

The [+] key adds two numbers.
The [−] key subtracts one number from another.
The [×] key multiplies two numbers.
The [÷] key divides one number by another.

We will be discussing calculators that perform multiplication and division in order, left to right, before performing addition and subtraction. This is the same order that is used in interpreting written mathematical expressions. A calculator that follows this order has *hierarchy*.

For example, key the following sequence into the calculator and watch the display as you do it.

Key sequence:	[2]	[+]	[3]	[×]	[4]	[−]	[6]	[=]
Display:	2	2	3	3	4	14	6	8

A calculator with hierarchy does not compute $2 + 3$ when you punch in the first three keys (other calculators will, however). When the [−] key is pressed, the calculator first multiplies 3 times 4 and then adds 2 to that product to get 14. The answer 8 is what we would normally get if we carry out the calculation $2 + 3 \times 4 - 6$; that is, $2 + 3 \times 4 - 6 = 8$.

If we want to perform the addition $2 + 3$ first and then multiply that sum by 4, we use parentheses, thus, $(2 + 3) \times 4 - 6$. The rule for written mathematical expressions is that operations in parentheses are performed first. The same is true for the calculator with hierarchy. To calculate the same expression on the calculator, we key in the sequence

Keying sequence:	[(]	[2]	[+]	[3]	[)]	[×]	[4]	[−]	[6]	[=]
Display:	0	2	2	3	5	5	4	20	6	14

which is consistent with the equation $(2 + 3) \times 4 - 6 = 14$.

EXERCISE

17. Write keying sequences for the mathematical expressions in the following exercises. Use your calculator to evaluate these expressions.

(a) $2 + 5 \times 20$ (b) $(2 + 5) \times 20$ (c) $2 + 5 \times 20 + 3$

(d) $(2 + 5) \times 20 + 3$ (e) $(2 + 5) \times (20 + 3)$ (f) $2 + 5 \times (20 + 3)$

So far the sequence of keys to be pressed corresponds closely to the symbols that occur in the mathematical expression that we want to calculate. Let's look at an example that might create a difficulty.

$$\frac{5 + 7 + 9}{3}$$

The horizontal line in this expression calls for division. We might try the following sequence to calculate it.

Keying sequence: [5] [+] [7] [+] [9] [÷] [3] [=]

The display on the calculator will calculate the answer to $5 + 7 + 9 \div 3$; that is, divide 9 by 3 and add this to the sum of 5 and 7. This gives you 15. But to evaluate

$$\frac{5 + 7 + 9}{3}$$

you want to calculate the sum of 5, 7, and 9 first and divide the sum by 3. Another way of writing this mathematical expression is $(5 + 7 + 9) \div 3$, which suggests how to key it into the calculator.

Key sequence: [(] [5] [+] [7] [+] [9] [)] [÷] [3] [=]

Try that sequence on your calculator and you will get the correct answer: $(5 + 7 + 9) \div 3 = 7$.

EXERCISES

18. For each of the following mathematical expressions, write a keying sequence that will give the value of the expression on the calculator.

(a) $\dfrac{4 + 5 + 6}{3}$ (b) $\dfrac{20}{4 + 6}$ (c) $\dfrac{10 + 12 + 16}{9 + 10}$

19. Use the calculator to evaluate the following mathematical expressions.
(a) $17 \times (13 + 3 \times (23 + 59) - 57) + 29$

(b) $\dfrac{12 \times 14 + 24 \times 33}{37 \times 42 + 57}$ (c) $\dfrac{7 \times (52 - 17) + 13}{83 - 35}$

The K Key or Other Constant Feature of Calculators

There are many situations where you might want to multiply a bunch of different numbers by a single number. (Filling in a table of numbers is one such.) For example, suppose you want to multiply each of the numbers 23, 47, 107, and 97 by 53. There is a feature on most calculators that enables you to do this without having to key in the [×] [5][3] four times. On some calculators you use a [K] key; on others you press the [×] key twice; and on others there are no special key presses, but you have to follow a certain sequence.

To simplify things in what follows, we will write the numbers in the keying sequences without brackets, thus, 7 [×] 5 for [7] [×] [5].

For a calculator with [K] key, the keying sequence for multiplying 23, 47, 107, and 97 by 53 would be

KEYING SEQUENCE	DISPLAY	MATHEMATICAL EXPRESSION
53 [×] [K] 23 [=]	1219	53 × 23
47 [=]	2491	53 × 47
107 [=]	5671	53 × 107
97 [=]	5141	53 × 97

For other calculators, the keying sequence for doing this will be

KEYING SEQUENCE	DISPLAY	MATHEMATICAL EXPRESSION
53 [×] [×] 23 [=]	1219	53 × 23
47 [=]	2491	53 × 47
107 [=]	5671	53 × 107
97 [=]	5141	53 × 97

For still other calculators, the keying sequence will be

KEYING SEQUENCE	DISPLAY	MATHEMATICAL EXPRESSION
23 [×] 53 [=]	1219	53 × 23
47 [=]	2491	53 × 47
107 [=]	5671	53 × 107
97 [=]	5141	53 × 97

Notice in the latter case that the factor that remains the same is keyed in second in the initial keying sequence.

You will have to experiment to find out which of the above procedures (or possibly some other procedure) is appropriate for your calculator.

EXERCISES

20. The procedure for *adding* 53 to each of the numbers 23, 47, 107, and 97 is similar. You replace [×] by [+]. Try this out with your calculator.

21. In a recent inventory of their branch stores, Safeland Supermarkets counted the quantities of jars of Sticky Peanut Butter shown in the table.

BRANCH STORE	NO. OF 8 OZ JARS STICKY	WHOLESALE VALUE
Lakeland	54	$64.80
Payson	89	
Verde Valley	123	
Los Alamos	65	
Lukeville	47	

Each jar of Sticky has a wholesale value of $1.20. Use your calculator to complete the Wholesale Value column in the table.

_1.12_ SUMMARY OF IMPORTANT IDEAS AND TECHNIQUES

- Using strategies to solve problems
  Drawing a picture
  Making a guess
  Organizing the data
  Breaking the big problem up into simpler problems
  Solving simpler, similar problems
  Making a model
  Getting out of a rut

- Combining strategies
  Organizing the consequences of guesses in a chart
  Making a plan; revising the plan if necessary
  Looking for a pattern

- Simplifying the labor of problem solving using calculators and computers

PROBLEM SET

PRACTICING
SKILLS

1. Mr. Lovejoy hired the twins to rake his yard, front and back, for $6. It was a large yard, but the front and back were about the same size. When the time came to start, Bill was not home from his music lesson, so Bryan started alone. Bryan was finished with the whole front before Bill

showed up; he had forgotten about the job and stopped at a friend's house. The two of them raked the back together. How should they split the money?*

2. A digger starts digging a hole at 8 A.M. on Monday and continues digging from 8 A.M. to 1 P.M. each day until the job is finished. She digs a depth of 5 ft each day, and the hole is to be 30 ft deep. However, due to the condition of the soil, 2 ft of dirt falls back in the hole each night while she is not working. When will she finish the hole?

3. You wake up in the morning. You look at your electric digital clock and notice that it is blinking. The time on the clock shows 5:00. "Hmm. The electricity went off during the night. I wonder when? I know that when the electricity goes off and then comes back on, the clock resets itself to 12:00." You notice that your wristwatch reads 8:30 (the correct time), and the conventional electric clock in the kitchen reads 6:00. How long was the electricity off and when did it go off?

4. You are planning to have champagne for your wedding reception and figure you will need 20 bottles. A special French brand costs $15 per bottle while an acceptable (but cheap) domestic brand costs $7 per bottle. You would like to buy only the French brand, but you can't since you have no more than $200 to spend on champagne. So you figure you will buy French champagne for serving early in the reception and the cheap kind for serving later. What is the largest number of French bottles you can buy, keeping to your budget of $200 and buying a total of 20 bottles?

5.   June 30, 1989

I really can't stand the heat today. It must be around 90° right now. Just a few days ago it was only 63°. I remember the heat wave we had in April; one day the temperature was 2° below freezing, and the next, it jumped to 95°.

I had some errands to run this morning before driving into Manhattan from Queens. We had run out of stamps, so I went to the post office and bought two rolls of 25¢ stamps, 100 to a roll, and a dispenser for 49¢. I also went to the Fast Copy Center to get 10 copies made of a recent newspaper article. They were 7¢ for the first 5 copies and 6¢ for each additional copy.

I had to stop for gas and only needed 4.8 gallons, which cost $4.15. I realized I had gotten pretty good mileage on my VW since I had gone 144 miles since my last fill up.

Joe and I met for lunch at La Garbage. Joe ordered a rare steak for $7.85 and coffee for $ .65. I had a chicken salad plate for $5.25 and coffee as well. The waiter put everything on one check, but we decided we would each pay for what we had ordered. We each left about a 15 percent tip.

At that point, I thought to myself, "Gee, I've spent a lot of money so far today. I wonder how much?"

How much did I spend?[†]

6. The Health Food Shop sells raisins at $3.70/lb and granola at $2.50/lb. The owner wants to make 90 lb of a hike mix consisting of granola and raisins and costing $3.50/lb. To figure out how many pounds of raisins and how many pounds of granola should go into the mix, the owner decides to make some guesses and organize them in a chart—with the hope that he can zero in on a solution. Here is the beginning of his chart, his first guess, and some consequences of his first guess.

---

* *Make It Simpler*, p. 71.
† *Mind over Math*, p. 61.

RAISINS (POUNDS)	COST—RAISINS	GRANOLA (POUNDS)	COST—GRANOLA	TOTAL COST OF MIX	TARGET COST OF MIX
45	$166.50	45	$112.50	$279.00	

What should the target cost of the mix be?

7. In problem 6, is the cost of the mix of 45 lb raisins and 45 lb granola bigger or smaller than the target cost? Choose the most reasonable of the following possible next guesses: (a) 50 lb raisins and 40 lb granola; (b) 40 lb raisins and 50 lb granola. What are the consequences of the guess you chose?

8. You are the same engineer of a switching locomotive as in the switching problem. Today three railroad cars are arranged as in the top picture. You want to interchange them so that they will be arranged as in the bottom picture. As before, the cars and locomotive can hook together in any combination so that locomotive can push or pull one, two, or three cars at once; the tunnel is big enough for each car but not for the locomotive; and each car is longer than the tunnel. How can you do the switching?

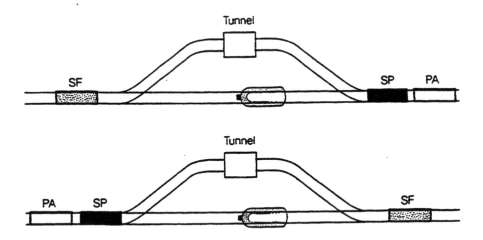

9. On my home's electric meter there is a little dial that goes around once for each 10 Wh (watthour, watthours) of electricity used. I wanted to figure out how much it costs to bake cookies. First of all, the oven is on for 20 min when I bake cookies. Also I discovered that 1000 Wh cost $ .13. To figure out how many watthours are used to bake cookies, I found that, with the oven off, the little dial on the meter took 10 sec to go around once. With the oven on, it took the little dial only 6 sec to go around once. With this information, I was able to solve my problem. How? How much does it cost me to bake cookies?

10. A team of five asphalt-spreading machines is laying asphalt on 21 mi of city streets. City Transportation figures it will take the team 30 working days to complete the work. At the end of 10 working days, one of the machines breaks down and will be in the shop for quite a while waiting for replacement parts. How much longer will it take the remaining four machines to complete the job?

11. Tomorrow you are planning a bike trip to Picacho Peak, leaving from your home in Tucson. Tomorrow night at 8 o'clock you have an appointment in Tucson, so you would like to know what's the latest time you can leave tomorrow morning to be back in time for your appointment.

You make the following list of facts to help you decide:

- Average biking speed from Tucson to Picacho Peak is 12 mph.
- Average biking speed from Picacho Peak to Tucson is 10 mph. (It's uphill from the peak to Tucson.)
- Distance from house to Picacho Peak is 60 mi.
- Spend an hour at Picacho Peak eating, resting, and enjoying the scenery.
- On return to Tucson, need 1 hr to eat and get cleaned up and dressed for appointment. Need 20 min to get from house to appointment.

When should you leave in the morning?

12. There are 15 people at a party and everybody shakes hands exactly once with each person present. How many handshakes will have taken place?

13. You want to figure out the occupations of Andres, Brown, and Cohen. You know the following facts:

- One is a bank teller, one a farmer, and one a chef.
- Andres is neither the teller nor the farmer.
- Cohen is not the teller.

What are the occupations of the three women?

14. The Southwestern gift shop chain mentioned in the best-price problem also sells herbariums for $20 each. At this price the chain sells 100 of them each week. Marketing consultants have told the chain management that for each decrease of $1 in the price, the chain can sell 10 additional herbariums each week. Should management lower the selling price to increase its income from herbariums? What should the price be so that its income from herbariums is as large as possible? The cost to the chain for each herbarium is $5.

15. If you have a chain saw with a blade 18 in. long, can you cut a log that is 16 ft long and 8 in. in diameter into 4-ft pieces by making only two cuts?

16. Modify BASIC program 2 from section 1.11 to figure out how many pounds of raisins and how many pounds of granola should be in the hike mix of problem 6 in order that the mix costs $3.50/lb.

USING IDEAS   *For each remaining problem in this problem set, write an essay explaining as clearly and completely as you can your solution to the problem. In your essay, describe the steps you take to solve the problem, mention the problems or solutions from the text that gave you ideas, and include the problem-solving strategies you used. You may want to outline and organize your work before writing your final essay.*

17. A bunch of students on a field trip to a local bottling plant were watching the machine that puts the tops on bottles. It was a circular device holding 36 bottles equally spaced around the outside. The students were trying to figure out how long it would take to cap all 36 bottles. One student started timing right after the top was put on the first bottle and found that it took 10 sec until the ninth bottle was completely capped. At that point, the students were dragged off to another part of the plant. How long would it have taken for the machine to cap all 36 bottles?*

18. Inspector Lee looked once again at the dead body of Horace Rimple and noted the time on the shattered watch: 1:10. The watch had undoubtedly been shattered by the bullet that killed old Mr. Rimple as he lay asleep in his bed.

---

* *Make It Simpler*, p. 165.

"Tell me what happened today," he instructed the butler.

"As always, on Sunday, it was Mr. Rimple's wish to have the family gather for the afternoon. On days such as today, when he was feeling unwell, the members of the family were to go in and sit by his bed to talk, even if he looked asleep. He could still hear them even if he did not make the effort to open his eyes.

"Today, as customary, Robert spent the time from 1:00 to 1:03 in the afternoon with him; Susan the time from 1:03 to 1:06; James, the time from 1:06 to 1:09; William, the time from 1:09 to 1:12; Lawrence, the time from 1:12 to 1:15; and Mary, the youngest, the time from 1:15 to 1:18. Mr. Rimple was very particular about those times. Each of them said he seemed to be asleep."

"Well," said Inspector Lee, "it seems very clear that William is the murderer."

"Unfortunately," said the butler, "it is not quite that simple. While Mr. Rimple loved that watch, it did not keep very good time. It lost exactly 6 minutes every 24 hours. I would set it correctly each night at 11:00 before going to bed. Thus, the watch was always incorrect."

"Ah." said Inspector Lee. "Then the murderer must be ... "
Who?*

19. On the track in the accompanying diagram, interchange the position of cars A and B and return the engine to its starting position. Only the engine can pass through the tunnel; the railroad cars are too big.

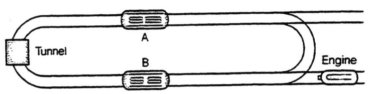

20. Ann, Becky, and Jane live in adjacent apartments. Becky has the middle apartment. They work as a chemist, a radio announcer, and a plumber, but not necessarily in that order. The radio announcer feeds Jane's cat when she goes away for the weekend. The chemist taps on Ann's wall when she wants to go jogging. What occupation does each woman have? (Hint: It might be useful to organize data and keep track of progress in a chart such as is shown.)

	CHEMIST	ANNOUNCER	PLUMBER
Ann			
Becky			
Jane			

21. Three singers, Conrad, Darlene, and Letha, met at the rehearsal of the Long Beach Choral Society. Their last names were Jacobs, Kaufman, and Nishio, not necessarily in that order, and their professions were accountant, plasterer, and teacher, again not necessarily in that order. Here are some things that you know about these people.

- The plasterer, who was starting her own solar installation firm, offered to design a sauna for Nishio.

- Kaufman jogged every morning on the beach, which was one block from his condo.

- Darlene's last name was not Nishio.

- Conrad was not the accountant.

---
* *Make It Simpler*, p. 223.

Match the singers' first names with their last names and professions. You may find the charts useful.*

	Jacobs	Kaufman	Nishlo	Accountant	Plasterer	Teacher
Conrad						
Darlene						
Letha						
Accountant						
Plasterer						
Teacher						

	Last Name	Profession
Conrad		
Darlene		
Letha		

22. You have two egg timers: an 11-min and a 7-min timer. How can you time the boiling of vegetables for 15 min using these two timers?

7-min egg timer

11-min egg timer

23. *Problems for the Quickening of the Mind*, a collection of problems dating from the Dark Ages, contains the following question:

If 100 bushels of corn are distributed among 100 people in such a manner that each man receives 3 bushels, each woman 2 bushels, and each child half a bushel, how many men, women, and children are there?

(Hint: There are several solutions. Try to find as many as you can.)

---

* Problem and charts from Ruth Afflack, *Beyond EQUALS*, Math/Science Network, Mills College, Oakland, Calif, 1982, prob. 2, p. 108.

24. Your French vineyard produces two types of champagne: dry and brut. This season you plan to create a third type, extra dry, as a mixture of brut and dry. You want the retail price of extra dry to be 53 francs per liter. You know that the retail price of brut is 55 francs/l and that the retail price of dry is 47 francs/l. Furthermore, you anticipate being able to sell the following amounts of each type:

- 800 liters extra dry
- 400 liters dry
- 300 liters brut

How many liters of dry and how many liters of brut should your vineyard produce?

25. You have 12 coins that are identical except for the fact that 1 of them is counterfeit and therefore heavier or lighter than the others. Using a balance scale, how can you find the counterfeit coin and also tell whether it is lighter or heavier than the others? What is the fewest number of tries that you need?

26. Quabbin Reservoir, located in the western part of Massachusetts, supplies most of the water for the Boston area. The water from Quabbin is pumped into several holding reservoirs in the immediate vicinity of Boston, and Boston and its suburbs draw water from these holding reservoirs. At the end of each day, Quabbin refills the holding reservoirs to replace exactly the water drawn during the day. You work for Quabbin Reservoir and need to know the contents of the reservoir at the end of today's activities. Here is what you know:

- There are three holding reservoirs.
- Holding reservoir A starts with 300 million gal each day.
- Holding reservoir B starts with 250 million gal each day.
- Holding reservoir C starts with 150 million gal each day.
- Boston takes 137 million gal each day from C.
- Cambridge and Watertown each take 125 million gal daily from A.
- Newton, Roxbury, and Waltham each take 25 million gal from B daily.
- Quabbin Reservoir started yesterday morning with 700 million gal.
- It rained this morning and Quabbin Reservoir received 400 million gal additional water.

What is the solution to your problem?*

27. La Dolce Vita apartment house has 100 identical apartments. The owner wants to know what the rent for each apartment should be so that her total profit from the whole building is largest. Local rental trends indicate that if the rent on each apartment is $200, then she can keep all apartments rented and that for each $10 increase in the monthly rent the number of vacancies will increase by two. For example, if the rent is $210, then there will be two vacancies. The cost (upkeep and mortgage) per apartment is $50/mo. What should the rent be so that total profit is largest?

28. There are five houses in a row. Each is occupied by a person of different nationality. You'd like to find out who drinks brandy and who owns a skunk. Here are some clues.

- The Spaniard owns a dog.
- The person who is English lives in the red house.
- Coffee is drunk in the green house.
- The Ukrainian drinks tea.
- The green house is immediately to the right of the ivory house.

---

* Adapted from Deborah Hughes Hallett, *The Math Workshop Algebra*, W. W. Norton & Company, New York, 1980, p. 18, problem 116.

- The doctor owns snails.
- The mathematician lives in the yellow house.
- Milk is drunk in the middle house.
- The Norwegian lives in the first house.
- The stockbroker lives next door to the person with the fox.
- The mathematician lives next to the house where horses are kept.
- The carpenter drinks orange juice.
- The Japanese is a salesperson.
- The Norwegian lives next door to the blue house.
- Each person has one home, one pet, one occupation, one nationality, and one drink.

ANSWERING QUESTIONS OF HOW MANY?
OUR SYSTEM OF WRITTEN NUMERALS

CH A P T E R

The goal of this chapter is to describe how our system of written numerals works. In subsequent chapters we will be discussing the methods we normally use for adding, subtracting, multiplying, and dividing whole numbers. Understanding these methods depends very much on how we represent numbers with written numerals. We show how this system of written numerals might have developed from basic needs and primitive solutions. We also look at other systems that have features in common with our own and can be used to illustrate how our methods for calculating work. Using these other systems will give us experiences similar to those of small children when they begin to use our own system.

The development begins with simple problems involving questions of How many? and with solutions to these that do not involve our number system but instead involve simpler systems based more directly on pairing and one-to-one correspondence. These "primitive" solutions could have been created either by young children or by people in a primitive culture. As we look at more complex problems in this development, it becomes apparent that more sophisticated tools are needed. In this hypothetical history these "more sophisticated tools" evolve into our number system.

At the same time we will see that some problems that we normally solve with our sophisticated tools can also be solved with primitive ones. A primitive solution may be more accessible, more natural, and more appropriate for a given child at his or her stage of development than the more sophisticated one.

THE PENCIL PROBLEM

Katie is in kindergarten. She has been asked to hand out pencils to the students in her class: a pencil for each student. She wants to know the answers to these questions: Will there be enough pencils for everybody? (Will there be more people than pencils?) Will there be more pencils than people? Will there be the same number of pencils as people?

How can Katie answer these questions?

The typical adult response to this problem is to count the pencils, count the students, and compare the two numbers. Katie can count a little. But her experience with numbers is minimal. It is unlikely that the adult solution is available to her. There is an alternative solution that doesn't involve counting.

She takes the box of pencils and hands them out to all the members of the class, a pencil for each student. If she runs out of pencils before everybody gets one, then there are not enough pencils for everybody: There are more people than pencils. If she has pencils left over after everybody gets one, there are more pencils than people. If everybody gets a pencil and there are no pencils left over, then there are the same number of pencils as people.

The Mathematical Idea: Questions of How Many? Decided by Pairing

Katie was able to answer the questions Which are there more of, pencils or people? or Is there the same number of both? by *pairing* the pencils with the people in her class.

She was trying to make what is called a *one-to-one correspondence* between the set of pencils and the set of people.

PAIRING AND ONE-TO-ONE CORRESPONDENCE

Suppose you have two sets A and B. You select an element of A and *pair* it up with an element of B. Only one element of B can be paired with an element of A; only one element of A can be paired with an element of B. When all the elements of one of the two sets are used up, you have a *pairing* of A and B.

A *one-to-one correspondence* between sets A and B is a pairing of the elements of A with the elements of B so that each element of A is paired with an element of B and each element of B is paired with an element of A. No elements of A or B are unpaired. In this case you say that *A and B have the same number of elements.*

If you have a pairing of A and B in which every element of A is paired with one element of B and there are elements of B that have not been paired, then there are *more elements of B than elements of A.* If you have a pairing in which every element of B is paired with an element of A and there are elements of A that have not been paired, then there are *more elements of A than elements of B.*

Same number of pencils as people

More people than than pencils

More pencils than people

Only in this case is there a one-to-one correspondence between the set of pencils and the set of people.

EXERCISE

1. You live in a civilization that hasn't learned to count yet. You are responsible for supplying a horse to each adult in the village. You have gathered a lot of horses into your corral. How do you find out if you have enough?

THE BIRTHDAY HAT PROBLEM

Katie will be celebrating her fifth birthday soon. She wants to give each of her guests a birthday hat. Will she have enough? (Though she can count to 10 or so, that won't help. To her, counting is just a series of sounds she has memorized.) How can she decide if she has enough before the guests arrive?

A Solution to the Birthday Hat Problem

Katie could wait until her guests arrive, place a hat on each guest, and see if there are more guests than hats, more hats than guests, or the same number of hats as guests. However, Katie doesn't want to be caught short when her guests arrive; she wants to know *ahead of time* whether she has enough hats. She does know the names of her guests. As she says the name of each guest, she puts a hat aside. If she has used up all the hats before all the names have been spoken, there are not enough hats. If all the names have been spoken and a hat has been put aside for each, there are enough hats.

The Mathematical Idea: Pairing Using an Intermediary Set

To decide whether there are enough hats, Katie—unable to pair each hat with a guest in person—tried to pair each hat with the name of a guest. Katie knows something like the following: There is a one-to-one correspondence between the names of the guests and the guests themselves. She knows that if there is a one-to-one correspondence between hats and names, then there is a one-to-one correspondence between hats and guests; if there are more hats than names, then there are more hats than guests. In either case, there will be enough hats. By the same reasoning, she knows that if there are more names than hats, then there are more guests than hats. This kind of reasoning is valuable to Katie, since it is a lot more convenient to try to pair hats with names than to pair hats with guests.

GUESTS   NAMES   HATS

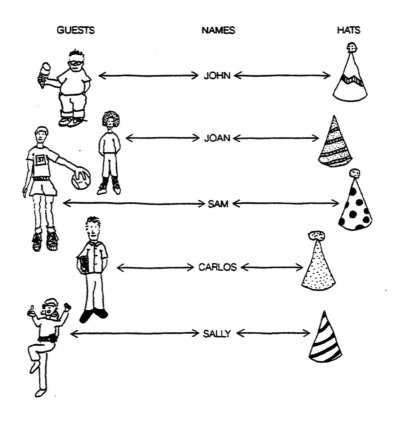

JOHN

JOAN

SAM

CARLOS

SALLY

Erase **names** and get this pairing:

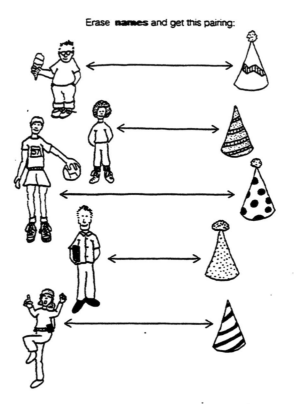

THE ERASER PROBLEM   Katie's teacher has asked her to go to the school storeroom and get erasers for all the students in her class. The teacher wants each student to have just one eraser, with no erasers left over. How can Katie solve this problem?

Katie suggests to the teacher that she take all the students to the storeroom and pair each student with an eraser. The teacher frowns at this idea, so Katie must think of something else. Katie also considers pairing the students' names with erasers, but there are too many names for her to remember. She thinks: "I could carry something belonging to each person, such as a shoe or a sock . . . Better yet, everybody can get a bead from the bead bin and give it to me. I'll take the beads to the storeroom and pair beads with erasers."

EXERCISE

2. The warriors in my primitive village need new spearheads, a spearhead for each warrior. Spearheads are made in the next village, and I plan a trip there to trade sheepskins for spearheads, one sheepskin for one spearhead. I want to be sure that I carry the right amount of sheepskins with me and I want to be sure that I bring back just the right amount of spearheads. How can I do this? (Remember, the people in my village can't count.)

Rancher Zor raises horses and Rancher Moq raises cattle. They meet in the village market to discuss a trade. They agree to trade some cattle for some horses, one cow for one horse. Zor doesn't want to bring to the village all the horses he wants to trade, because he may want to trade more horses than Moq has cattle to trade. And Moq doesn't want to bring all his cattle to the village for the same reason. But since they can't count, they need some way to compare the collection of cattle Moq wants to trade with the collection of horses Zor wants to trade. Help them solve this problem using pairing.

Try this problem first!

Zor says aloud: "What if I pair each horse I want to trade with a stone, one stone for one horse?" And Moq says: "What if I pair one cow I want to trade with a stone, one stone for one cow? Then we could try to pair my stones with your stones, stone for stone. If we pair all my stones with your stones and some of your stones are unpaired, then you will have some horses I cannot trade for. If we pair my stones with all your stones and some of my stones are left over, then I will have cattle that I cannot trade with you. If neither of these happens, then both of us will be able to trade all the cattle and horses we want to."

The Mathematical Idea: Convenient Sets for Pairing

The problems we have discussed so far in this chapter are ones of comparing the sizes of two sets using pairing. In the birthday problem, the eraser problem, and the ranchers' trade problem it was not convenient to pair the two sets directly. In each situation at least one of the sets to be compared was replaced by a convenient, intermediate set having the same number of elements. The intermediate set was used to make the comparison.

As the sets to be compared get bigger, another difficulty appears. The intermediate sets themselves become cumbersome. If Zor and Moq had had several hundred cattle and horses to trade, then the weight of the stones and the amount of work involved in pairing the two sets would have been too much. Something new is needed.

A natural response to this new problem would be to group stones together systematically and replace each group by another object. For example, Zor and Moq could group 10 stones together and replace the bunch of 10 stones by a stick. Every time they see a stick used in an intermediate set, they can pair it with another stick or with 10 stones.

3. Ugboo is trading sheepskins for Lagor's spears, one sheepskin for each spear. The collection of sticks and stones in the left-hand drawing is an intermediate set representing the sheepskins that Ugboo wants to trade. Each stone represents 1 sheepskin; each stick represents 10 stones. The collection of sticks and stones in the right-hand drawing represents the spears that Lagor wants to trade. Again, each stone represents 1 spear, and each stick represents 10 stones. By comparing the two collections, decide which set is biggest, the set of sheepskins or the set of spears.

The Mathematical Idea: Grouping

In exercise 3, a group of 10 stones is replaced by a stick. In this system, to compare two sets A and B, you first create two intermediate sets of stones, the first set in one-to-one correspondence with A, the second set in one-to-one correspondence with B. Second, in each of the two intermediate sets, group the stones into bunches of 10 and replace each bunch with a stick. (This grouping can be done while you form the one-to-one correspondence, much as we do when we tally: ||||| ||||| ||||| ||||| ||| . . ..) Each intermediate set has been replaced by a collection of sticks and stones. Finally, you make a pairing of the sticks and stones in one collection with the sticks and stones in the other. Pairing has become a bit more sophisticated.

REPLACEMENT NUMBERS

The scheme that we have described in which 10 stones can be replaced by a stick could be extended by allowing 10 sticks to be replaced by an arrowhead, and 10 arrowheads by something else, and so on.

In this system, 10 objects of lesser value can be exchanged for a single object of the next higher value, and vice versa. The number 10 is not special here: One civilization might use the number 12 and another might use the number 5. Historically, however, the numbers 5, 10, and 20 occur most often in this context because a person has 5 fingers on a hand, 10 fingers in all, and 20 digits in all on hands and feet.

In some systems of this kind, the numbers for replacement and exchange are not the same at all levels. For example, a twentieth-century coinage system used the "replacement" numbers: 4, 12, 5, 4. These are the replacement numbers for the old British farthing, pence, shilling, crown, pound system, in which

1 pence = 4 farthings
1 shilling = 12 pence
1 crown = 5 shillings
1 pound = 4 crowns

Citizens of the United States use a system of measuring for which the replacement numbers are 12, 3, 220, 8, and 3. These are the replacement numbers for our inch-foot-yard-furlong-mile-league system for linear measurement.

4. A common system of measurement in use throughout the world uses the replacement numbers 60, 60, 24, 7, and 52. What is the system of measurement, and what do the replacement numbers stand for?

5. What are the replacement numbers for the system of liquid measurement traditionally used in the United States?

3.2 THE DEVELOPMENT OF OUR HINDU-ARABIC, DECIMAL NUMERAL SYSTEM

The Counting Board

As an alternative to the stick-and-stone system, suppose that instead of replacing each group of 10 stones from your main pile of stones with a stick, you replace each group of 10 stones from the main pile with another stone placed in a second pile. In this system each set to be compared will have two piles associated with it, a "10s" pile and a main pile. You may want to separate the two piles with a line.

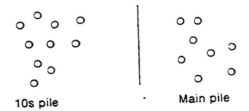

10s pile   Main pile

When the 10s pile gets large, you can create a third pile. You can replace each group of 10 stones from the 10s pile by putting a stone in a third pile, the "10s of 10s" (or "100s") pile. When the 10s of 10s pile gets large, you can replace each group of 10s of 10s stones in it with a stone placed in the "10s of 10s of 10s" (or "1000s") pile. And so on.

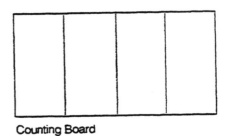

Counting Board

This system could easily have evolved into a *counting board*, a flat surface divided by parallel lines into separate spaces called *columns*. Stones are placed on the counting board between the lines, in the columns; the different columns correspond to the different piles in the system above. The main pile is the right-most column, the 10s pile goes in the column just to its left, and so on.

RULES FOR A COUNTING BOARD

A stone in the right-most column represents a single element. (Such a stone is called a *unit*.) A stone in any other column is worth 10 stones in the column just to its right. For example:

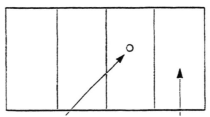

The stone here is worth 10 stones here.

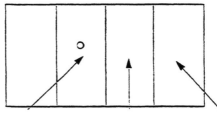

The stone here is worth 10 stones here or 100 stones here.

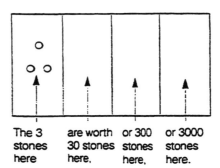

| The 3 stones here | are worth 30 stones here, | or 300 stones here, | or 3000 stones here. |

EXERCISE 6. Farida wants to trade her wheat for Milor's sheep—1 bushel of wheat for 1 sheep. Farida wants to know if she has enough wheat to obtain all Milor's sheep. Here are some clues.

Farida has this many bushels of wheat:

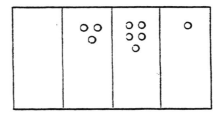

Milor has this many sheep:

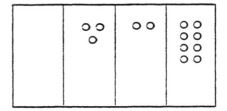

Solve this problem using the rules of the counting board.

Numbers and Numerals

Two sets that can be put in one-to-one correspondence have the same number of elements. What do we mean by the phrase "the number of elements in a set"? (A phrase that has the same meaning is "the number of a set.") When we say that the number of elements in a set A is 3, we mean that there is a one-to-one correspondence between A and the set $\{a,b,c\}$. The number 3 is the attribute in common to all sets for which there is a one-to-one correspondence with the set $\{a,b,c\}$. The number of a set S is the attribute in common to all sets for which there is a one-to-one correspondence with the set S.

We normally use the symbol 3 to represent the number 3. This symbol is called a *numeral* in our standard system of numerals, the Hindu-Arabic system. In any system of numerals there is a numeral for each number, and different numbers must be represented by different numerals.

A requirement for a good system of numerals is that given a set, you can easily figure out the numeral that represents the number of the set. One crude system of numerals is the one that represents a set by a set of stones in one-to-one correspondence with it.

Representing a Number Uniquely on a Counting Board

Another system of numerals involves representing a number by a collection of stones on a counting board, as we have just been discussing. For a counting board there are rules for passing from a set to the numeral that represents its number. Another requirement of a good system of numerals is that you can use it to compare numbers. Let's see how we can compare numbers using a counting board. Consider three numbers represented by the following counting board numerals:

Which numeral represents the largest number? You notice that in (a) and (c) there are columns in which there are more than 10 stones. You decide to reduce the number of stones used in the numerals as shown.

Thus all three numerals represent the same numbers! To tell at a glance which of two numerals represents the largest number, it might be useful to require that

■ There be only one numeral representing a given number.
■ Each numeral use the fewest possible number of stones.

The counting board system of numerals will satisfy these requirements if we adopt a rule.

NEW RULE FOR A COUNTING BOARD

The largest number of stones allowable in any column is 9.

As we mentioned earlier, a good system of numerals should have the ability to represent a given number without too much difficulty. To use a counting board to record a given number directly, suppose that you have a set of bushels (of wheat) and you want to represent its number on the counting board. You start with the right-hand column of the counting board and place a stone on the board, 1 for each bushel, as if you were pairing stones with bushels. When you have 10 stones in the right-hand column, you remove them and place 1 stone in the next column to the left. You keep doing this: For each bushel you place a stone in the right-hand column until you get 10, which you then remove and replace by a single stone in the column to its left. Whenever you accumulate 10 stones in *any* column, you immediately remove them and replace them with a single stone in the column just to its left.

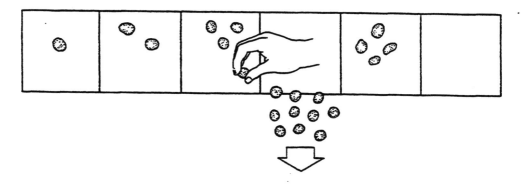

This rule works like an odometer in an automobile.

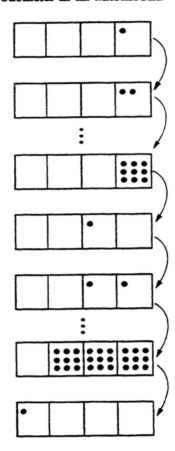

In the end you have represented the number so that there are no more than 9 stones in a column: The fewest possible stones are used (within the context of the original rules of the counting board), and this way of representing the quantity is unique: Two distinct numerals represent different numbers. You have also "counted" the bushels of wheat one by one, from whence the name, counting board.

FARIDA'S WHEAT PROBLEM   Farida now has this many bushels of wheat:

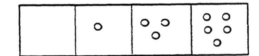

Milor has this many sheep:

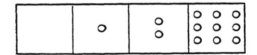

Farida wants to trade wheat for sheep—1 bushel for 1 sheep. Does she have enough wheat to buy all Milor's sheep?

A Solution to Farida's
Wheat Problem
Farida thinks: "Knowing how to represent a number directly on the counting board by 'counting' also tells me which of two counting board numerals represents the larger number.

"As I count a number on the counting board, stones begin to occupy more and more of the columns to the left.

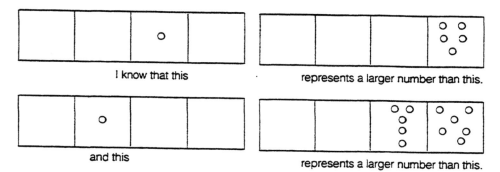

I know that this   represents a larger number than this.

and this   represents a larger number than this.

In fact, to decide which of two numerals represents the larger number, I start with the left-most column and compare the stones in that column from the two numerals. If they are the same, I move to the next column to the right. I keep doing this until I reach a column where the number of stones differs for the two numerals. The numeral with more stones there represents the larger number.

(a) represents the larger number because (a) has more stones in this column.

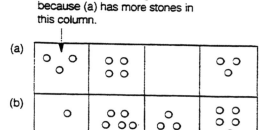

These columns are the same.

(b) represents the larger number because (b) has more stones in this column.

"Let's try this method with my bushels and Milor's sheep. Here they are, represented on a counting board.

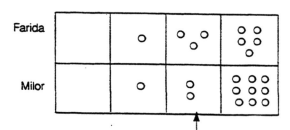

This is the first column (from the left) where the two numerals differ. Farida has more wheat because her numeral has more stones in this column.

The ancient Egyptian system of numerals is very close to the system of counting board numerals. The chart shows the system.

Unit = |

∩ = 10 | = 10 units

𝟫 = 10 ∩   = 100 units

⚶ = 10 𝟫   = 1000 units

⌐ = 10 ⚶   = 10,000 units

⌐ = 10 ⌐   = 100,000 units

⚱ = 10 ⌐   = 1,000,000 units

Take a look at some sample numerals and their Hindu-Arabic equivalents.

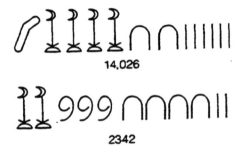

14,026

2342

A numeral in this system is called an *Egyptian numeral.*

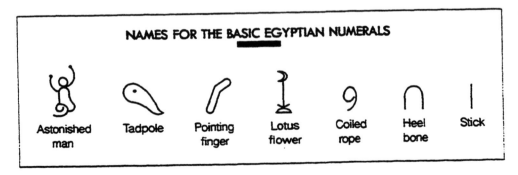

NAMES FOR THE BASIC EGYPTIAN NUMERALS

Astonished man   Tadpole   Pointing finger   Lotus flower   Coiled rope   Heel bone   Stick

It is easy to convert a counting board numeral to the Egyptian numeral representing the same number. (Two numerals, one from one numeral system and the other from another system, are *equivalent* if they represent the same number.) In fact, each of the columns of the counting board can be labeled with an Egyptian symbol so that each stone in that column represents the same number as the symbol.

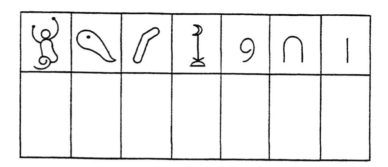

A counting board numeral consists of stones placed on a counting board. An Egyptian numeral is written. There are advantages to the latter. A written numeral is portable. You can use written numerals to keep permanent records of the numbers.

You may want to calculate with your numeral system. The Egyptian system is not very convenient for this. For example, multiplication of Egyptian numerals (using methods we use with our Hindu-Arabic numerals) would involve a lot of writing with a stylus on papyrus, a slow and tedious process. The Egyptian system was designed to record the outcomes of calculations, not to do the calculations. To calculate, Egyptians would have used a counting board, or something like it, by converting the Egyptian numerals to stones on the counting board, calculating there, then converting the counting board answer to the equivalent Egyptian numeral. The illustration shows two examples of the conversion of an Egyptian numeral to a counting board numeral.

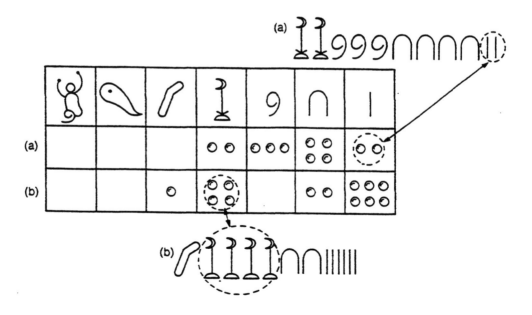

7. Write the Egyptian numeral equivalent to the following counting board numeral.

8. Two Egyptian numerals are shown. Draw pictures of the equivalent counting board numerals to decide which represents the larger number.

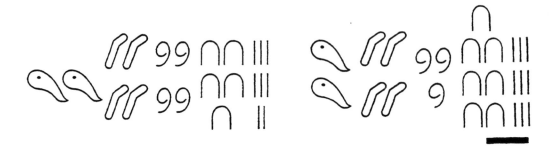

The Mathematical Idea: Egyptian Numerals, the Counting Board, and Our Own Decimal Numerals

The way an Egyptian might have used a counting board is similar to the way we use a calculator. We transfer our numerals to the calculator (we "punch in the numbers"), carry out calculations there, and, if we need to remember the results, we save the written numerals somehow. The counting board is an ancient calculator.

We do not normally use a counting board for making computations, but it can be useful for describing and understanding how our own system of written numerals works. It's easy for us to write the numeral in our system that corresponds to a quantity represented by stones on a counting board. For example, consider the following counting board setup.

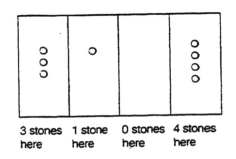

3 stones here   1 stone here   0 stones here   4 stones here

This counting board numeral is equivalent to the *decimal numeral* 3104. To go the other way, the counting board numeral equivalent to the decimal numeral 7065 is

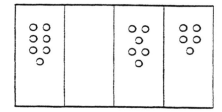

Going back and forth between counting board numerals and decimal numerals is so easy that it seems as if they were designed for each other. For an Egyptian to convert stones on a counting board into an Egyptian numeral, she has to remember which symbol goes with which column of the counting board: A stone in the third column from the right converts to φ; a stone in the sixth column converts to $\varnothing$, and so on. For us, we have to remember the 10 digits to which each configuration of stones in a column converts.

STONES IN COLUMN	DECIMAL CONVERSION
	0
O	1
O O	2
O O O	3
•	•
•	•
•	•

A typical decimal numeral consists of a row of digits. In converting a counting board numeral to the equivalent decimal numeral and back, the columns of the counting board correspond to *places* (or positions) in this row of digits. Thus, if the fourth column from the right of the counting board has 5 stones in it, then the converted decimal numeral has a 5 in the fourth place from the right.

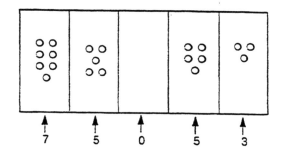

Each stone in the fourth column (from the right) represents the number one thousand. So 5 stones in the fourth column represents the number five thousand. However, 5 stones in the second column represents the number 5 tens (fifty). The symbol 5 in the numeral 75053 occurs at two different positions. It represents different numbers for each of the two occurrences. Because a given digit in a numeral represents a different number depending on its place in the row of digits, our system is called a *place value* system. The Egyptian system is not a place value system. For an Egyptian, the two symbols shown represent the same quantity.

The Egyptian digit 9 represents the number one hundred no matter what position it holds in the entire numeral. Furthermore, as a new column is added on the left of the counting board, a new Egyptian digit must be created to which a stone in that column can be converted. For a place value system, all that is needed is an additional place.

Our number words (or spoken numerals) correspond nicely to counting board numerals. In fact, if we label a column of the counting board with our word for the value of a stone occurring in that column, we would have

TEN THOUSANDS (10,000s)	THOUSANDS (1000s)	HUNDREDS (100s)	TENS (10s)	UNITS (1s)

These labels are also the names of the places of the digits in one of our written numerals. For example, 3154 is spoken as "three thousand, one hundred, five tens, four units." We don't quite say this, however. The word "unit" is dropped, and "five tens" has been condensed over the years to "fif-ty." So the spoken numeral equivalent to the written numeral 3154 is "three thousand one hundred fifty-four."

When there are no stones in a given column of the counting board, the digit 0 (zero) is placed in the corresponding position in the decimal numeral. In a place value system, it is important to have a symbol indicating no stones in a column of the counting board. In the Egyptian system there is no analogue to our written 0. There is no need for it. In our spoken numeral, no stones in a column is indicated by omitting the name of the column. We say "three thousand one hundred four" for 3104—and understand by omission that there are no tens. We say "three thousand one hundred forty" for 3140—and understand by omission that there are no units. The Egyptians write

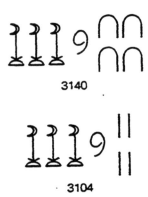

3140

3104

Our decimal system of numerals originated in India, was used in Arabic countries beginning in the eleventh century A.D. and was introduced into Western Europe by Fibonacci, a thirteenth-century Italian. The system is sometimes referred to as the *Hindu-Arabic system.*

We all know that the decimal numeral 3104 can be rewritten, using our symbols for addition and multiplication as $3104 = 3 \times 1000 + 1 \times 100 + 0 \times 10 + 4$. Similarly, $5673 = 5 \times 1000 + 6 \times 100 + 7 \times 10 + 3$.

These are examples of *expanded form* for a decimal numeral. They are possible because decimal numerals are a place value system and show in symbolic form the close connection of decimal numerals and counting board numerals. The standard methods we use for adding, subtracting, multiplying, and dividing depend heavily on being able to write decimal numerals in expanded form. Thus we will be able to use counting board numerals to show how these operations work in a tangible way, using stones instead of the decimal digits.

We will also use *expanded form on a counting board,* in which the digits of a numeral are written directly on a counting board.

	10,000s	1000s	100s	10s	1s
5673 =		5	6	7	3

EXERCISE

9. Write the expanded form for each of these decimal numerals:
   (a) 165   (b) 4073   (c) 17,078   (d) 245,673

Place Value Blocks

Another system for representing numbers that is close to our written numerals and that we will use in subsequent chapters uses a set of blocks of different sizes. These are called *place value blocks* and are related as follows:

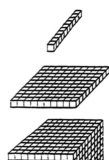

The unit is a centimeter cube:

A *long* is equal to 10 units:

A *flat* is equal to 10 longs:

A *cube* is equal to 10 flats:

The following table shows conversions of place value blocks and our numerals.

PLACE VALUE BLOCK   DECIMAL NUMERAL

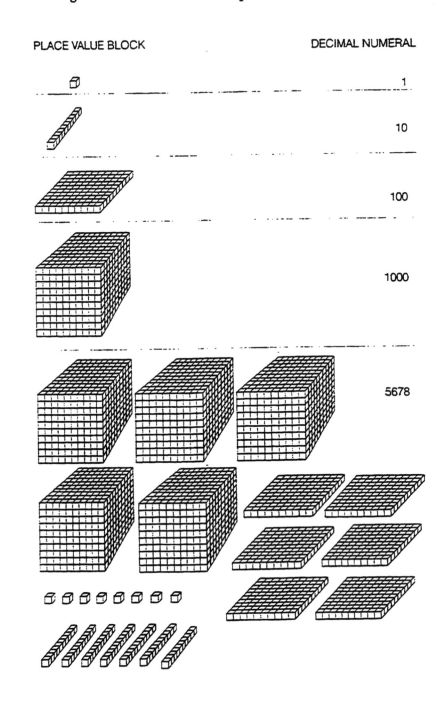

1

10

100

1000

5678

10. Write the decimal numeral equivalent to the collection of place value blocks shown below.

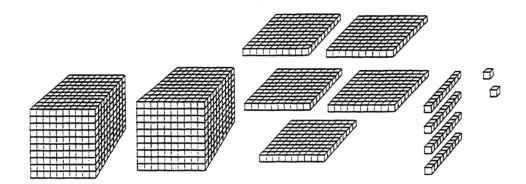

11. Draw the place value blocks equivalent to each of the following decimal numerals.
(a) 27   (b) 270   (c) 207   (d) 456   (e) 5063

The Abacus

The *abacus* is a device closely related to the counting board. There are many types of abaci; we shall describe a particularly simple version. Instead of the columns of the counting board, this abacus has wires or rods attached vertically to a board. The base of the board rests flat on the ground.

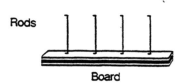

Beads are used instead of stones, and these slide on the rods.

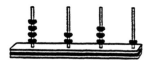

The first rod (on the right) of the abacus corresponds to the first column (on the right) of the counting board. The second rod corresponds to the second column, and so on. Thus, the counting board numeral and the abacus numeral shown in the illustration are equivalent.

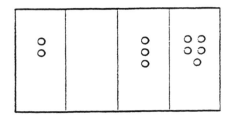

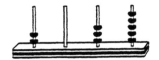

THE RUSSIAN ABACUS

This Russian abacus consists of beads on wires stretched from the top side of a frame to the bottom. There are 10 beads on each wire. The illustration shows how to "set" the decimal number 5,123,012 on the abacus.

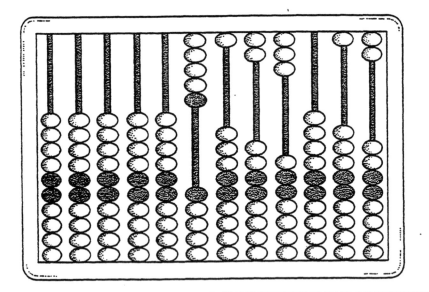

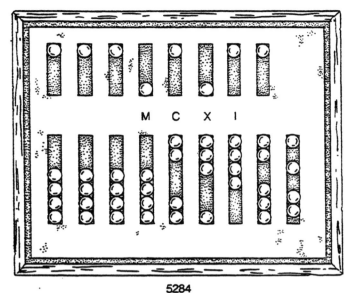

5284

A Roman abacus

Stones (*calculi*) slide in grooves carved on a board, making the Roman abacus as much a counting board as an abacus. (The two right-most grooves are reserved for fractions.)

European counting boards of the Renaissance

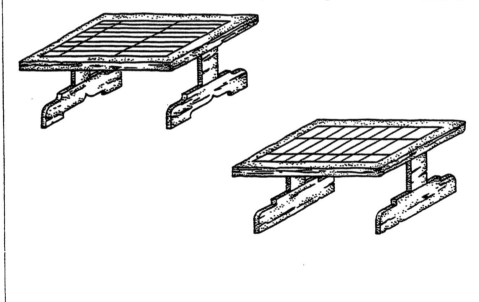

(*continues on next page*)

(continued from page 115)

The woodcut from the Renaissance shows two people calculating, one using a counting board, the other using written numerals. The female figure in the background personifies Arithmetic and appears to be deciding the debate between those on the one hand who think the abacus is the best way to calculate and those on the other hand who think the newly introduced (into Western Europe) Arabic numerals with pencil and paper are the way to go.

(Cartoon drawn by Ellen Champagne.)

In the cartoon, a takeoff on the Renaissance woodcut, the debate is between those who think the personal computer or electric calculator (modern-day abacus) is the best way to calculate and those who think Arabic numerals with pencil and paper are the way to go.

Japanese abacus (twentieth century)

For addition and subtraction, it is faster for experienced operators to use a modern abacus than it is to use either standard paper and pencil methods or a hand-held calculator.

EXERCISES

12. Write the decimal numeral equivalent to the following abacus numeral.

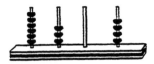

13. Draw the abacus numeral equivalent to the decimal numeral 3506.

Base Systems

For our counting board a stone in a given column is worth 10 stones in the column just to its right. This is called a *base 10* counting board. One can imagine another counting board for which a stone in a given column is worth B stones in the column just to its right. Such a counting board is called a *base B* counting board. One can also have a base B abacus. (The abacus described above is, of course, a base 10 abacus.) A system of numerals closely tied to such a counting board is called a *base system*. The base of the corresponding counting board is called the *base* of the system of numerals. The common base of the Egyptian system, our numeral system, and place value blocks is 10.*

Our system of written numerals is called a *decimal* system because it is a base 10 system. (*Decem* is the Latin word for "ten.")

Stick Numerals

Besides working with the counting board, expanded form on a counting board, place value blocks, and an abacus, we will also work with another numeral system.

Imagine a base 5 abacus. For this abacus

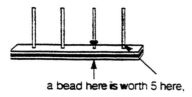
a bead here is worth 5 here,

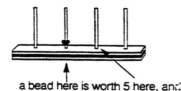
a bead here is worth 5 here, and

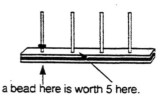
a bead here is worth 5 here.

Each bead on the first rod corresponds to an element of the set; each bead on any other rod is worth 5 beads on the rod just to its right. For example,

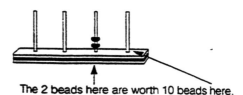
The 2 beads here are worth 10 beads here.

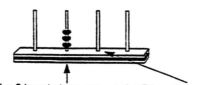
The 3 beads here are worth 15 beads here.

---

* There are place value blocks for bases other than 10. In the lab manual designed to accompany this text, there are base 5, 6, and 10 place value blocks to cut out and assemble.

Let us create a place value system of written numerals closely related to these base 5 abacus numerals. A written numeral will look very much like the equivalent abacus numeral. The table gives the "digits":

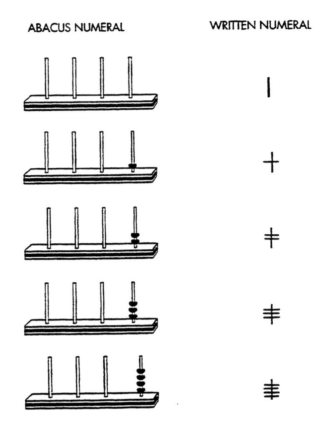

The next table gives some equivalents.

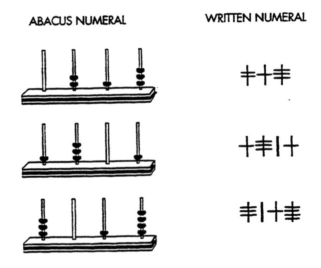

We will call these written numerals *stick numerals*.

Why Stick Numerals?

In the next few chapters we will be discussing methods for adding, subtracting, multiplying, and dividing whole numbers. In these discussions we will use stick numerals in addition to counting boards and our own numerals. We will use stick numerals because they are very much like our own. We will discuss methods for computing with stick numerals that are very much like standard methods for computing with our own numerals. Although stick numerals and the methods for working with them will seem strange, there is a purpose to using them. Their use will enable us to experience feelings similar to those felt by small children when they begin to work with our standard numerals—a system that feels strange to *them*.

In working with stick numerals it is important to remember that like the base 5 abacus from which they came, the system of stick numerals is a base 5 place value system. There are some important facts to remember.

To get a feel for stick numerals and how they work, look at the following equivalents between stick numerals and decimal numerals.

Each bead on the second rod is worth 5, so the following number is equivalent to 10.

A bead on the third rod is worth 5 on the second rod and each bead on the second rod is worth 5. So a bead on the third rod is worth 5 × 5 = 25. Thus, the following numeral is equivalent to 75.

The following numeral is equivalent to $75 + 10 + 4 = 89$.

$$\text{丰十丰}$$

The numeral 丰丰丰 is equivalent to $2 \times 25 + 3 \times 5 + 2 = 50 + 15 + 2 = 67$. Note the similarity to expanded form for our numerals.

Converting stick numerals to decimal numerals may help in understanding stick numerals. However, frequently we will work entirely within the stick numeral system and not resort to conversion from that system to ours.

Counting with stick numerals, like counting on a counting board and counting with our own numerals, works like an automobile odometer.

14. The picture below shows a farmer's calendar from the city of Styria (now in Austria) in the late Middle Ages.

The letters stand for days of the week. The symbols along the very bottom are numerals equivalent to

2 10 18 5 15 4 12 1 9 3 11 21 8 16 5 13

How does this numeral system work?

15. Represent the following collection of stones as a stick numeral. (No fair using decimal numerals as an crutch! Count using stick numerals as described in the text.)

16. For each of the following pairs of stick numerals, decide which of the two numerals represents the larger number. (No fair converting to decimal numerals! Refer to the method of comparing with base 10 counting board numerals.)

$$\overline{\overline{+}}\,\overline{\overline{\overline{+}}}\,|\,\overline{\overline{\overline{+}}}\quad\text{vs.}\quad\overline{\overline{+}}\,\overline{\overline{\overline{+}}}\,\overline{+}|\qquad\overline{\overline{\overline{+}}}\,||\,\overline{\overline{+}}\quad\text{vs.}\quad\overline{\overline{+}}\,\overline{\overline{\overline{+}}}\,\overline{\overline{+}}\,\overline{\overline{\overline{+}}}$$

$$\overline{\overline{\overline{+}}}\,\overline{+}\,|\,\overline{+}\quad\text{vs.}\quad\overline{\overline{\overline{+}}}\,\overline{+}\,\overline{+}|$$

Modeling Standard Numerals

Counting boards, abaci, and place value blocks make the standard numeral system concrete and tangible and thus help us to understand how it works. These tangible systems are models for ours and will enable us later to use the problem-solving strategy, *make a model*, when working with our numerals.

i

When we say that the number of elements in a set S is 3, we mean that there is a one-to-one correspondence between S and the set $\{1,2,3\}$. We write $n(S) = 3$ to express this fact. Thus $n(\{a,b,c\}) = n(\{@,\#,\&\}) = n(\{1,2,3\}) = 3$. Following are some definitions related to this notation.

DEFINITIONS RELATED TO NUMBERS

If S is a set, then $n(S)$ denotes the *number of S*, or the *number of elements in S*.
If S is in one-to-one correspondence with the set $\{1,2,\ldots,N\}$, then we write $n(S) = N$.

If ϕ is the empty set, the set with no elements, then we say that the number of elements in ϕ is zero and write $n(\phi) = 0$.

A *natural number* is any member of the set $\{1,2,3,\ldots\}$.

A *whole number* is any member of the set $\{0,1,2,3,\ldots\}$.

Exponential Notation

The numbers 10, 100, 1000, 10,000, ... are important to our system of numerals. They are related as shown.

$$100 = \text{ten } 10\text{s} = 10 \times 10$$
$$1000 = \text{ten } 100\text{s} = 10 \times 100$$
$$10{,}000 = \text{ten } 1000\text{s} = 10 \times 1000$$
$$100{,}000 = \text{ten } 10{,}000\text{s} = 10 \times 10000$$

And so on.

We can also write them this way.

$$100 = 10 \times 10$$
$$1000 = 10 \times 10 \times 10$$
$$10{,}000 = 10 \times 10 \times 10 \times 10$$
$$100{,}000 = 10 \times 10 \times 10 \times 10 \times 10$$

And so on.

There is a shorthand way to write these numbers using the convention of exponential notation.

EXPONENTIAL NOTATION

For any number N,

$$\underbrace{N \times N \times \cdots \times N}_{p \text{ times}} = N^p.$$

The number p is called the *exponent* of N^p.

Using exponential notation, we can write

$$10 = 10^1$$
$$100 = 10^2$$
$$1000 = 10^3$$
$$10000 = 10^4$$
$$100000 = 10^5$$

and, in general,

$$\underbrace{100\ldots00}_{n \text{ zeros}} = 10^n.$$

The numbers 10^n are called the *powers of 10*. Note the economy of symbols achieved using exponential notation.

How does expanded form for a whole number look when exponential notation is used?

$$5843 = 5 \times 10^3 + 8 \times 10^2 + 4 \times 10^1 + 3.$$
$$9,234,705 = 9 \times 10^6 + 2 \times 10^5 + 3 \times 10^4 + 4 \times 10^3 + 7 \times 10^2 + 0 \times 10^1 + 5.$$

EXERCISES

17. Write the numbers in exponential notation as powers of 10:
    (a) 1 million   (b) 1 billion   (c) 1 trillion

18. Write the numbers in expanded form using exponential notation:
    (a) 12,378   (b) 508,122   (c) 89,142,693

3.4   EXTENDING THE IDEAS: OTHER NUMERAL SYSTEMS

Bases Other than 10

Recall the stick numerals and their equivalents, shown in the table.

STICK NUMERAL	DECIMAL NUMERAL	DECIMAL NUMERAL IN EXPONENTIAL NOTATION
⊣	5	5^1
⊣I	25	5^2
⊣II	125	5^3
⊣III	625	5^4
⊣IIII	3125	5^5
⊣IIIII	15,625	5^6
⋮	⋮	⋮

The stick numeral ‡┼∥‡┼ converts to a decimal numeral as shown.

$$‡┼∥‡┼ = 3 \times 5^4 + 2 \times 5^3 + 0 \times 5^2 + 4 \times 5^1 + 1.$$

The expression on the right-hand side, using exponential notation, allows you to determine the equivalent decimal numeral.

Commonly, the expression $3 \times 5^4 + 2 \times 5^3 + 0 \times 5^2 + 4 \times 5^1 + 1$ is written 32041_{five}. The numeral 32041_{five} is called a *standard* base 5 numeral. Of course, a stick numeral is also a base 5 numeral. However, the standard base 5 numerals are the ones you are most likely to encounter in other sources. Incidentally, 34_{five} is read as "three four, base five," *not* "thirty-four, base five." Thirty-four means three 10s and 4, not three 5s and 4. Likewise, 201_{five} is read as "two zero one, base five" (and also as "two oh one, base five").

The notation for standard base 5 numerals is commonly used for other bases. For example,

$$57032_{eight} = 5 \times 8^4 + 7 \times 8^3 + 0 \times 8^2 + 3 \times 8^1 + 2.$$

The numeral on the left is pronounced "five seven zero three two, base eight." The 5, 7, 0, 3, and 2 are the *digits* of this base 8 numeral. The possible digits of a standard base 8 numeral are 0, 1, 2, 3, 4, 5, 6, and 7, just as the possible digits of a standard base 5 numeral are 0, 1, 2, 3, and 4.

Notice that if you multiply out the right-hand side of the 57032_{eight} equation, you get

$$5 \times 8^4 + 7 \times 8^3 + 0 \times 8^2 + 3 \times 8^1 + 2$$
$$= 5 \times 4096 + 7 \times 512 + 0 \times 64 + 3 \times 8 + 2$$
$$= 20{,}480 + 3584 + 0 + 24 + 2$$
$$= 24{,}090.$$

Thus, $57032_{eight} = 24090_{ten}$. The $_{ten}$ usually is omitted from a base 10 numeral.
Another example is

$$100101_{two} = 1 \times 2^5 + 0 \times 2^4 + 0 \times 2^3 + 1 \times 2^2 + 0 \times 2^1 + 1.$$

Multiplying out the right-hand side of this equation, we get

$$1 \times 2^5 + 0 \times 2^4 + 0 \times 2^3 + 1 \times 2^2 + 0 \times 2^1 + 1$$
$$= 1 \times 32 + 0 \times 16 + 0 \times 8 + 1 \times 4 + 0 \times 2 + 1$$
$$= 32 + 4 + 1$$
$$= 37.$$

That is, $100101_{two} = 37$. Notice that the digits of a standard base 2 numeral are 0 and 1.

Both base 8 and base 2 numerals are used internally in computers. Another base used by computers is base 16. Since a base 16 system of numerals needs 16 digits, we will need some additional digits in addition to the traditional ones. The digits commonly used for base 16 numerals are 0, 1, 2, 3, 4, 5, 6, 7, 8, 9, A, B, C, D, E, and F. In this system $A_{sixteen} = 10$, $B_{sixteen} = 11$, $C_{sixteen} = 12$, and so on, for example,

$$7 \times 16^4 + 11 \times 16^3 + 0 \times 16^2 + 14 \times 16^1 + 5 = 7B0E5_{sixteen}.$$

19. Find the base 10 numeral equivalent to $9A3F_{sixteen}$.

20. Find the base 10 numeral equivalent to 11001011_{two}.

21. Find the base 10 numeral equivalent to 605_{seven}.

EXAMPLES OF SPOKEN SYSTEMS OF NUMERALS

	WORD	MEANING
1	tai	
2	lua	
3	tolu	
4	vari	
5	luna	hand
6	otai	other one
7	olua	other two
8	otolu	other three
9	ovair	other four
10	lua luna	two hands

A base 5 spoken system of numerals: the Api language of the New Hebrides.

1	urapun	3	okosa-urapun	5	okosa-okosa-urapun
2	okosa	4	okosa-okosa	6	okosa-okosa-okosa

A base 2 spoken system of numerals: a western tribe of Torres Straits.

Converting from One Base to Another

As you can see from the previous discussion, it is easy to convert a numeral in a base other than 10 to a standard base 10 numeral. It is also easy to convert from a base 10 numeral. Let's do an example.

Let's write the base 6 numeral for 967 (base 10 numeral). First divide 967 by 6 getting a quotient and remainder.

$$\begin{array}{r} 161 \text{ R1} \\ 6\overline{)967} \end{array}$$

(If you have 967 unit place value blocks and convert as many of them as you can into base 6 *longs*, you get 161 longs with 1 unit left over.) Then do the same thing with 161: Divide it by 6 getting a quotient and remainder.

$$\begin{array}{r} 26 \text{ R5} \\ 6\overline{)161} \end{array}$$

$$\begin{array}{r} \text{R1} \\ 6\overline{)967} \end{array}$$

If you convert the 161 base 6 *longs* into base 6 *flats*, you get 26 flats with 5 longs left over. Then do the same thing with 26: Divide it by 6 getting a quotient and a remainder.

$$\begin{array}{r} 4 \text{ R2} \\ 6\overline{)26} \end{array}$$

$$\begin{array}{r} \text{R5} \\ 6\overline{)161} \end{array}$$

$$\begin{array}{r} \text{R1} \\ 6\overline{)967} \end{array}$$

If you convert the base 6 flats into base 6 *cubes*, you get 4 cubes with 2 flats left over. Since the last quotient you get is less than the base, you are finished. This last quotient and the previous remainders are your digits.

$$967_{ten} = 4251_{six}.$$

EXERCISES
22. Find the base 6 numeral equivalent to 1425.

23. Find the base 8 numeral equivalent to 967.

24. Find the base 2 numeral equivalent to 967.

Numeral Systems of Historical Importance

The chart on page 127 illustrates several examples of different numeral systems used historically.

HINDU-ARABIC	GREEK	ROMAN	CHINESE	EGYPTIAN	BABYLONIAN
1	α	I	丨	丨	𒁹
2	β	II	丨丨	丨丨	𒈫
3	γ	III	丨丨丨	丨丨丨	𒐈
4	δ	IV	丨丨丨丨	丨丨丨丨	𒐉
5	ε	V	丨丨丨丨丨	丨丨丨 丨丨	𒐋
6	ϛ	VI	⊤	丨丨丨 丨丨丨	𒐌
7	ζ	VII	⊤	丨丨丨丨 丨丨丨	𒑅
8	η	VIII	⫪	丨丨丨丨 丨丨丨丨	𒑆
9	θ	IX	⫫	丨丨丨 丨丨丨 丨丨丨	𒑇
10	ι	X	一〇	∩	〈
20	κ	XX	=〇	∩∩	〈〈
30	λ	XXX	≡〇	∩∩∩	〈〈〈
40	μ	XL	≣〇	∩∩ ∩∩	〈〈 〈〈
50	ν	L	≣〇	∩∩∩ ∩∩	〈〈〈 〈〈
60	ξ	LX	⊥〇	∩∩∩ ∩∩∩	𒁹
70	ο	LXX	⊥〇	∩∩∩∩ ∩∩∩	𒑖
80	π	LXXX	⊥〇	∩∩∩∩ ∩∩∩∩	𒑗
90	ϟ	XC	⊥〇	∩∩∩ ∩∩∩ ∩∩∩	𒑘
100	ρ	C	丨〇〇	𖢁	𒑖〈〈
200	σ	CC	丨丨〇〇	𖢁𖢁	
300	τ	CCC	丨丨丨〇〇	𖢁𖢁𖢁	
400	υ	CD	丨丨丨丨〇〇	𖢁𖢁𖢁𖢁	
500	φ	D	丨丨丨丨丨〇〇	𖢁����	
600	χ	DC	⊤〇〇	�×6	〈
700	ψ	DCC	⊤〇〇	�×7	
800	ω	DCCC	⫪〇〇	�×8	
1000	͵α	M	一〇〇〇	𓆼	

Babylonian Numerals

The Babylonian system, in use before 2000 B.C., is of particular interest and is worthy of more explanation. It is a base 60 place value system. There are 59 "digits," each one made of the two symbols ⟨ and ⟨. Some examples are shown in the chart of equivalent historical numerals. Here are some more.

BABYLONIAN "DIGIT"	EQUIVALENT DECIMAL NUMERAL
⟨ꟷꟷꟷ	13
⟨ ꟷꟷꟷ	37
ꟷ	59

The Babylonian digit ꟷ is equivalent to 1, and the digit ⟨ is equivalent to 10. The other 57 nonzero digits are constructed from these. For example, to construct the Babylonian digit equivalent to the decimal numeral 48, take 4 Babylonian digits for 10 and 8 Babylonian digits for 1 and put them together in the following way.

To construct the Babylonian digit equivalent to the decimal numeral 25, take 2 Babylonian digits for 10 and 5 Babylonian digits for 1 and put them together in the following manner.

These two examples and the other Babylonian digits that appear in the chart should give you a good idea of what the pattern is.

A typical Babylonian numeral will be a sequence of these digits. For example, the Babylonian numeral

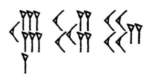

has the digits $\langle\text{𝟛𝟛}$ $\langle\text{𝟚𝟚}$ and $\langle\langle\text{𝟚}$ in succession. The decimal equivalents, in succession, are 17, 34, 42.

The Babylonian numeral [cuneiform symbols]

has the digits [cuneiform], [cuneiform], [cuneiform], and [cuneiform]

in succession. The decimal equivalents, in succession, are 7, 23, 5, and 38.

Here are two examples of conversions of Babylonian numerals to our standard base 10 numerals.

[cuneiform symbols]

$$= 17 \times 60^2 + 34 \times 60^1 + 42.$$

[cuneiform symbols]

$$= 7 \times 600^3 + 23 \times 60^2 + 5 \times 60^1 + 38.$$

In early uses of Babylonian numerals there was no symbol equivalent to our zero to "hold a place." One would have had to decide from the context which was meant by the symbol 𝟙. However, around 400 B.C. the Greeks began to use the symbol o (this is the Greek letter *omicron*) as a place holder. Thus 60 would be written 𝟙o and 1 would be written 𝟙. Moreover,

[cuneiform symbols] o [cuneiform]

$$= 23 \times 60^2 + 0 \times 60^1 + 11.$$

As you can see from the chart of equivalent historical numerals, the Greeks of classical time had their own system of written numerals. However, whenever involved calculations had to be made, the Greeks used the Babylonian system because it was much more efficient. This is what the mathematician Archimedes (287–212 B.C.) and the astronomer Ptolemy (2d century A.D.) did. It is likely that the Babylonian system was developed because of the need to make large numbers of astronomical calculations. The number of minutes in an hour (60), the number of seconds in a minute (60), and the number of angle degrees in a circle (360) are all vestiges within our own measurement systems of the Babylonian base 60 system.

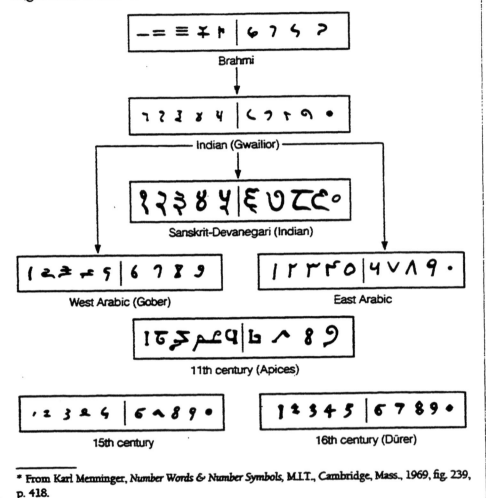

THE EVOLUTION OF WRITTEN DIGITS IN THE HINDU-ARABIC NUMERAL SYSTEM

The chart* shows the evolution of the written forms of digits for the Hindu-Arabic system of numerals. The changes are due mostly to the fact that they were written by hand. In the sixteenth century, just after the invention of the printing press, the forms of the digits stabilized to forms very much like what they are today. The symbol for zero (a place holder) is presumably of Greek origin from around 400 B.C.

Brahmi

Indian (Gwailior)

Sanskrit-Devanegari (Indian)

West Arabic (Gober)

East Arabic

11th century (Apices)

15th century

16th century (Dürer)

* From Karl Menninger, *Number Words & Number Symbols*, M.I.T., Cambridge, Mass., 1969, fig. 239, p. 418.

EXERCISES

25. Convert the following Babylonian numerals into standard decimal numerals.

(a) 𒐈𒌋𒐕   (b) 𒌋𒐉𒌋𒐈   (c) 𒌍𒐕 𒌍𒐕

(d) 𒌋𒐕𒌍𒐉𒌋   (e) 𒐈𒌋𒐕 0 𒌋𒌋𒌍𒐉𒌍

26. Convert the expressions in decimal numerals to Babylonian numerals.

(a) $12 \times 60 + 32$ (b) $23 \times 60^2 + 44 \times 60 + 7$

(c) $7 \times 60^3 + 15 \times 60^2 + 39$

PROBLEM SET

1. A certain shepherd wants to be sure that he has the same number of sheep when he brings them in from pasture in the evening as he had when he let them out for pasture in the morning. How can he do this even though he knows nothing about counting?

2. Here are some pairs of (base 10) counting boards. The stones on each counting board represent a number. Some boards do not satisfy the "new" rule: There are columns with more than 9 stones in them. Put each board in compliance with the rule but make sure that it still represents the same number as before. Indicate which board of the pair represents the larger number.

(a)

(b)

(c)

3. Several counting board numerals are shown below. Find the standard numeral equivalent to each.

(a)

(b)

(c)

(d)

4. Draw the counting board numerals equivalent to the standard numerals
   (a) 68   (b) 4057   (c) 4507   (d) 4570   (e) 70,000

5. Here are two Egyptian numerals. Decide which represents the larger number.

(a)

(b)

6. The standard numeral 3104 can be written in expanded form in the following two ways:

   $3104 = 3 \times 1000 + 1 \times 100 + 0 \times 10 + 4$ and $3104 = 3 \times 10^3 + 1 \times 10^2 + 0 \times 10^1 + 4$.

   Write each of the following numerals in expanded form in the same two ways.
   (a) 452   (b) 31   (c) 701   (d) 89,425   (e) 30,016   (f) 2,708,280

7. For each pile of place value blocks shown below write the standard numeral equivalent to it.

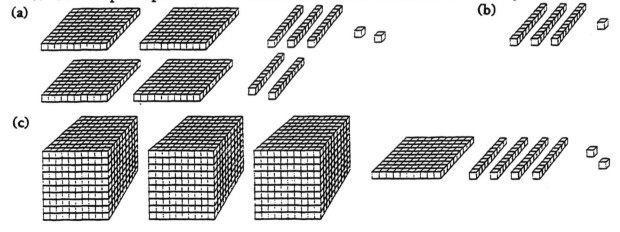

(a)

(b)

(c)

8. For each of the standard numerals, draw a pile of place value blocks equivalent to it.
   (a) 17   (b) 3172   (c) 2003   (d) 513

9. Here are base 10 abaci with beads on them. For each abacus write the equivalent standard numeral.
   (a)   (b)

10. For each of the standard numerals, draw the equivalent base 10 abacus numeral.
    (a) 5690   (b) 90,073

11. For each of the stick numerals write the next largest stick numeral.
    (a)   (b)   (c)
    (d)   (e)   (f)

12. Write each of the stick numerals in expanded form (write "plus" in place of a plus sign, +).
    (a)   (b)   (c)
    (d)   (e)   (f)

13. For each pair of stick numerals, decide which represents the larger number.
    (a)
    (b)

14. Write the following standard decimal numerals in expanded form using exponential notation.
    (a) 37,153   (b) 498,000   (c) 17,320,508   (d) 223,606,798

15. For each of the following numerals, find the base 10 numeral equivalent to it.
    (a) $CAB_{sixteen}$ (b) 110110101_{two} (c) 430_{five} (d) 873_{nine}

16. Find the standard numeral equivalent to 377 in each base.
    (a) base 16   (b) base 2   (c) base 5   (d) base 9

17. Find the standard base 10 numeral equivalent to each Babylonian numeral.
    (a)   (b)

18. Draw a number line to include the numbers from zero to 100. Mark on this number line the powers of 2, 3, 5, and 10 that are between zero and 100 inclusive. Distinguish the different sets of powers in some way, perhaps by using different colors. Use what you have done to determine the number of digits needed to represent 100 in each of these different bases.

For each problem remaining, document as clearly and completely as you can your solution to the problem. Include the steps you took to solve the problem, mention the problems or solutions from the text that gave you ideas, and include the problem-solving strategies you used. Outline and organize your work before writing your final report in essay form.

Problems 19–22 are ones that people in an innumerate society may have encountered. Solve them as they might have—by pairing elements of sets, but without our numerals, our methods of counting, and our sophisticated operations on whole numbers.

19. The citizens of Dotta represent a number by making dot marks on sheepskin, one dot for each element of a set. The law of Dotta requires that each business negotiation be recorded by a pair of these Dotta numerals. A copy of the document for one day's business activities is provided. The numeral on the left is either the offer or the asking price (in dottas, the monetary unit), depending on who began the negotiations, the buyer or the seller. The numeral on the right is the actual price paid. A Dotta buyer never pays more than the seller asks, and a Dotta seller never asks less than a buyer offers. Determine who initiated each negotiation and describe how you figured it out.

(a)

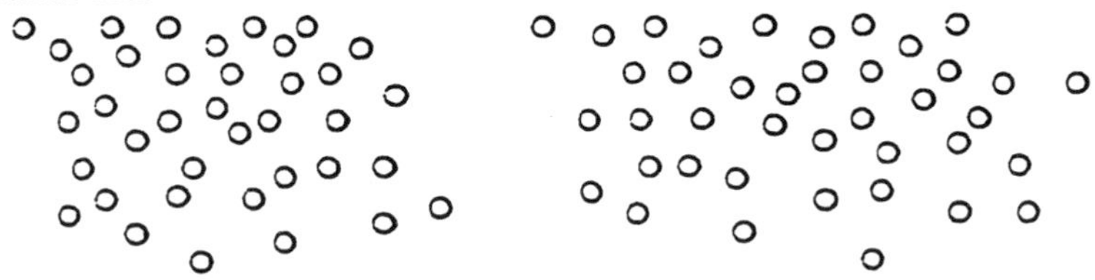

(b)

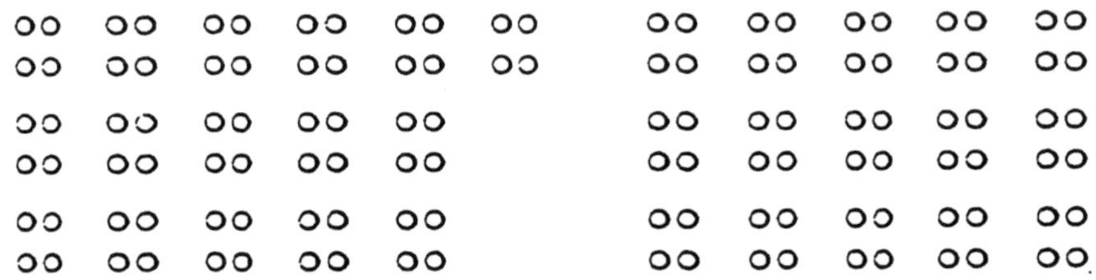

(c)

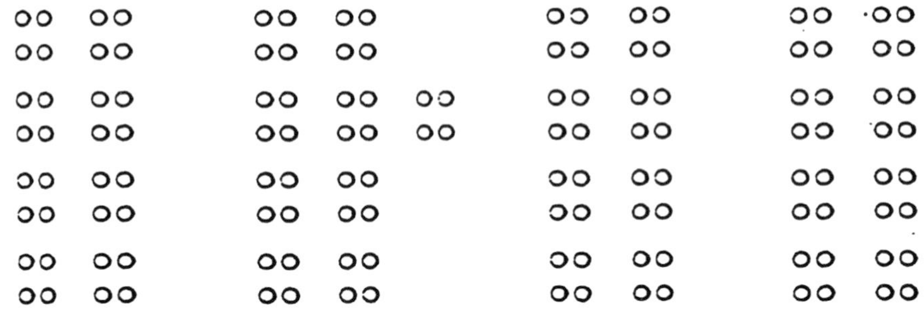

20. Ugboo, his mother and father, his brother Nip, his sisters Snip and Snap, and little brother Norum are planning a trip to a faraway village of Dom. Ugboo's friend Lagor once took a trip to Dom and kept track of it by bringing back a pile of sticks, one for each day of traveling. These are shown on the left. On the right is a pile of stones, one for each loaf of bread Ugboo's mother has baked for the trip. In the middle is a pile of square tiles, one for each member of Ugboo's family.

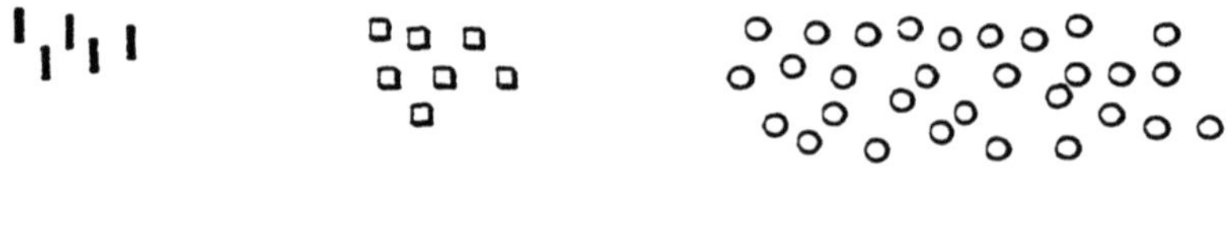

Lagor has told Ugboo that each person must have one loaf of bread for each day of travel. Make a copy of the items in the picture above and do (a) or (b), whichever is appropriate.

(a) On the copy of the picture, circle the stones representing the loaves that will be left over from the trip.

(b) Draw a balloon and in it draw pictures of stones representing the loaves of bread that yet must be baked if there is to be enough bread for the trip.

21. On the left in the illustration is a pile of sticks, 1 for each blanket that Lagor has. On the right is a pile of stones, 1 for each sheep Ugboo has. Lagor wants to trade all the blankets for sheep. Ugboo has said, | | | blankets for each sheep. Lagor agrees to this.

On a copy of the items in the illustration, either circle the sticks representing the blankets Lagor has left over (after "buying") all of Ugboo's sheep or circle the sheep Lagor cannot buy after he has used up all his blankets.

$$||\,|\,|\,|\,|\,|\,|\,|\,| \qquad \circ \; \circ \; \circ \; \circ$$
$$||\,|\,|\,|\,|\,|\,|\,|\,|\,| \qquad \circ \quad \circ \quad \circ \quad \circ$$

22. Lagor now wants to buy horses and cows from Gorul. Again, Lagor has blankets to trade as represented by the sticks on the left in the illustration, 1 stick for each blanket. Gorul's horses are represented by the pile of square tiles, 1 tile for each horse; his cows are represented by stones, 1 stone for each cow. Gorul and Lagor agree that the prices are | | | for each cow and | | | | for each horse. Lagor will trade blankets for all of Gorul's cows and buy as many horses as he can with the remaining blankets. On a copy of the illustration, circle a set of stones in one-to-one correspondence with the horses Lagor can buy and circle the set of sticks in one-to-one correspondence with the blankets Lagor uses to buy cows and horses.

$$||\,|\,|\,|\,|\,|\,|\,|\,|\,|\,| \qquad \circ \qquad \square \quad \square$$
$$||\,|\,|\,|\,|\,|\,|\,|\,|\,|\,| \qquad \circ \;\; \circ\,\circ \qquad \square \; \square$$
$$\qquad\qquad\qquad\qquad \circ \quad \circ \qquad \square\,\square\,\square$$

23. Farida wants to trade wheat for Milor's sheep—1 bushel of wheat for 1 sheep. Farida wants to know if she has enough wheat. Here are some clues:

■ Farida has this many bushels of wheat:

■ Milor has this many sheep:

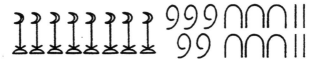

Help Farida solve this problem. Don't convert Egyptian numerals to standard numerals; work completely within the Egyptian system.

24. Ruut grows barley and Pilan raises goats. Ruut wants to trade the barley he has raised this month and last month for goats, 1 bushel of barley for 1 goat. Ruut wants to know whether he has enough barley to buy all the goats. Here are some clues.

■ Ruut harvested this many bushels of barley last month:

■ Ruut harvested this many bushels of barley this month:

■ Pilan has this many goats for trade:

Help Ruut solve this problem. As in problem 21, work completely within the Egyptian system.

25. Convert the collection of base 5 place value blocks into an equivalent one in which there are no more than 4 blocks of one type.

26. Decide which of the following two collections of base 5 place value blocks represents the larger number. Stay within the system of place value blocks while you do this.

(a)   (b)

27. Mina, a child in Ugboo's village many generations later, is learning about stick numerals in school. Below are shown homework sheets in which she is being asked to convert some bunches of stones to stick numerals and vice versa. Help her finish her homework.

(a)

○ ○ ○ ○ ○ ○ ○	++
○ ○ ○ ○	
○○○○○ ○ ○○○○	
○ ○ ○ ○ ○○○○	

(b)

‡‡	○○○○○○ ○○○○○○
+‡	
≢|	
+|||	

28. Three prosperous chicken farmers from Glapora have decided to trade in the market of Mina's village. Each comes with a bag of stones, a stone for each chicken he wants to sell. To trade in the village market, the farmers from Glapora must convert their stones to the village's stick numeral system. Help them do this. Here are the stones from each farmer's bag.

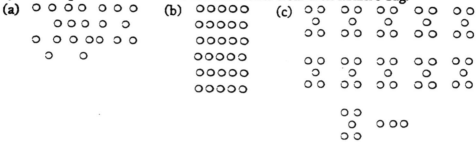

(a) ○ ○ ○ ○   ○ ○ ○
   ○ ○ ○ ○   ○ ○
   ○ ○ ○ ○ ○○ ○ ○
   ○   ○

(b) ○○○○○
   ○○○○○
   ○○○○○
   ○○○○○
   ○○○○○
   ○○○○○

(c) ○○ ○○ ○○ ○○ ○○
    ○   ○   ○   ○   ○
   ○○ ○○ ○○ ○○ ○○

   ○○ ○○ ○○ ○○ ○○
    ○   ○   ○   ○   ○
   ○○ ○○ ○○ ○○ ○○

   ○ ○
    ○   ○ ○ ○
   ○ ○

29. On the homework sheet below, Mina is being asked—for various pairs of stick numerals—to determine which represents the larger number. Help her.

(a) ≢≢++≢ or ≢+≢+≢   (b) ≢++ or ≢|≢   (c) ≢≢≢≢ or +||||

(d) ≢|| or +++   (e) +|| or +||| (f) ≢≢+≢ or ≢≢+|

30. To help her learn about stick numerals, Mina is using base 5 place value blocks and a base 5 counting board. Help her fill in the blanks in the table.

STICK NUMERAL	PLACE VALUE BLOCKS	COUNTING BOARD NUMERAL
+≢≢	(flat, 2 longs, 3 units)	(○ | ○ ○ | ○ ○ ○)
	(3 cubes, 3 flats, 2 units)	
		(○ ○ ○ ○ | ○ ○ | ○)
≢|+|		

31. Archaeologists are studying a scroll discovered on the site of Mina's ancient village. They found some stick numerals on the scroll.

(a) +| (b) +|| (c) +||| (d) +|||| (e) ≠≢

(f) ≢+| (g) +≢ (h) +≢|≢ (i) +≢+ (j) +|≢≢|

To complete their study, they must convert these numerals to standard numerals. Help them do this.

32. You have come across a copy of a Mayan "manuscript" showing a list of numerals in the Mayan system.

(a) You suspect that this list has a purpose and want to figure out what it is. You have heard that the Mayan numeral system is a place value system with a base. You wonder: What is the base of the system? What are the digits? What is the symbol for zero? Answer these questions as you break the puzzle of the list.

(b) Based on what you learned in (a), determine which Mayan numeral in each pair represents the larger number.

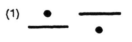

(c) Convert the following sets of stones into Mayan numerals.

(d) As an archaeologist, you need to convert Mayan numerals into standard decimal numerals. Do this for the numerals shown.

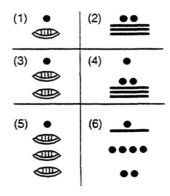

MULTIPLE-CHOICE QUESTIONS

Several possible answers are given for each question. Choose the item that answers the question best.

1. Table Top sells kitchen table tops that are either round or square and either plastic or wooden. The manager denotes the set of all table tops she has on hand by *T*, the set of round table tops by *R*, and the set of plastic table tops by *P*. Then she draws a diagram:

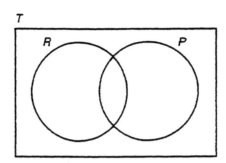

Consider the set of table tops corresponding to the shaded portion of the next diagram:

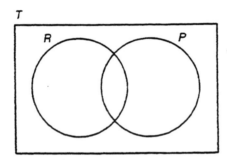

The best description of this set is
  (a) The set of tops that are round but not plastic
  (b) The set of tops that are round and wooden
  (c) The set of tops that are either wooden or square but not both
  (d) The set of tops that are both round and plastic
  (e) The set of tops that are round or wooden or both

2. Table Top is having a sale. In its advertisement you read that in the sale there will be 22 round table tops and 15 wooden table tops. You are opening a café, need to buy a large quantity of table tops, and are considering buying your table tops at the Table Top sale. Based on the information in the ad, the most accurate conclusion you can reach concerning the total number of table tops for sale is
  (a) A minimum of 15 and a maximum of 22
  (b) A minimum of 7 and a maximum of 15
  (c) A minimum of 22 and a maximum of 37
  (d) A minimum of 15 and a maximum of 37
  (e) A minimum of 7 and a maximum of 22

3. A clothing factory inspector examines shirts for the following types of defects: buttons missing, defects in the cloth, and defects in the stitching. He has examined a 100 shirt lot and tabulated his results in a Venn diagram:

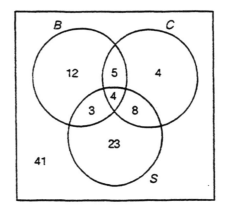

Here B = set of shirts with buttons missing, C = set of shirts with defects in the cloth, and S = set of shirts with defects in the stitching.

The number of shirts with no buttons missing but with a defect in stitching is
(a) 26   (b) 31   (c) 38   (d) 76   (e) 7

4. Shown is a collection of base 4 place value blocks. This is equivalent to which standard decimal numeral?

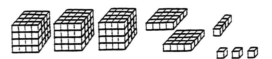

(a) 135   (b) 231   (c) 3213   (d) 9   (e) 59

5. The Health Food Shop sells raisins at \$3.65/lb and granola at \$2.35/lb. The owner wants to make 80 lb of a hike mix consisting of granola and raisins and costing \$3.30/lb. To figure out how many pounds of raisins and how many pounds of granola should go into the mix, the owner decides to make some guesses and organize them into a chart, hoping that he can zero in on a solution. Here is the beginning of his chart and his first guess:

RAISINS IN HIKE MIX (POUNDS)	GRANOLA IN HIKE MIX (POUNDS)	COST OF RAISINS IN MIX	COST OF GRANOLA IN MIX	TOTAL COST OF MIX	TARGET COST OF MIX
30	50	\$109.50	\$117.50	\$227.00	

The target cost of the mix is
(a) \$240   (b) \$227   (c) \$292   (d) \$188   (e) \$264

6. The owner makes another guess and continues to fill in the chart.

RAISINS IN HIKE MIX (POUNDS)	GRANOLA IN HIKE MIX (POUNDS)	COST OF RAISINS IN MIX	COST OF GRANOLA IN MIX	TOTAL COST OF MIX	TARGET COST OF MIX
30	50	$109.50	$117.50	$227.00	
45	35	?			

The amount that should go in the space marked "?" is
(a) $246.50   (b) $105.75   (c) $127.75   (d) $164.25   (e) $82.25

7. The collection of stones on a (base 10) counting board is equivalent to which standard decimal numeral?

(a) 4125   (b) 3025   (c) 3026   (d) 3036   (e) 4025

8. Ugboo wants to trade as many blankets as he can for Lagor's sheep. This many blankets (I I I) are to be traded for this many sheep (o o o o). Here are Ugboo's blankets

        I I I   I
        I I I I
        I I I   I
              I I   I
        I I I   I

and here are Lagor's sheep

What will be left over after all the trading has taken place?
(a) II O O O   (b) O O   (c) II O O   (d) II   (e) I O O O

9. This quantity of stones

    ooooo ooooo ooooo ooooooo
    ooooo ooooo ooooo
    ooooo

converted to stick numbers is
(a) ≢⊣⊦   (b) ⊣⊦⊦   (c) ≢⊦   (d) ⊣≢I   (e) ⊣≢⊦

10. A universal set U has subsets A and B. The subset $A' \cap B$ corresponds to the shaded portion of which diagram below?

(a) U
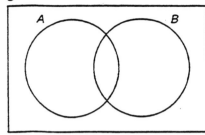

(b) U
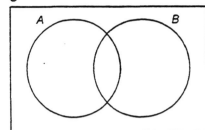

(c) U
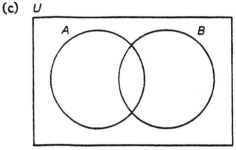

(d) U
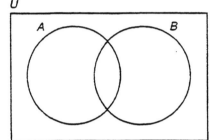

(e) U
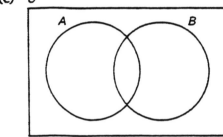

ESSAY QUESTIONS
For each of the remaining problems, document your solution carefully in the form of an essay.

11. A personnel director is trying to narrow the selection process in hiring a new computer specialist. Of the 80 applicants, he wants to know how many have both a college education as well as at least four years of work experience with computers. He has tabulated the following information so far:

42 have a college education.

37 have had at least four years of work experience with computers.

13 have had no college education and have less than four years of work experience with computers.

Use the information to help him solve his problem.

12. You are hiking from the bottom of Death Valley (at 289 ft below sea level) to the top of Telescope Peak (at 10,811 ft above sea level), a mountain at the edge of the Valley.

When you leave on your hike the temperature at the bottom of Death Valley is 50°C and drops by 1°C for every 300 ft in elevation gain. What will the temperature be when you reach the top of the mountain?

13. In the country of Xoran the money system is as follows:

Yellow (Y) is the basic coin.
Green (G) is worth (Y)(Y)(Y)(Y).
Red (R) is worth (G)(G).
Blue (B) is worth (R)(R)(R).

You wish to buy a camel whose price is

(B)(B)(B)(B) (R) (G)(G)(G) (Y)(Y).

With you, you have

(G)(G) (Y)(Y)(Y)(Y)(Y)(Y)(Y)
(B) (R)(R)(R)(R)(R).

Can you buy the camel? Why or why not?

14. We were driving across the desert, but my father refused to turn on the air conditioning. "You know that if I turn on the air conditioning, we only get 16 miles to the gallon. Right now we're getting 18." I began to figure just how much it would cost us to keep cool. We were going 55 mph out there in the desert, and gas cost $1.20 gal. Just how much would it cost us to keep cool?*

---

* From Carol Meyer and Tom Sallee, *Make It Simpler*, Addison-Wesley, Reading, Mass., 1983, p. 261.

ADDITION AND SUBTRACTION OF WHOLE NUMBERS

C H A P T E R 4

In the previous chapter we considered the development of our system of written numerals. In this and the next two chapters we will discuss the standard operations with whole numbers. We devote this chapter to addition and subtraction. In this context, an *operation* takes a pair of numbers and associates with the pair a third number, the *sum* of two numbers in the case of addition, the *difference* of two numbers in the case of subtraction. Our aim is to describe what the operations mean at a primitive level (of sets) and to show how and why the standard methods for computing the sum and difference work. We will start with simple problems and work up to more complicated ones. The solutions to the problems will build on each other.

As in chapter 3, we will try to put ourselves in the shoes of children and solve these problems from their point of view. As adults, we have computed so much and for so long that we can do these operations with ease and without thinking. This is not so for people just learning. Solving problems from their point of view will show us how the standard methods evolved, how they work and what mathematical stages one must go through to learn, use, and understand them. We will use the various devices introduced in chapter 3 for *making concrete models* of numbers such as counting boards and place value blocks. We will also use expanded notation as well as the standard decimal numerals.

UGBOO AND LAGOR'S PROBLEM

Ugboo has this many sheep

● ● ● ● ● ● ● ●

and Lagor has this many

● ● ● ● ● ● ● ● ● ● ●

Do they have enough sheep together to buy this many blankets

● ●,

Try this problem yourself first.

1 sheep for 1 blanket? Help them solve their problem using the fact that the only technique they have for comparing quantities is pairing the elements of a set. They do not have our decimal numerals to work with.

A Solution to Ugboo and Lagor's Problem

Take the set S of stones representing Ugboo's sheep and the set L of stones representing Lagor's sheep and form the union $S \cup L$ of the two sets. Then pair the elements of $S \cup L$ with the set B of stones representing the blankets.

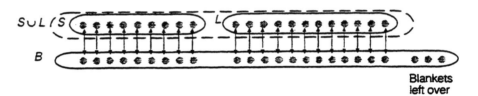

Blankets left over

Every element of $S \cup L$ has been paired with an element of B, and there are elements of B left over. Ugboo and Lagor have enough sheep to buy the blankets.

The Mathematical Idea: Primitive Addition

Ugboo and Lagor know how to compare one set with another by pairing the elements. In this problem they want to compare two sets: $S \cup L$ and B. The set $S \cup L$ is a union of the sets S and L. Since Ugboo and Lagor do not have numerals to represent numbers, addition for them means forming the union of two sets having no elements in common.

DEFINITION OF DISJOINT SETS

Sets A and B having no elements in common are called *disjoint*. A and B disjoint means

$$A \cap B = \varnothing.$$

For example, if A is the set of letters of the word *heat*, B is the set of letters of the word *song*, and C is the set of letters of the word *chime*, then A and B are disjoint while A and C are not disjoint.

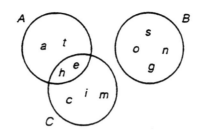

EXERCISE

1. In the circles are stones representing, from left to right, the camels that Roga has, the camels that Luxora has, and people requesting camels for a caravan leaving this weekend. Are there enough camels for people? Solve this without counting.

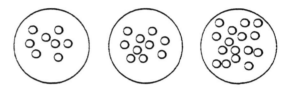

THE BIRTHDAY FAVOR
PROBLEM

Solve this yourself!

John is having a birthday party. He wants to give each of his 10 guests a favor. He has saved up money and bought 5 hats; his mom gave him 7 more hats. Will he have enough? John is in the first grade; he can count to 50 and knows how to compare numbers by counting. How would he solve this?

A Solution to the Birthday
Favor Problem

"Let me take the favors I bought and the favors Mom gave me. I'll put the two bunches together. Then I'll count the whole bunch. I get 12 altogether. I know that 12 is bigger than 10, the number of guests. So I'll have enough!"

The Mathematical Ideas: Addition and Addition Facts

In chapter 3 we learned that it is more efficient to compare two "large" sets by comparing the numbers of the sets (using the numerals that represent them) than it is to compare them by pairing elements. When we have two sets that we want to compare, then, we count the two sets, obtain their numbers, and compare them. We do the same when one of the sets S is a union of two other disjoint sets A and B: $S = A \cup B$, $A \cap B = \emptyset$. Finding the number that corresponds to $n(A \cup B)$ is called *addition*. The number $n(A \cup B)$ is the *sum of the addends* $n(A)$ and $n(B)$ and is written $n(A \cup B) = n(A) + n(B)$.

After solving a lot of addition problems like the one above, where each set has fewer than 10 items in it, young John will begin to remember the answers to them. He will remember that the disjoint union of a set with 5 items and a set with 7 items in it is a set with 12 items in it; he will say "7 plus 5 is 12" and will write $7 + 5 = 12$ for this fact. In other words, he will begin to learn his addition tables and to write these elementary addition facts in symbols.

A Solution to the Math Book
Problem

The two second grade classes at George Washington Elementary School have received a shipment of new math books. Sam and Carlotta have been assigned the task of determining whether there are enough books for the two classes, 58 students in all. Sam has a box of 24 books and Carlotta has a box of 38 books. The two of them have had lots of experience adding numbers less than 10 but no experience adding larger numbers. How can they figure out whether there will be enough books?

Sam and Carlotta realize that they must figure out the number of books in the two boxes combined. They consider forming the union of the two sets and counting the new set from scratch.

"You know," Carlotta says, "there might be a way easier than counting to figure out what we would get. Let's try *making a model* of the two numbers using place value blocks."

"Sure," Sam responds, "do you remember how they work?"

"Well, each little cube is a unit. Each long stands for 10 units. Do you see, if you glued 10 units together, you'd get a long? Here are 38 and 24 in place value blocks.

If you put all the blocks together, you'd have

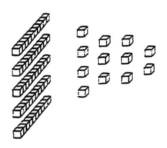

There are 5 longs and 12 units. Trade 10 units for 1 long.

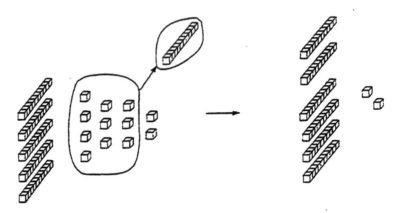

Now you have 6 longs and 2 units. That's 6 tens and 2 units. That makes 62, which is more than 58. There will be enough books for everybody."

2. Find the following sum using place value blocks and the solution to the math book problem as a plan: $46 + 38 =$.

3. Find the sum of the stick numbers $\mp$$\equiv$ and $+$$\equiv$ using base 5 place value blocks.

THE PTA PROBLEM

The PTA has an annual fair to raise money for special school needs. Each classroom sponsors a booth. The booth for one third grade class raised $376 while the booth for the other third grade class raised $548. Third graders Adam and Samantha have been given the job of figuring out how much the two third grades raised together. They have decided to *make models* of the numbers and use place value blocks. They've had experience adding two-digit numbers with place value blocks but no experience adding three-digit numbers. Help them solve the problem using place value blocks.

A Solution to the PTA Problem

Adam and Samantha set up the place value blocks for the two numbers as shown.

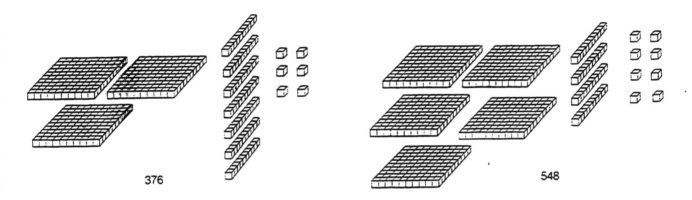

376   548

Samantha: "We've *solved similar problems* with two-digit numbers. Let's do what we did there and put all the flats together, all the longs together, and all the units together from the two piles. The new pile of place value blocks represents the sum of the two numbers."

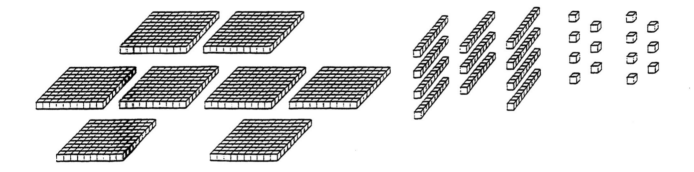

Adam: "There are 8 flats, 11 longs, and 14 units. What number corresponds to that? Wait, you just told me that I can trade 10 longs for a flat.

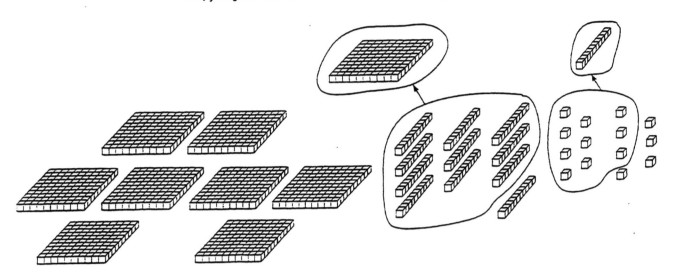

That makes 9 flats, 1 long, and 14 units."

Samantha: "I can trade 10 of the 14 units for a long. Then we would have 9 flats, 2 longs, and 4 units. That's 9 hundreds, 2 tens, and 4. Nine hundred twenty-four dollars. The two classes together raised $924."

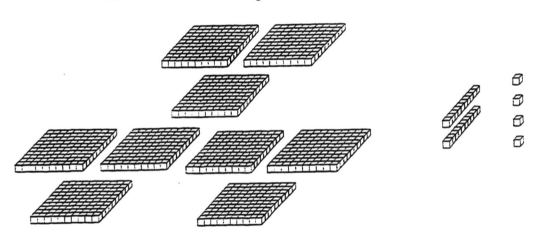

EXERCISES   4. Solve the addition problems using place value blocks:
(a) 357 + 486   (b) 746 + 569
5. Solve the problem of adding ≢⊣≢ to ⊣|≢ using base 5 place value blocks.

The Mathematical Idea: From the Concrete to the Abstract

Since place value blocks consist of unit blocks glued together in convenient combinations, the solution to the PTA problem using place value blocks is very concrete. You can see and feel the union of the two sets being formed when the two collections of place value blocks are shoved together. A certain amount of trading then occurs to determine the number associated with the union.

We will look at three more solutions to the PTA problem. Each solution will use a different device, and each succeeding solution will be slightly more abstract than the one that precedes it. The third solution will use the standard method.

A Solution to the PTA Problem Using a Counting Board

Make models of 376 and 548 on a counting board.

100s	10s	1s	
o o o	o o o / o o o / o	o o o / o o o	376
o o / o o o	o o / o o	o o o o / o o o o	548

To find the sum, in each column lump the stones from the two numbers together.

100s	10s	1s
o o / o / o o / o o o	o o o / o o o / o / o o / o o	o o o / o o o / o o o o / o o o o

There are 14 stones in the 1s column, 11 stones in the 10s column, and 8 stones in the 100s column. There must be fewer than 10 stones in each column. Start with the units column and replace 10 stones there by another stone in the 10s column.

100s	10s	1s		100s	10s	1s
o o / o / o o / o o o	o o o / o o o / o / o o / o o	o o o / o o o o / o o o o		o o / o / o o / o o o	o o o / o o o / o / o o / o o	o o o / o

Now there are 4 stones in the 1s column, 12 in the 10s column, and 8 in the 100s column. The units column is satisfactory.

Move to the 10s column where there are now 12 stones. Replace 10 of those stones by a stone in the 100s column.

100s	10s	1s
o o / o / o o / o o o	o o o / o o o / o / o o / o o o	o o o / o

The result is

100s	10s	1s
○ ○ ○ ○ ○ ○ ○ ○ ◎	○ ○	○ ○ ○ ○

That makes 4 stones in the 1s column, 2 in the 10s column, and 9 in the 100s column. There are now fewer than 10 stones in each column. The number represented on the counting board is 9 hundreds, 2 tens, and 4, or 924.

EXERCISES 6. Solve the problems using stones on a counting board:
   (a) 357 + 486   (b) 746 + 569
7. Add the stick numerals ≢+≢ and ≢|≢ using a base 5 counting board.

A Solution to the PTA Problem Using Expanded Notation on a Counting Board

Expand 376 and 548 on a counting board:

100s	10s	1s
3	7	6
5	4	8

Add the two quantities in the units column and get $6 + 8 = 14$. Do the same thing in each of the other columns: In the 10s column, $7 + 4 = 11$; in the 100s column, $3 + 5 = 8$.

100s	10s	1s
3	7	6
5	4	8
8	11	14

To interpret the numbers in the bottom row, each must be 9 or less. In the first column you notice that $14 = 10 + 4$. You can exchange 10 in the units column with a 1 in the second column. So you replace the 14 by 4 in the units column and add 1 to the 10s column.

100s	10s	1s
3 5	7 4	6 8
8	~~11~~ 12	~~14~~ 4

Finally, you notice in the 10s column that $12 = 10 + 2$. That means 10 tens (or 1 hundred) plus 2 tens. You can exchange the 10 for a 1 in the 100s column. So replace the 12 by 2 in the 10s column and add 1 to the 100s column.

100s	10s	1s
3 5	7 4	6 8
~~8~~ 9	~~11~~ ~~12~~ 2	~~14~~ 4

Now you have 9 in the 100s column, 2 in the 10s column, and 4 in the units column. That's 924.

EXERCISES

8. Use expanded notation on a counting board to solve the addition problems.
   (a) $357 + 486$ (b) $746 + 569$
9. Use expanded notation on a base 5 counting board to add ≢≢≣ to ≢|≣ .

A Solution to the PTA Problem Using the Standard Method

Here is another solution using expanded notation on a counting board. This time we do the trading as we go, column by column. We start with the units column, add the numbers in that column, and, if the sum is greater than 9, trade 10 from that column for 1 in the column just to its left; then we move to the 10s column and do the same thing there; then to the 100s column; and so on.

This solution is so close to the standard method that we show the two methods in parallel, with the standard method on the right. The word for *trade* in the standard method has traditionally been *carry*, literally from the act of carrying a stone to the next column of the counting board.

	100s	10s	1s
Add in units column	3 5	7 4	6 8
		1	4

```
      1  ←—— "Carry" 1
    376
    548
   -----
      4
```

	100s	10s	1s	
				"Carry" 1
Add everything in 10s column	3	7	6	1 1
	5	4	8	376
	1	1	4̸	48
		2̸		———
				24

	100s	10s	1s	
Add everything in 100s column	3	7	6	1 1
	5	4	8	376
	1	1	4̸	548
	9̸	2̸		———
				924

EXERCISE 10. Use the standard method to add ⧻╪⧻ to ╪I⧻.

4.2   SUBTRACTION OF WHOLE NUMBERS

We now turn to subtraction. As with addition, we begin with primitive subtraction, build on that, and wind up eventually with the standard method of subtraction.

UGBOO'S HORSE PROBLEM   Ugboo has this many stones

○○○○○○○○○○○○○○○○○○○○○○○○○○○○○○○○

He wants to buy a horse from Neevil, who will sell the horse for this many stones

○○○○○○○○○○○○○○○○

Try this first.

Ugboo needs to know what will be left over after paying for the horse because he wants to buy a saddle for the horse, too. How can Ugboo find out what he'll have left? Remember that Ugboo does not have our numerals to work with; his only technique for deciding how many is pairing the elements of two sets.

A Solution to Ugboo's Horse Problem

Let U be the set of stones Ugboo has. Find a subset S of U that is in one-to-one correspondence with the set representing Neevil's price. With U as the universal set, what Ugboo would have left over after buying Neevil's horse is S', the complement of S in U.

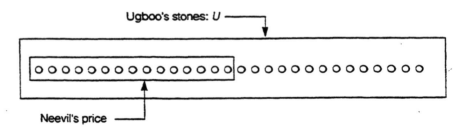

The Mathematical Idea: Primitive Subtraction

In Ugboo's horse problem Ugboo wants to find the set S', where $S \subset U$ and S represents Neevil's price. Finding the number of S' is called *subtraction of $n(S)$ from $n(U)$*, and we write $n(S') = n(U) - n(S)$.

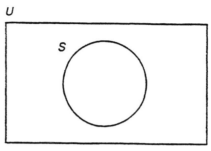

Shaded part is S'

THE TOY PROBLEM

Solve this first!

A Solution to the Toy Problem

Miguel is in the first grade and has been given a gift of $8 (in single dollar bills) for his birthday. With $5 of this money he plans to buy a toy. He wants to know how much he will have left. Help him solve this. Miguel has had a lot of experience adding single-digit numbers. He has not yet learned about subtraction.

From the eight dollar bills, Miguel counts out five dollar bills for the toy. He counts what is left and gets three dollar bills.

Price   The rest

The Mathematical Ideas: Subtraction and Subtraction Facts

Start with a set U. Identify a subset S. If you know the standard decimal numbers $n(U)$ and $n(S)$, you would like an efficient way to find the standard decimal number $n(S') = n(U) - n(S)$.

After solving a lot of subtraction problems like the toy problem—in which the number of the larger set is no bigger than 19 and the number of the subset to be identified is no bigger than 10—Miguel will begin to remember the answers to these problems. He will remember that a 5-element subset of an 8-element set has a complement of 3 elements. At the same time, he will begin to say "5 subtracted from 8 is 3" and write $8 - 5 = 3$ for this fact. Such a fact is called an *elementary subtraction fact*.

EXERCISE

11. What are the basic addition facts and the basic subtraction facts for standard base 6 numerals?

THE PAPER PAD PROBLEM

Try this yourself, first!

The school secretary has given Adam and Samantha's class 57 paper writing pads for use in the next two months. The students know that they use up about 23 pads per month. They want to know if, after going through 23 pads this month, there will be enough for the following month. The students have had experience subtracting single-digit numbers but have not had experience subtracting two-digit numbers. The students in the class decide to solve this by *making models* of standard numerals and using place value blocks. Help them do this.

A Solution to the Paper Pad Problem

The students set up the place value blocks corresponding to 57.

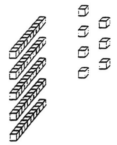

They think: "There are 5 longs (tens) and 7 units. In those blocks we want to identify the number 23—2 longs and 3 units. We identify 3 units in the 7 units, with 4 units remaining. We identify 2 longs in the 5 longs, with 3 longs remaining. What makes up the difference (the complement) after identifying 23 is 3 longs and 4 units. That's 34. There will be enough pads left over for another month."

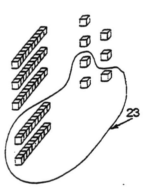

EXERCISES

12. Solve the paper pad problem using stones on a counting board, assuming no previous experience with two-digit subtraction.

13. Solve 89 − 42 in two ways: (a) using place value blocks and (b) using stones on a counting board.

14. Subtract ⊞ from ⊞⧻ in two ways: (a) using base 5 place value blocks and (b) using stones on a base 5 counting board.

THE ASSEMBLY TICKET
PROBLEM

STOP

First, try it yourself!

A Solution to the Assembly
Ticket Problem

Willow Elementary School will have an assembly, primarily for the students; but it would like to issue tickets for parents and others according to the availability of seats. The auditorium will seat 542 people. The number of students, teachers, and school staff who will be attending is 375. The students of Adam's and Samantha's class have been given the task of finding out how many tickets can be issued for parents and others. The students in Adam's and Samantha's class are feeling good about having *solved a simpler, similar problem,* the paper pad problem. So they decide to tackle this problem with place value blocks also. Help them do this.

The students *make a model* of 542 in place value blocks.

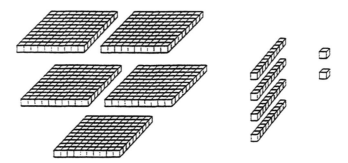

In this collection they want to identify 375: 3 flats, 7 longs, and 5 units. They notice right away that things are not quite as nice as they were for the paper pad problem. For one thing, there are 2 unit blocks in the 542 collection and 5 unit blocks in the 375 collection. "How can we identify a subset having 5 units when there are only 2 units in the large set?" they ask.

Somebody suggests, "Why don't we do some trading so that we *can* find 5 unit blocks? Trade one of the 4 longs of 542 for 10 unit blocks. That gives us 5 flats, 3 longs, and 12 units."

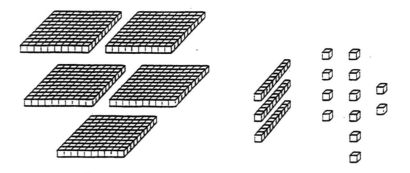

"Now we can identify a subset of 5 units. Now for the longs. We want to identify a subset with 7 longs, but there are only 3 there," another says. "We can trade one of the 5 flats in 542 for 10 longs. The collection of blocks representing 542 now has 4 flats, 13 longs, and 12 unit blocks. Now we can identify a subset—consisting of 3 flats, 7 longs, and 5 units—in the set of blocks for 542."

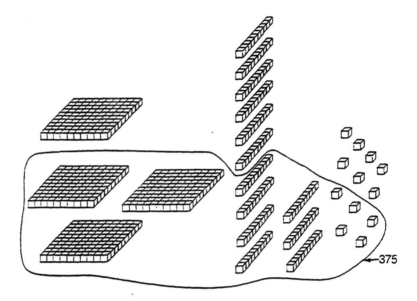

←375

What's left in 542 is 1 flat, 6 longs, and 7 units. The number is 167."

EXERCISES

15. Solve the assembly ticket problem using stones on a counting board. Use the same idea as in the solution using place value blocks. Make a model of 542 on a counting board and trade until you can identify a subset of stones corresponding to 375. Then figure out what's left.

16. Solve the problem using place value blocks: 735 − 468.

17. Subtract ┼╪╪ from ╪┼┼ using base 5 place value blocks.

The Mathematical Idea: Trading Systematically

In the paper pad and assembly ticket problems the trick is to identify a certain subset in a set of blocks. If this is not possible at first, you trade blocks in the set until it is possible.

To be systematic, you do this one block size at a time, starting with the smallest block size. You want to identify the units of the number you are subtracting as a subset of the unit blocks; if you can't do this, trade a long for 10 units. Then you should be able to identify a subset of the unit blocks equal to the units of the number you are subtracting. Next, you move to the longs; if you can, identify the 10s of the number you are subtracting with the longs; if you can't, trade a flat for 10 longs. There will now be enough longs. Then move to the flats, and so on.

A Solution to the Assembly Ticket Problem Using the Counting Board

First we place 542 on the counting board.

100s	10s	1s
○ ○	○ ○	○ ○
○	○ ○	
○ ○		

We want to identify a subset of these stones corresponding to 375. We do it one place at a time starting with the units. There are only 2 unit stones on the counting board, and we need at least 5. On the counting board we trade a stone from the 10s column for 10 stones in the units column.

100s	10s	1s
O O	O O	O O
O	O →	O O O O
O O		O O O O
		O O

Then we identify 5 stones in the units column of the counting board:

100s	10s	1s
O O	O O	O O
O	O	O O O O
O O		O O O O
		O O

Next, the 10s column. We need to identify a subset of 7 stones here, but there are only 3 there now. Again, we exchange 1 stone from the 100s column for 10 stones in the 10s column.

100s	10s	1s
O O	O O	O O
O O	O	O O O O
→	O O O O	O O O O
	O O O O	O O
	O O	

Then we identify 7 stones in the 10s column.

100s	10s	1s
O O	O O	O O
O O	O	O O O O
	O O O O	O O O O
	O O O O	O O
	O O	

Finally we identify 3 stones in the 100s column.

The remaining stones are our answer.

100s	10s	1s

A Solution to the Assembly Ticket Problem Using Expanded Form on a Counting Board and the Standard Method

What follows is a solution similar to the previous one. The difference is that we use expanded form on a counting board, and we determine what is left in each column as we go. (Identifying a subset and determining what is left in a column is called *subtracting in such and such a place* in the standard method.) On the left below is the solution using expanded form and in parallel, on the right, the solution using the standard method. Traditionally, the word *borrow* has been used in place of *trade*. Thus, in place of "trade 1 long for 10 units," one might say "borrow 1 long for 10 units."

Can't subtract in 1s column.

100s	10s	1s
5	4	2
(3	7	5)

5 4 2
3 7 5

Trade 1 in 10s column
for 10 in 1s column.

100s	10s	1s
5	$\not4$3	12
(3	7	5)

3
5 $\not4$^{1}2
3 7 5

Subtract in 1s column.
Can't subtract in 10s column.

100s	10s	1s
5	$\not4$3	12
(3	7	5)
		7

3
5 $\not4$^{1}2
3 7 5
7

Trade 1 in 100s column
for 10 in 10s column.

100s	10s	1s
$\not5$ 4	$\not4$13	12
(3	7	5)
		7·

4 ^{1}3
$\not5$ $\not4$^{1}2
3 7 5
7

Subtract in 10s column

100s	10s	1s
$\not5$4	$\not4$13	12
(3	7	5)
	6	7

4 ^{1}3
$\not5$ $\not4$^{1}2
3 7 5
6 7

Subtract in 100s column

100s	10s	1s
$\not5$4	$\not4$13	12
(3	7	5)
1	6	7

4 ^{1}3
$\not5$ $\not4$^{1}2
3 7 5
1 6 7

Notice that to use these techniques with ease, you must know the elementary subtraction facts.

EXERCISES

18. Solve the subtraction problems
    (a) $804 - 456$ (b) $5641 - 2825$
    using each of the following devices: (i) place value blocks, (ii) stones on a counting board, and (iii) expanded form on a counting board. (For the latter, subtract at each place value before moving on to the next.)

19. Solve the subtraction problems
    (a) $403_{six} - 345_{six}$ (b) $3210_{six} - 1542_{six}$
    using each of the following devices: (i) base 6 place value blocks, (ii) a base 6 counting board, and (iii) expanded form on a base 6 counting board. (For the latter, subtract at each place value before moving on to the next.)

A Solution to the Assembly Ticket Problem Using the Method of Equal Additions

There is another "standard" method for subtracting called the *method of equal additions*. It is commonly taught in European countries; as recently as the 1950s it was commonly taught in this country but now only rarely.

We will illustrate the method of equal additions by solving the problem $542 - 375$. The method is related to this observation: If a friend has $25 more than you and someone gives both of you $10, then your friend still has $25 more than you.

PRINCIPLE BEHIND METHOD OF EQUAL ADDITIONS

Suppose that A and B are whole numbers and $A > B$. Then

$$A - B = (A + S) - (B + S)$$

for any whole number S.

Here is the method of equal additions used to solve the problem 542 − 375.

	100s	10s	1s
Can't subtract	5	4	2
in 1s column.	(3	7	5)

	100s	10s	1s
Add 10 to both 542 and 375	5	4	12
allowing subtraction in 1s column.	(3	7̇8	5)
			7

	100s	10s	1s
Can't subtract in 10s column.	5	14	12
Add 100 to both numbers allowing	(3̸4	7̇8	5)
subtraction in 10s column.		6	7

	100s	10s	1s
Subtract in 100s column.	5	14	12
	(3̸4	7̇8	5)
	1	6	7

EXERCISE   20. Solve the problems using the method of equal additions.
(a) 804 − 456   (b) 5641 − 2825

We Know How to Subtract But __When__ Do We Subtract?

THE EGG PROBLEM   Miguel plans to fix breakfast for his family. He will need 9 eggs. He has 5 eggs already. He has decided to borrow the rest from neighbors. How many eggs will he need to borrow? Remember, Miguel is in the first grade. He has solved the toy problem and is beginning to learn the elementary subtraction facts.

You know that the answer is the same as the answer to "5 subtracted from 9." But does Miguel know this? The toy problem feels different from the egg problem. Miguel might approach the latter in this way: "I've got 5 eggs. How many more do I need to make 9? I need to figure out what I add to 5 to get 9—5 + ? = 9."

Later, he might think: "Let me *draw a picture* of the 9 eggs that I need and of the 5 eggs that I have.

Need: O O O O O O O O O
Have: O O O O O

Let me cross off the 5 eggs that I have from the eggs that I need.

Need: Ø Ø Ø Ø Ø O O O O
Have: O O O O O

It's subtraction! The 4 eggs that remain I have to borrow from the neighbors."

The Mathematical Idea: Subtraction as Finding
the Solution to a Missing Addend Problem

What Miguel has discovered here is that solving a subtraction problem $542 - 375$ is the same as solving the *missing addend* problem $375 + ? = 542$, and vice versa. Recall that the two numbers being added in an addition problem are called *addends*.

The egg problem is a simple problem; it is naturally a missing addend problem. For a person just learning to use subtraction, it takes a little bit of effort to show that it is a subtraction problem. The standard method of subtraction is based more on the method used to solve the toy problem. In section 4.4 we will describe a method of subtraction based on the idea of finding a missing addend.

More Problems in Which Subtraction Is Used to Find Solutions

Here are more problems that call for subtraction in their solutions. Note the language used in each situation.

- Washington Elementary PTA took in $4357 in their fund-raising; Jefferson Elementary PTA took in $3802. You are interested in knowing *how much more* Washington took in than Jefferson did. Answer: $4357 - $3802 = $555.

- The car trip from Tucson to Phoenix is 110 mi. You have already traveled 48 mi. You want to know *how much farther* you have to travel. Answer: $110 - 48 = 62$. You must travel 62 more miles.

- John's family has agreed to pay $55 toward the price of a new bike and John has agreed to pay the *difference*. The price of the bike is $129. John wants to know how much he will be paying. Answer: $129 - $55 = $74.

EXERCISE

21. Show that subtraction really does solve each of the preceding problems by showing how the original definition of subtraction given at the beginning of this chapter applies.

Why Do We Need to Do All This?

Imagine the following third grade scene:

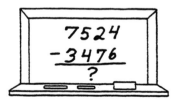

"Class, today we are going to learn how to subtract with large numbers. To illustrate the method, we will subtract 3476 from 7524. First, write down the larger number.

7524

Then subtract each digit of the smaller number 3476 from 9 and write your answers from left to right under the 7524.

$$7524$$
$$6523$$

Now add the two numbers together.

$$7524$$
$$+\ 6523$$
$$\overline{14,047}$$

Next cross out the 1, the leftmost digit of the sum, and add it underneath.

$$7524$$
$$+\ 6523$$
$$\overline{14,047}$$
$$\rightarrow +\ 1$$
$$\overline{4048}$$

This last number, 4048, is your answer.

$$7524$$
$$-\ 3476$$
$$\overline{4048}"$$

The Method of Complements for Subtraction

The method of subtraction we have just described is called the *method of complements*. You probably feel about our discussion of this method just as a third grader would feel if he were given the standard method without experiences and explanations leading up to it.

Here is another example of subtraction using the method of complements. To subtract 23,875 from 51,324, add

the larger of the two numbers	51,324
to the smaller number subtracted from 99,999	+ 76,124
and get this sum	127,448.

Cross out the leftmost digit of the sum (It will always be a 1. Why?) and add it to what's left.

$$27,448$$
$$+\ 1$$
$$\overline{27,449}$$

This most recent sum is the answer to your problem.

$$51,324$$
$$-\ 23,875$$
$$\overline{27,449}$$

22. Use the method of complements to solve the subtraction problems.

(a) 6407 − 2358

(b) 75,432 − 43,094

(c) 5316 − 728 (Careful with this one!)

4.6 SUMMARY OF IMPORTANT IDEAS AND TECHNIQUES

- Primitive addition
- The definition of addition of whole numbers using the union of two disjoint sets
- Stages in the development of the standard method for addition
  Elementary addition facts
  Addition using place value blocks
  Addition using a counting board
  Addition using expanded form on a counting board
- Primitive subtraction
- The definition of subtraction for whole numbers using the complement of a set
- Stages in the development of the standard method for subtraction
  Elementary subtraction facts
  Subtraction using place value blocks
  Subtraction using stones on a counting board
  Subtraction using expanded form on a counting board

- Unusual methods of subtraction
  The method of equal additions
  The method of complements
  The cashier method
- Recognizing problem situations that call for subtraction
- Formal properties of addition
  Zero, an identity for addition
  Commutative property of addition
  Associative property of addition
- The use of symbols and letters: a glimpse at algebra
  Rules for working with symbols
  Substitution principle
  Addition and subtraction properties of equality
  Cancellation property of addition
- The relationship of order to addition and subtraction
  The add-subtract slide rule
  Definition of order using addition
  The order properties of addition and subtraction
  Using order properties to estimate solutions or check the reasonableness of solutions to addition and subtraction problems

PROBLEM SET

PRACTICING SKILLS

1. Curious George, the irrepressible monkey, is going on a picnic with his relatives. Every monkey wants to wear a hat. George brings out his hats from his closet. He has this many hats:

   o   o   o   o   o

   His cousin Martha gets her hats from her closet. She has this many hats:

   o   o   o   o   o   o   o   o

   George and Martha and the rest of the monkeys line up to choose hats.

   o   o   o   o   o   o   o   o   o   o   o   o

   Will every monkey have a hat to wear? Solve this problem without counting.

2. Solve the addition problems using place value blocks.
   (a)   469 + 375   (b)   582 + 740

   Record your steps using [cube] for a cube, [flat] for a flat, [long] for a long, and □ for a unit.

3. Solve the addition problems using stones on a counting board.
   (a)   683 + 299   (b)   756 + 849
   Record your steps by drawing pictures of counting boards with stones.

4. Use expanded form on a counting board to solve the addition problems.
   (a) $258 + 493$ (b) $954 + 867$

5. Max has counted 37 pieces of candy, all that he collected at Halloween. He wants to know how much will be left for himself if he gives 1 piece of candy to each student in his first grade class. He knows there are 26 students in his class. He has had a lot of experience with single-digit numbers, but he has not yet learned about subtraction. How could Max solve this problem?

6. Solve the following subtraction problems using (i) place value blocks and (ii) stones on a counting board.
   (a) $79 - 46$ (b) $685 - 423$ (c) $873 - 498$ (d) $4365 - 3896$

7. Use expanded form on a counting board to solve the subtraction problems.
   (a) $483 - 289$ (b) $8602 - 1953$

8. Use the method of equal additions to solve the subtraction problems.
   (a) $765 - 289$ (b) $6843 - 4788$

9. Use the method of complements to solve the subtraction problems.
   (a) $8213 - 3629$ (b) $7644 - 5087$

10. Use the rules developed for working with symbols to solve the problems.
    (a) Find a whole number A so that $A + 58 = 97$.
    (b) Find a whole number B so that $259 - B = 147$.

11. Use the rules developed for working with symbols to solve the problems.
    (a) Find whole numbers A and B so that $A = 35 + B$ and $241 = A + B$.
    (b) Find whole numbers C and D so that $C = 23 - D$ and $D = 57 + C$.

12. Use the order properties of addition and subtraction to estimate the answers.

(a)	(b)	(c)	(d)
5329	$74{,}618$	8971	$65{,}702$
$+\ 856$	$+\ 97{,}864$	$-\ 2089$	$-\ 28{,}738$

13. Complete the following addition table for stick numerals. This table should include all the elementary addition facts for stick numerals.

Plus	$+$	$\ddagger$	$\not\equiv$	$\equiv$	$+\!\mid$
$+$					
$\ddagger$					
$\not\equiv$		$+\!\mid$			
$\equiv$					
$+\!\mid$					

14. Use the table completed in problem 13 to solve the following stick numeral subtraction problems as missing addend problems.

(a) $+\!\equiv\ -\ \equiv$ (b) $+\!\ddagger\ -\ \ddagger$

(c) $+\!\equiv\ -\ +\!\mid$ (d) $+\!+\ -\ \not\equiv$

For each problem remaining, document as clearly and completely as you can your solution to the problem. Include the steps you took to solve the problem, mention the problems or solutions from the text that gave you ideas, and include the problem-solving strategies you used. You might want to outline and organize these details before assembling your final report.

15. Find the sum of stick numerals ⌗╪╪ and ╪≡╪ by *making models* of them in two different ways: (a) using base 5 place value blocks and (b) using a base 5 counting board. Record your solutions using pictures.

16. Subtract stick numeral ╪≡╪ from ⌗╪≡ by making models of them in two different ways: (a) using base 5 place value blocks and (b) using a base 5 counting board. Record your solutions using pictures.

17. Find the sum of the base 7 place value block numerals shown, working entirely within the system of blocks. Record your steps in solving this with pictures.

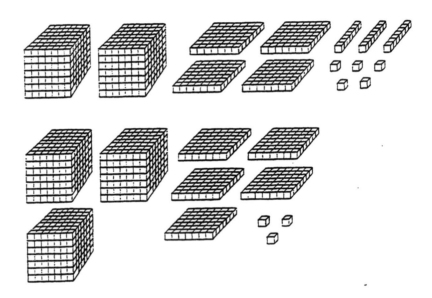

18. In problem 17, subtract the smaller place block numeral from the larger. Again, work entirely with the base 7 system of place value blocks. Record your steps with pictures.

19. Find the sum of the base 8 counting board numerals shown, working entirely within the counting board system. Record the steps of your solution with pictures of stones on counting boards.

(a)

8²s	8s	1s
o o o o	o o o o o	o o o o o

(b)

8²s	8s	1s
o o	o o o o o o o	o o o o o o

20. In problem 19, subtract the smaller counting board numeral from the larger. Work entirely within the base 8 counting board system and record your steps with pictures.

21. Addition of stick numerals can also be carried out using a base 5 abacus, which allows in the early steps of a solution an unlimited number of beads on a post. First, go through a sample problem and solution.

   Problem: Add the stick numerals ╪╪╪ and ┼╪╪.
   Solution: Convert the first numeral to beads on an abacus.

   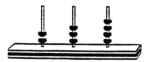

   Post by post, from the second numeral add beads to the abacus equal to the number of horizontal cross bars of the numeral.

   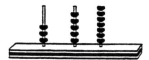

   Trade 5 beads on any post for a single bead on the post just to its left. Do this until there are no more than 4 beads on any post.

   (a) 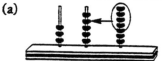   (b) 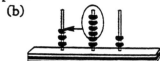   (c)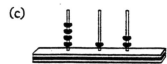

   Use this method to add these stick numerals: ╪│╪ and ┼╪┼.
   Record the steps you take with pictures of beads on abaci.

22. The method of problem 21 can be altered so that at any stage no more than 4 beads on a post are allowed. For example, to add the stick numerals ╪╪╪ and ┼╪╪, convert one of them to an abacus as before.

   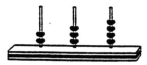

   Then add the other numeral to it, post by post, as follows.

   (i) *First post:* The abacus has ╪ here. The other numeral has ╪. The sum of these is the stick numeral ┼╪. So, on the abacus you remove 2 beads from the first post, leaving 2, and add 1 to the second.

   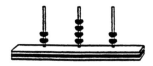

(ii) *Second post:* The abacus now has ⬚ on this post; the numeral has ⊤. The sum of these is the stick numeral ⊤⊤. So, on the abacus you remove 3 beads from the second post, leaving 1, and add 1 to the third:

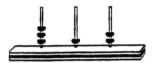

(iii) *Third post:* The abacus has ⬚ on this post and the numeral has ⊤. The sum is the numeral ≡. Thus, you add 1 to the fourth:

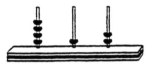

(a) Use this method to add the stick numerals

$$≣+≣ \quad \text{and} \quad +≣⊤$$

(b) Try this method with the stick numerals

$$⊤≣⊤ \quad \text{and} \quad +≣⊤$$

What happens with this pair that didn't happen with the worked out example above and that creates a problem? What do you do to resolve this problem?

23. A base 5 abacus can also be used to subtract stick numerals.
   (a) In the manner of problem 21, outline a method of subtracting one stick numeral from another on a base 5 abacus that allows an unlimited number of beads on each post in the early stages of the solution. Illustrate your method by subtracting ⊤≣≣ from ≣⊤≣ and +≣≣ from ≣|≣.
   (b) In the manner of problem 22, alter the method of problem 23(a) so that at most 4 beads are allowed on a post at any stage of the solution. Illustrate your method with the same pairs of stick numerals as in (a).

24. How you would adapt the standard method of addition for decimal numerals to one for stick numerals? (*Suggestions:* One way you might answer this is to display an annotated solution using expanded notation on a counting board, in parallel with the standard method, as was done in the text. The particular numerals in your illustration should be chosen carefully so that the solution contains all variations of your method. For instance, numerals that don't involve trading would not be a good choice.)

25. How would you adapt the standard method of subtraction for decimal numerals to one for stick numerals? (See suggestions in prob. 24.)

26. Find the missing digits in the following stick numeral addition and subtraction problems.
   (a) ☐≣≣☐   (b) +☐|≣   (c) +|☐⊤   (d) ☐+☐⊤
(plus)   ≣☐≣   (plus) ≣+☐☐   (minus) ☐+≣   (minus) ⊤≣+·☐
   ─────   ─────   ─────   ──────
   ≣☐|≣   ☐⊤|⊤   ≣☐   +☐|⊤

27. Here is a stick number addition problem in code. Each letter stands for one of the stick digits I , +, ‡, ‡, or ‡. Different letters stand for different digits. (Obviously, the left-most digit in any stick numeral can't be I .) Decode the problem by finding X, B, and A.

$$\begin{array}{r} X\ X\ X \\ B \\ \hline B\ A\ A\ A \end{array}$$

28. Jatora lives in the kingdom of Xapho, where the basic monetary unit is the xaph. She uses a base 6 counting board having four columns as shown on the far left below. Each pebble in the right-most column (marked with an X) is worth 1 xaph. Jatora wants to buy a camel that costs the amount indicated in the diagram below; she also wants to buy a saddle that costs the amount indicated second from the right. Jatora has the amount also indicated in the diagram. Figure out how much Jatora will have left after she pays for the camel and the saddle.

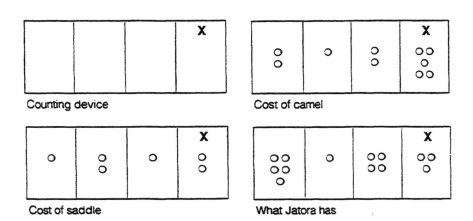

Counting device

Cost of camel

Cost of saddle

What Jatora has

Use only the base 6 counting board system to solve this problem. Draw pictures of counting boards showing how you solved it.

29. You are in charge of ordering emergency phone boxes to go along the interstate from Tucson to Nogales. How many should you order? You know that

The phones are to be placed every 1056 ft on both sides of the road.
The length of the road to be covered is 55 mi.
No phones are needed at either end of the road to be covered.
1 mi = 5280 ft.

30. Here is an addition problem in code for decimal numerals. Each letter stands for one of the digits 0 through 9. Different letters stand for different digits. Each letter stands for the same digit for all its occurrences. For example, if the E in MORE stands for 3, then the E in MONEY also stands for 3. (By convention, the left-most digit of any decimal numeral cannot be 0.)

$$\begin{array}{r} S\ E\ N\ D \\ +M\ O\ R\ E \\ \hline M\ O\ N\ E\ Y \end{array}$$

Decode the problem by finding out what digit each letter stands for. (You might want to make a guess or two to get started.)

31. Here is a subtraction problem in code. Each letter stands for one of the digits 0 through 9. Different letters stand for different digits. (The rules are the same as for prob. 30.)

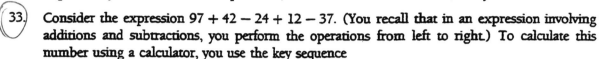

$$
\begin{array}{r}
S\ P\ E\ N\ D \\
-\ M\ O\ R\ E \\
\hline
M\ O\ N\ E\ Y
\end{array}
$$

Find out what each letter stands for. (*Hint:* More than one answer is possible. For a start, make a guess for M from among 1, 2, 3, 4, 5, 6, 7, 8, 9 and see what the consequences are.)

32. Explain why the method of complements, as a method for subtraction, always works.

33. Consider the expression $97 + 42 - 24 + 12 - 37$. (You recall that in an expression involving additions and subtractions, you perform the operations from left to right.) To calculate this number using a calculator, you use the key sequence

$$97\ [+]\ 42\ [-]\ 24\ [+]\ 12\ [-]\ 37\ [=].$$

(a) Here is a list of your checking account transactions for the month of November:

Nov. 1: Balance from October $573
Nov. 5: Check for rent $275
Nov. 7: Deposit $435
Nov. 13: Check for food $72
Nov. 17: Check for car payment $135
Nov. 20: Check for clothing $110
Nov. 22: Check for insurance $153
Nov. 25: Deposit $127
Nov. 29: Check for food $84

Use a calculator to determine the balance at the end of the month.

(b) Below is a table of annual 1988 budgets for the major zoological parks in the Southwest.

Arizona-Sonora Desert Museum $2,500,000
Dallas Zoo   2,400,000
Houston Zoo   2,600,000
Los Angeles Zoo   1,400,000
Phoenix Zoo   2,600,000
San Antonio Zoo   5,700,000
San Diego Zoo   28,000,000
San Diego Wild Animal Park   16,000,000

Use your calculator to determine the total amount spent by these parks in 1988.

MULTIPLICATION OF WHOLE NUMBERS

CH A P T E R

In this chapter we will discuss the multiplication of whole numbers. Our goal is to understand what multiplication is, where it is used, and why the familiar methods we use for multiplication actually do what they are supposed to. The main part of the chapter consists of a series of problems each of which can be solved by multiplying two whole numbers and which progresses from simple problems involving single-digit numbers to problems containing several-digit numbers. We will solve the problems from the point of view of a person who has had no previous experience with multiplication but who has had a lot of experience with addition and subtraction. As the problems increase in complexity, this person gains experience, and we are able to see just what new mathematical skills are needed for solving the new problems. In this way we will experience for ourselves the evolution of the standard method for multiplying several-digit numbers and understand how it works. Since the method evolves from real problems and their solutions, the person will gain the ability to recognize many situations where the method can be used and believe that it does the job it is supposed to.

A discussion of some formal properties of multiplication follows, which, in turn, leads to rules for solving equations with unknowns. We will also discuss the relationship of multiplication to order and its use in estimating products of large numbers.

In the early parts of the chapter, we think of multiplication first as repeated addition and then as counting the number of items in an array. Later in the chapter, we look at two additional ways of thinking about multiplication: (1) as counting the number of branch ends in certain *tree diagrams* and (2) as counting the number of elements in the *cartesian product* of two sets.

We begin the chapter with a problem that involves large numbers in order to show that a person can solve a complicated multiplication problem without knowing anything about multiplication and—since the nontraditional solution we offer involves a lot of work—to motivate the development of a more systematic method for multiplying two numbers.

THE HOTEL PROBLEM

You run a hotel. All the rooms in Our Hotel are filled for the evening. You'd like to know what your receipts for the night should be. (For one thing, you'd like to know whether the amount of money you have in your cash register matches the amount of money you ought to have taken in.) Here are some clues:

The charge for each room is $45.
Your hotel has 68 rooms.

Try this yourself before reading on.

You are also a person who knows how to add and subtract two- and three-digit numbers. But you don't know about multiplication. How would you solve this?

Solution to the Hotel Problem

You might think like this: "One room costs $45. Two rooms would cost

$$\begin{array}{r} \$45 \\ + 45 \\ \hline \$90 \end{array}$$

Three rooms would cost $45 more than that.

$$\begin{array}{r} \$90 \\ + 45 \\ \hline \$135 \end{array}$$

Hey, I get it. For 68 rooms, just add $45 consecutively 68 times.

$45
$45
$45
$45
$45
$45
$45
$45
$45
$45
⋮

Wait a minute. SIXTY-EIGHT TIMES? I can't get that all on one page. Suppose I were to add the $45s up in bunches of 10 at a time.

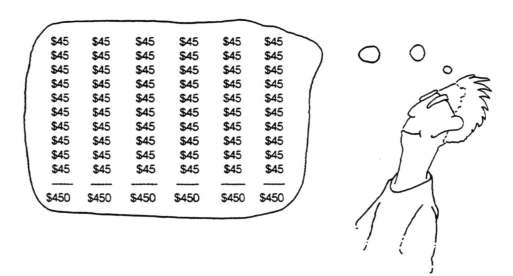

$45	$45	$45	$45	$45	$45
$45	$45	$45	$45	$45	$45
$45	$45	$45	$45	$45	$45
$45	$45	$45	$45	$45	$45
$45	$45	$45	$45	$45	$45
$45	$45	$45	$45	$45	$45
$45	$45	$45	$45	$45	$45
$45	$45	$45	$45	$45	$45
$45	$45	$45	$45	$45	$45
$45	$45	$45	$45	$45	$45
———	———	———	———	———	———
$450	$450	$450	$450	$450	$450

"I wouldn't have to total all of the columns; I'd only have to do one of them. The others would add to the same thing—$450. Let me add up the amounts for the six columns.

$$
\begin{array}{r}
\$450 \\
\$450 \\
\$450 \\
\$450 \\
\$450 \\
\$450 \\
\hline
\$2700
\end{array}
$$

"That accounts for the receipts for the first 60 rooms. There are 8 more rooms to account for.

$$
\begin{array}{r}
\$45 \\
\$45 \\
\$45 \\
\$45 \\
\$45 \\
\$45 \\
\$45 \\
\$45 \\
\hline
\$360
\end{array}
$$

"That's it. All I have to do is add the $2700 to the $360.

$$
\begin{array}{r}
\$360 \\
\$2700 \\
\hline
\$3060
\end{array}
$$

"That does it!"

Too Much Work to Solve the Problem?

The solution to the hotel problem seems like a lot of work, especially since you know that it can be solved easily with the standard method for multiplication of two-digit numbers.

Nevertheless, it is an appropriate solution for someone who isn't acquainted with the standard method. After working a few such problems this long way, this person will feel the need for a "better way." When he is acquainted with the better way, he will know and appreciate what is being accomplished when he uses it. Now, let's build up to the method by considering problems with smaller numbers.

EXERCISE
1. You own the wheat field shown below. You know that each of the little squares in the picture produces a bushel of wheat. You'd like to know how much wheat the whole field produces. You have solved the hotel problem, so you know how to add three- and four-digit numbers. But you know nothing about multiplication. How would you solve this?

THE BOOK PROBLEM

Try this.

Sarah is in the third grade. She knows nothing about multiplication. She plans to sell 7 books at $8 each and wants to know what her total receipts will be from this sale. How could she solve this?

A Solution to the Book Problem

You, Sarah, add up $8 seven times: $8 + $8 + $8 + $8 + $8 + $8 + $8 = $56.

The Mathematical Idea: Multiplication as Repeated Addition

Sarah solved the book problem by adding $8 to itself repeatedly. You solved the hotel problem by adding 45 repeatedly: there were 68 addends, and each addend was the whole number 45. This method of solution is called repeated addition and leads to the following definition.

DEFINITION OF *MULTIPLICATION*

For any whole numbers A and B,

$$A \times B = \underbrace{B + B + B + \ldots + B.}_{A \text{ addends}}$$

The whole number $A \times B$ is called the *product* of A with B. The whole numbers A and B are called the *factors* of $A \times B$. Given A and B, finding the whole number $A \times B$ is called *multiplication*. In particular, for $1 \times B$ there is one addend so that $1 \times B = B$, and for $0 \times B$ there are *no* addends so that $0 \times B = 0$.

At some point Sarah will be told that 7×8 is shorthand for "7 times 8," which is shorthand for adding 8 repeatedly with 7 addends. After solving many such problems in this way, Sarah will begin to remember the answers to them and would be able to solve the book problem by thinking "$8 added to itself 7 times is $7 \times \$8$ or $56." She will begin to memorize the multiplication tables, the *elementary multiplication facts*.

In earlier grades Sarah and her friends will have had lots of experience with repeated addition when the number to be repeated is 2 or 5 or 10. This occurs in what is called skip counting.

2, 4, 6, 8, 10, ... (skip counting by 2s)
5, 10, 15, 20, 25, ... (skip counting by 5s)
10, 20, 30, 40, ... (skip counting by 10s)

For example, to figure out 4×5, you skip count: 5, 10, 15, 20. The fourth number in the sequence, 20, is the answer.

EXERCISES

2. Mina uses (base 5) stick numerals and doesn't know her multiplication tables. How would she solve ≢ × ≣ ?

3. Suppose that your system of numerals is the base 8 system and that you don't know the base 8 multiplication tables. How would you solve $7_{eight} \times 5_{eight}$ completely within the base 8 system? How about $5_{eight} \times 7_{eight}$?

4. Make a multiplication table for the base 8 system.

DEVELOPMENT OF THE STANDARD METHOD FOR MULTIPLICATION

THE CLASSROOM SEAT PROBLEM

The seats in John's classroom are arranged as shown.

U U U U U U U U
U U U U U U U U
U U U U U U U U
U U U U U U U U
U U U U U U U U
U U U U U U U U
U U U U U U U U

Try this yourself, first!

John, in the third grade, wants to know how many seats there are. He knows that multiplication is repeated addition and has just learned his multiplication tables. How could he figure out many seats there are?

A Solution to The Classroom Seat Problem

John thinks: "I could count the seats one by one. But maybe there is an easier way. Let me count the seats in the first row: There are 8 of them. All the other rows have 8 seats too. Then, 8 in the first plus 8 in the second, plus 8 in the third . . . Wait! To figure out the number of seats, all I have to do is add 8 to itself as many times as there are rows. Let's see: I count 7 rows. So the answer is 8 added to itself 7 times. Hey, that's just 7 × 8 = 56. The answer is 56 seats!"

The Mathematical Idea: Arrays and Multiplication

A bunch of objects arranged in a rectangular formation such as in the illustration of the seats in John's classroom or in that of the marching band, following, is called an *array.*

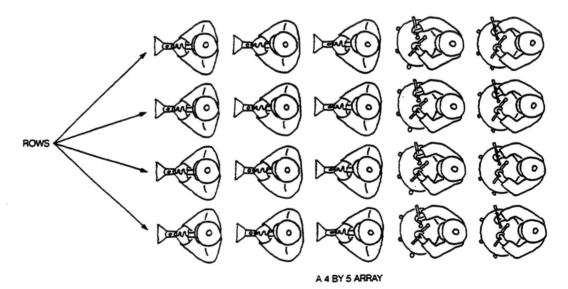

ROWS

A 4 BY 5 ARRAY

The horizontal lines of the array are called *rows*. One row must have the same number of objects as any other. In the case of the array of seats, there are 7 rows and each row has 8 seats. In the case of the marching band, there are 4 rows with 5 players in each row.

John made the connection between the number of items in an array having 7 rows with 8 in a row and the number gotten by adding 8 to itself 7 times. (He knew that this number is the product 7×8, which is equal to 56.) This may be an obvious connection for us, but it isn't for someone making it for the first time. We can make a general statement connecting arrays with multiplication.

THE NUMBER OF ITEMS IN AN ARRAY

A certain array has R rows with C items in each row.

$$C$$

$$
\begin{matrix}
\bullet & \bullet & \bullet & \bullet & \bullet & \bullet & \bullet & \bullet & \bullet & \bullet & \bullet & \bullet \\
\bullet & \bullet & \bullet & \bullet & \bullet & \bullet & \bullet & \bullet & \bullet & \bullet & \bullet & \bullet \\
\bullet & \bullet & \bullet & \bullet & \bullet & \bullet & \bullet & \bullet & \bullet & \bullet & \bullet & \bullet \\
\bullet & \bullet & \bullet & \bullet & \bullet & \bullet & \bullet & \bullet & \bullet & \bullet & \bullet & \bullet \\
\bullet & \bullet & \bullet & \bullet & \bullet & \bullet & \bullet & \bullet & \bullet & \bullet & \bullet & \bullet \\
\bullet & \bullet & \bullet & \bullet & \bullet & \bullet & \bullet & \bullet & \bullet & \bullet & \bullet & \bullet \\
\bullet & \bullet & \bullet & \bullet & \bullet & \bullet & \bullet & \bullet & \bullet & \bullet & \bullet & \bullet \\
\end{matrix}
$$

R

This is called an R by C array. The total number of items in an R by C array is $R \times C$.

Let's look at another example where you want to find the number of items in an array. You are purchasing a rectangular rug that is 10 ft long and 12 ft wide.

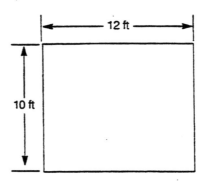

You pay for a rug according to how many square feet it contains. To determine how many square feet in the rug in this example, you superimpose a grid on the rug so that each square is a foot on a side.

This gives you a 10 by 12 array of squares. As you know, 120, the number of squares (each square a square foot) in this array is the *area* of the rug. We will discuss area in more detail beginning in chapter 17.

EXERCISE 5. Here is a picture of the vines in a vineyard.

John wants to know how many vines there are in this vineyard. How would John figure this out?

THE MOTEL PROBLEM   John runs a motel, Our Motel. All rooms are booked for the night. How much money will this bring him? He knows that

The charge for each room is $68.
The motel has 45 rooms.

Don't forget. Try it!

John solved the hotel problem at the beginning of the chapter. John has also solved the classroom seat problem and knows the connection between repeated addition (multiplication) and arrays. All he knows about multiplication is the tables. Help John solve this problem.

A Solution to the Motel   Here is one way John might go about solving the problem. "In the hotel problem
Problem   there were 68 rooms, and the charge for each was $45. We *solved that similar problem* by adding $45 to itself 68 times. For the motel problem I should add $68 to itself 45 times. That's a lot of work. Is there another way? I wonder if it means anything that the pairs of numbers are the same—$45 and 68 in one, $68 and 45 in the other. Let me *look at a simpler and similar problem.*

"Suppose I have Cheap Hotel with 7 rooms at $9 a room and Cheap Motel with 9 rooms at $7 a room. All the rooms are filled in Cheap Hotel and in Cheap Motel. I know that the total amount of money taken in for Cheap Hotel is $9 + $9 + $9 + $9 + $9 + $9 + $9 = $9 × 7 = $63 and that the amount of money taken in for Cheap Motel is $7 + $7 + $7 + $7 + $7 + $7 + $7 + $7 + $7 = $7 × 9 = $63. Is it a coincidence that these two totals are the same? Will the same thing happen with the big numbers? I just solved the classroom seat problem. Let me arrange the dollars for Cheap Hotel in an array like this,

$$\$ \ \$ \ \$ \ \$ \ \$ \ \$ \ \$ \ \$ \ \$$$
$$\$ \ \$ \ \$ \ \$ \ \$ \ \$ \ \$ \ \$ \ \$$$
$$\$ \ \$ \ \$ \ \$ \ \$ \ \$ \ \$ \ \$ \ \$$$
$$\$ \ \$ \ \$ \ \$ \ \$ \ \$ \ \$ \ \$ \ \$$$
$$\$ \ \$ \ \$ \ \$ \ \$ \ \$ \ \$ \ \$ \ \$$$
$$\$ \ \$ \ \$ \ \$ \ \$ \ \$ \ \$ \ \$ \ \$$$
$$\$ \ \$ \ \$ \ \$ \ \$ \ \$ \ \$ \ \$ \ \$$$

with 7 rows (the 7 rooms) and 9 dollar signs in each row (the charge for each room). The total number of dollars in that array is $9 × 7 or $63. If I turn Cheap Hotel's array on its side, I'll get the array for Cheap Motel:

$$\Leftrightarrow \ \Leftrightarrow \ \Leftrightarrow \ \Leftrightarrow \ \Leftrightarrow \ \Leftrightarrow \ \Leftrightarrow$$
$$\Leftrightarrow \ \Leftrightarrow \ \Leftrightarrow \ \Leftrightarrow \ \Leftrightarrow \ \Leftrightarrow \ \Leftrightarrow$$
$$\Leftrightarrow \ \Leftrightarrow \ \Leftrightarrow \ \Leftrightarrow \ \Leftrightarrow \ \Leftrightarrow \ \Leftrightarrow$$
$$\Leftrightarrow \ \Leftrightarrow \ \Leftrightarrow \ \Leftrightarrow \ \Leftrightarrow \ \Leftrightarrow \ \Leftrightarrow$$
$$\Leftrightarrow \ \Leftrightarrow \ \Leftrightarrow \ \Leftrightarrow \ \Leftrightarrow \ \Leftrightarrow \ \Leftrightarrow$$
$$\Leftrightarrow \ \Leftrightarrow \ \Leftrightarrow \ \Leftrightarrow \ \Leftrightarrow \ \Leftrightarrow \ \Leftrightarrow$$
$$\Leftrightarrow \ \Leftrightarrow \ \Leftrightarrow \ \Leftrightarrow \ \Leftrightarrow \ \Leftrightarrow \ \Leftrightarrow$$
$$\Leftrightarrow \ \Leftrightarrow \ \Leftrightarrow \ \Leftrightarrow \ \Leftrightarrow \ \Leftrightarrow \ \Leftrightarrow$$
$$\Leftrightarrow \ \Leftrightarrow \ \Leftrightarrow \ \Leftrightarrow \ \Leftrightarrow \ \Leftrightarrow \ \Leftrightarrow$$

"The same thing would work for Our Hotel and Our Motel! For Our Hotel, let me make an array of little squares with 68 rows (a row for each room) and with 45 squares in each row (a square for each dollar of a room's price).

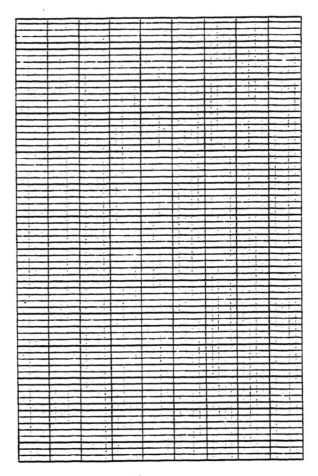

"Then let me tilt this array on its side.

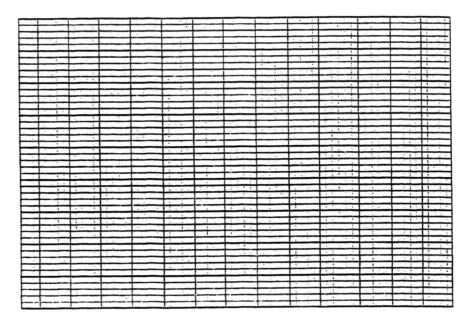

"The array tilted on its side is an array with 45 rows (one row for each room in Our Motel) and 68 squares in each row (the price for a room in Our Motel). The number of dollars for the hotel and the motel problem is the same! The answer to the hotel problem was $3060. The answer to the motel problem is also $3060."

John solved the motel problem first by relating it to the hotel problem and then by looking at a pair of simpler problems, Cheap Hotel and Cheap Motel. He noticed that a 7 by 9 array has the same number of elements as a 9 by 7 array, or, in terms of multiplication, that $7 \times 9 = 9 \times 7$. Children learning their multiplication tables will notice that $3 \times 4 = 4 \times 3$, that $7 \times 9 = 9 \times 7$, ... and be amazed. It is not surprising that they are amazed because the *problems* that give rise to the products 7×9 and 9×7 can be quite different, as we saw with Cheap Hotel and Cheap Motel. However, by viewing a product as the number of objects in a suitable array, we see that $7 \times 9 = 9 \times 7$ and $4 \times 8 = 8 \times 4$ are not coincidences and that this sort of thing works for the product of any pair of whole numbers, no matter how big they might be. An array with A rows of B items each (having a total of $A \times B$ items in the whole array) that is tilted on its side becomes an array with B rows of A items each (having a total of $B \times A$ items in the whole array). This demonstrates the *commutative* property of multiplication.

COMMUTATIVE PROPERTY OF MULTIPLICATION

For every pair of whole numbers A and B, $A \times B = B \times A$. The whole number $\underbrace{B + B + \cdots + B}_{A \text{ addends}}$ is the same as the whole number $\underbrace{A + A + \cdots + A}_{B \text{ addends}}$.

The commutative property of multiplication can be used to help organize the *elementary multiplication facts*. Once you know that $5 \times 9 = 45$, then by the commutative property you also know that $9 \times 5 = 45$.

EXERCISES

6. John knows that the answer to the wheat field problem (exercise 1) is 962 bushels of wheat. Help him solve the corresponding problem for another wheat field.

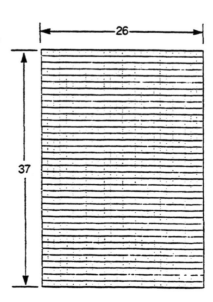

7. Mina's friend Ila has a field of cabbages.

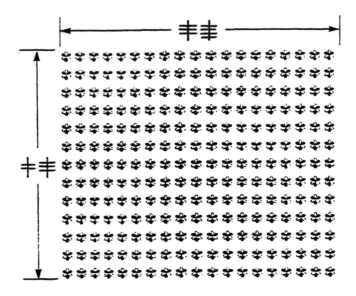

Ila knows that there are +‡‡+ cabbages in the field and has told Mina that Mina has a field of cauliflowers.

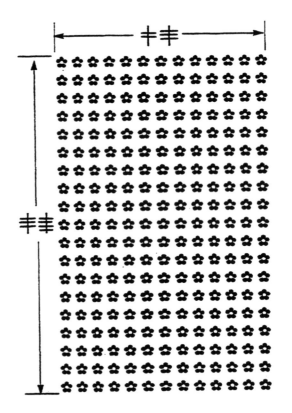

Mina wants to know how many cauliflowers she has. Help her find out. (Mina and Ila both use stick numerals to represent numbers.)

Maria is trying to find out how many linoleum tiles will be needed to tile the family room in her house. She has figured out that the tiles will look like this when placed on the family room floor.

Solve this yourself, first.

Maria knows her multiplication tables up through the 10s, and she knows the connection between multiplication and the number of objects in an array. But that's all. If you were Maria, how would you solve the problem?

A Solution to the Floor Tile Problem

Maria thinks: "This is an array of tiles. There are 7 rows and 19 tiles in each row. If it were smaller—such as a 7 by 9 array—then I could solve it. A 7 by 9 array would have $7 \times 9 = 63$ tiles in all. My array has too many tiles in each row. Wait! What if I were to cut up the array into two smaller arrays?

"Now I have two arrays of tiles. One is a 7 by 10 array; the other is a 7 by 9 array. I can figure out the number of tiles in each of the two small arrays: $7 \times 10 = 70$ in one and $7 \times 9 = 63$ in the other. I could add the two answers together to get the total number of tiles in the 7 by 19 array: $7 \times 19 = 70 + 63 = 133$ tiles."

The Mathematical Idea: Multiplication as Distributive over Addition

Maria solved the floor tile problem by *breaking the main problem into smaller problems* that she could solve. She did this by breaking the large array into two smaller arrays.

What does this look like in symbols? You want to find the product 7×19. You know that $19 = 10 + 9$. So $7 \times 19 = 7 \times (10 + 9)$. You find 7×19 by first finding 7×10, then 7×9, and finally adding the two quantities together: $7 \times 19 = 7 \times (10 + 9) = 7 \times 10 + 7 \times 9$. This is an instance of a general property of multiplication and addition.

DISTRIBUTIVE PROPERTY OF MULTIPLICATION OVER ADDITION

$$A \times (B + C) = (A \times B) + (A \times C)$$

for all whole numbers A, B, C. Also, since multiplication is commutative,

$$(A + B) \times C = (A \times C) + (B \times C).$$

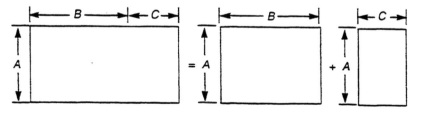

The distributive property can be used to figure out the elementary multiplication facts for "larger" numbers if you know them for "smaller" numbers. For example, suppose you want to figure out 6 × 9. You can write 9 as 9 = 4 + 5 and use the distributive law: 6 × 9 = 6 × (4 + 5) = 6 × 4 + 6 × 5. Because you know the multiplication tables for smaller numbers, you can calculate the right-hand side. It's 24 + 30 = 54. So 6 × 9 = 54.

EXERCISES 8. Maria must figure out the number of trees in her uncle's orchard.

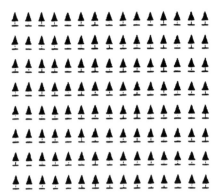

All Maria knows about multiplication is the tables. Help Maria solve this problem using the distributive law.

9. Your system of numerals is the base 8 system, and now you know the base 8 multiplication tables; but that's all you know about multiplication. Use what you know and the distributive law to figure out the number of vines in the vineyard across the road.

THE SECOND FLOOR TILE PROBLEM Maria now has the problem of figuring out the number of parquet tiles needed for her living room. She has figured out that the tiles will be arranged as shown.

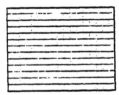

Try it, please! If you were Maria how would you solve this new problem?

Maria thinks: "It's another array. This time, the number of tiles in each row and the number of rows are *both* too big! Before I give up why don't I do what I did before and cut down on the number of objects in each row. I'll try this.

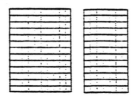

That's a little better. Now I need to cut down on the number of rows. But that's no problem. Let me try this.

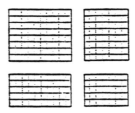

I have *broken the problem up into simpler problems*. Now there are four arrays, each of a size I can handle. I can figure out the number of tiles in each one, then add them all up to get the answer."

The Mathematical Idea: Using the Distributive Law Several Times

Maria used the distributive law several times. Here's what her solution looks like in symbols and pictures.

$$13 \times 17 = 13 \times (10 + 7)$$
$$= 13 \times 10 + 13 \times 7$$
$$= (8 + 5) \times 10 + (8 + 5) \times 7$$
$$= 8 \times 10 + 5 \times 10 + 8 \times 7 + 5 \times 7$$
$$= 80 + 50 + 56 + 35$$
$$= 221.$$

	17		10	7
13	13 X 17	= 8	8 X 10	8 X 7
		5	5 X 10	5 X 7

10. Help Maria find the number of trees in *this* orchard.

11. Your system of numerals is the base 8 system, and now you know the base 8 multiplication tables; but that's all you know about multiplication. Use what you know and the distributive law to figure out the number of vines in the vineyard on the edge of town.

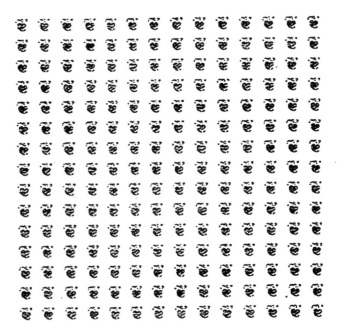

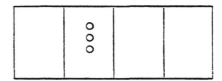

A Solution to the Computer
Handbook Problem

At Saul's school, the PTA plans to raise enough money to buy a computer handbook for every student in the school. Saul would like to know how much the PTA will have to raise. He knows that there are about 325 students in his school and that each handbook costs about $10. Saul knows his multiplication table (through the 10s), has solved many different multiplication problems—such as the classroom seat problem, the hotel and motel problems, and the floor tile problem—using the commutative and distributive properties of multiplication, but he doesn't know the standard method for multiplying many-digit numbers.

Saul thinks: "I can find the answer by adding up $10 to itself 325 times. Let's see. I know that ten 10s is 100. So twenty 10s would be 200. And five more 10s would make 250. Twenty-five 10s is 250. Now what about three hundred 10s? That's a lot more work. All these 10s make me think of a counting board. Let me *make a model* of 300 on a counting board.

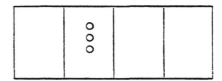

Three stones are in the 100s column. Repeated addition of that 10 times yields 30 stones in the 100s column. Each 10 of the stones is worth a single stone in the column to the left. That gives me 3 stones in the 1000s column.

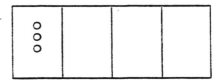

So $10 \times 300 = 3000$. Putting all that I know together, I get $10 \times 325 = 3000 + 250$."

The Mathematical Idea: Multiplication by 10

If a person can skip count by 10 or has a good knowledge of place value, then it is easy for that person to learn the 10s multiplication table: $1 \times 10 = 10$, $2 \times 10 = 20, \ldots, 10 \times 10 = 100$. A next step might be to learn how to multiply 10 by any number.

Saul's solution to the problem of finding 10×300 involved a counting board. Let's look at another multiplication problem using this device. Consider the problem 10×457. Here is 457 on the counting board.

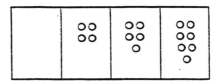

Multiplication of this by 10 (using repeated addition) means replacing each stone by 10 stones, then replacing each of those 10 stones by a stone in the column to its left. The net effect is to move each original stone one column to its left.

In terms of written numerals, multiplication by 10 amounts to placing a zero to the right of the numeral! (*You* knew that, of course, but did Saul?)

Here is another way to see that $10 \times 325 = 3250$ by *making a model* of 325 with place value blocks.

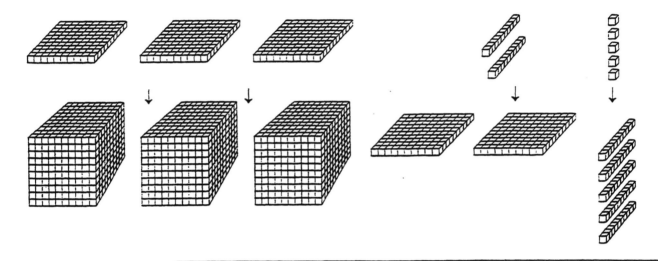

MULTIPLICATION BY 10

To multiply a decimal numeral by 10, place a 0 to the right of the numeral.

EXERCISES

12. Find a rule for multiplication of a stick numeral by $+1$ and justify your rule.

13. Find a rule for multiplication of a base 8 numeral by 10_{eight} and justify your rule.

THE AUDITORIUM SEAT PROBLEM

The seating arrangement of the auditorium in Sarah's school looks like the picture.

∩∩∩∩∩∩∩∩∩∩∩∩∩∩∩∩∩∩∩∩∩∩∩∩∩∩∩∩∩∩∩∩∩∩∩∩
∩∩∩∩∩∩∩∩∩∩∩∩∩∩∩∩∩∩∩∩∩∩∩∩∩∩∩∩∩∩∩∩∩∩∩∩
∩∩∩∩∩∩∩∩∩∩∩∩∩∩∩∩∩∩∩∩∩∩∩∩∩∩∩∩∩∩∩∩∩∩∩∩
∩∩∩∩∩∩∩∩∩∩∩∩∩∩∩∩∩∩∩∩∩∩∩∩∩∩∩∩∩∩∩∩∩∩∩∩
∩∩∩∩∩∩∩∩∩∩∩∩∩∩∩∩∩∩∩∩∩∩∩∩∩∩∩∩∩∩∩∩∩∩∩∩
∩∩∩∩∩∩∩∩∩∩∩∩∩∩∩∩∩∩∩∩∩∩∩∩∩∩∩∩∩∩∩∩∩∩∩∩
∩∩∩∩∩∩∩∩∩∩∩∩∩∩∩∩∩∩∩∩∩∩∩∩∩∩∩∩∩∩∩∩∩∩∩∩
∩∩∩∩∩∩∩∩∩∩∩∩∩∩∩∩∩∩∩∩∩∩∩∩∩∩∩∩∩∩∩∩∩∩∩∩
∩∩∩∩∩∩∩∩∩∩∩∩∩∩∩∩∩∩∩∩∩∩∩∩∩∩∩∩∩∩∩∩∩∩∩∩

Sarah wants to know the number of seats in the auditorium (so she'll know whether or not extra seats have to be brought in for the assembly). Sarah now knows the multiplication tables, the connection between repeated addition and arrays, how to multiply any number by 10, and the commutative and distributive properties of multiplication—at least as they relate to arrays. Help Sarah solve this problem.

Sarah thinks: "There are 9 rows with 30 in each row. I can organize the seats this way.

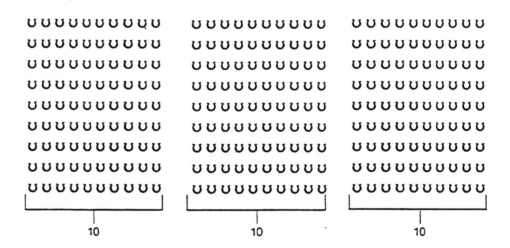

"This breaks the big array up into three smaller arrays. A row in each of the small arrays has 10 seats in it. If I replace each row in the small arrays with a dash, I'd get something like this:

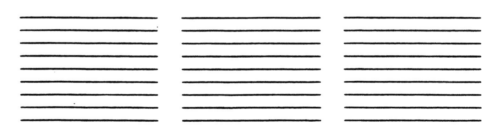

This is an array of dashes. The array has 9 rows with 3 dashes in each row. So this array has $9 \times 3 = 27$ dashes. Since each dash represents 10 seats, there are $27 \times 10 = 270$ seats in all."

The Mathematical Idea: Multiplication as Associative

To figure out 9×30, Sarah first noticed that $30 = 3 \times 10$ and split each row of 30 into three 10s. Replacing each 10 by a dash gave her a 9 by 3 array of dashes. She multiplied 9 times 3 to get 27. Then she multiplied 27 times 10 to get 270. In symbols, this is $9 \times 30 = 9 \times (3 \times 10) = (9 \times 3) \times 10$. The equation says that multiplying 3 by 10 and then multiplying the answer by 9 is the same as multiplying 9 by 3 and then multiplying the answer by 10. This is an instance of the *associative* property of multiplication of whole numbers.

ASSOCIATIVE PROPERTY OF MULTIPLICATION

$$A \times (B \times C) = (A \times B) \times C$$

for all whole numbers A, B, and C.

Together with the commutative property of multiplication, the associative property can be used to help organize the elementary multiplication facts. For example, if a person knows multiplication tables for "small" numbers, she can figure out the product 3×8 this way: $3 \times 8 = 3 \times (2 \times 4) = (3 \times 2) \times 4 = 6 \times 4 = 24$.

EXERCISE

14. Use the associative law to help John find the product 8×70.

THE SCHOOL CAFETERIA FLOOR PROBLEM

Maria is looking at a picture of her school cafeteria floor.

The picture shows an array of linoleum tiles that has 35 rows with 100 in each row. Maria wants to know how much all the tiles will cost. Since each tile costs $1, she needs to know how many tiles there are. Maria knows her multiplication tables, knows about arrays, has experience with the commutative, associative, and distributive properties of multiplication, and can multiply any number by 10—and that's all. Help Maria solve this problem.

Try it!

A Solution to the School Cafeteria Problem

Maria thinks about *simpler problems she has solved.* She thinks: "I want to figure out 35×100. I know that $100 = 10 \times 10$ so that $35 \times 100 = 35 \times (10 \times 10)$. I know how to multiply by 10, and I know the associative property. So

$$35 \times 100 = 35 \times (10 \times 10) = (35 \times 10) \times 10$$
$$= 350 \times 10$$
$$= 3500.$$

That's 3500—35 with two zeros placed to the right of the numeral."

The Mathematical Idea: Multiplication by 100, 1000, . . .

Maria just figured out an instance of the rule for multiplication by 100.

MULTIPLICATION BY 100

To multiply a decimal numeral times 100, you place two zeros to the right of the numeral.

Why it works is that to multiply 100 times 4567 means that you first think of 100 as 10×10; then you use the associative property of multiplication.

$$4567 \times 100 = 4567 \times (10 \times 10) = (4567 \times 10) \times 10 = 45{,}670 \times 10 = 456{,}700.$$

| Place one zero. | Place a second zero. |

Multiplication by 1000 can be dealt with in the same way. For example, to multiply 1000 times 1234, we think $1000 = 10 \times 100$ and use associativity. Then

$$1234 \times 1000 = 1234 \times (10 \times 100) = (1234 \times 10) \times 100$$
$$= 12{,}340 \times 100 = 1{,}234{,}000.$$

Place a new zero (from 10).   Place two more zeros (from 100).

Here is the general rule.

MULTIPLICATION OF A DECIMAL NUMERAL BY 10^n

To multiply a decimal numeral by 10^n, place n zeros to the right of the numeral. For example, $10^5 \times 1234 = 123{,}400{,}000$.

Exponent 5   5 zeros

EXERCISES

15. Maria must figure out the answer to this multiplication problem: $10{,}000 \times 472$. *You* know that the answer is 4,720,000. Explain this to Maria so that she will know and understand how to multiply any number by 10,000. Use the ideas just presented but not the general rule for multiplication by 10^n.

16. Find and justify a rule for multiplication of a stick numeral by $+|\,|$. Do the same for $+|\,|\,|$.

17. Find and justify a rule for multiplication of a standard base 8 numeral by 100_{eight}. Do the same for 1000_{eight}.

Third graders Sarah, John, Maria, and Saul have solved the multiplication problems that we have seen, starting with the book problem and ending with the school cafeteria floor tile problem. They haven't yet learned the standard method for multiplying two-digit numbers. They need to solve the problem 34 × 57. With their knowledge and experience how might they solve it?

A Solution to a Harder Problem

They sketch a 34 by 57 array.

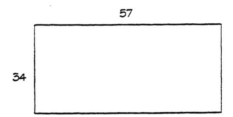

They think of using the distributive law to break up the 34 by 57 array into smaller arrays. Expanded form suggests to them where to make the break.

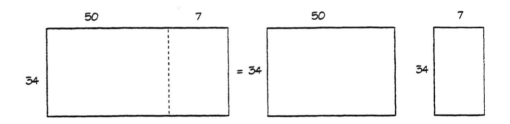

And again:

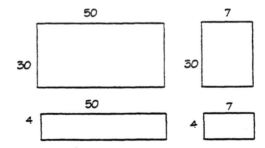

They now have four sub-arrays to deal with. They notice that the one in the lower right-hand corner is easy: There are 4 × 7 = 28 items in the array.

John says: "The array in the lower left-hand corner, 4 × 50, is also easy! We can *use a solution to another problem*, the auditorium seat problem, and organize it like this.

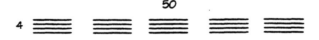

Each dash represents 10 items, making a 4 by 5 array of dashes. The array has 4 × 5 = 20 dashes. That's 20 × 10 = 200 original items."

Sarah says: "The upper right-hand corner can be handled in the same way. Organize its array this way.

Once again, each dash represents 10 items. It's a 3 by 7 array of dashes. So 3 × 7 = 21 dashes, and 21 × 10 = 210 items."

To handle the 30 by 50 sub-array in the upper left-hand corner, Maria suggests that they use the distributive law again and organize it to look like this.

5
3 □□□□□
   □□□□□
   □□□□□

Every big square represents a 10 by 10 array or 10 × 10 = 100 original items.

Maria says: "We have a 3 by 5 array of large squares. So there are 3 × 5 = 15 large squares or 15 × 100 = 1500 original items in the 30 by 50 sub-array."

Finally, they put all this together in one picture, wrote down the numbers they calculated from various parts of the picture, and added them up.

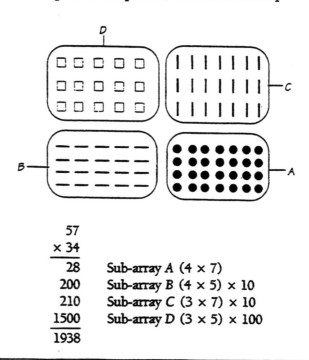

57
× 34
─────
28   Sub-array A (4 × 7)
200   Sub-array B (4 × 5) × 10
210   Sub-array C (3 × 7) × 10
1500   Sub-array D (3 × 5) × 100
─────
1938

The Mathematical Idea: Organizing the Array into Sub-Arrays of Dots, Dashes, and Squares

Sarah, John, Maria, and Saul solved the problem 34×57 first by *drawing a picture* of the product as an array (of dots, say). Then they organized the array into sub-arrays of dots, dashes, and squares. Let's solve exercise 1 (the wheat field problem) in the same way.

First *draw a picture* of the wheat field as an array of squares on a piece of graph paper.

Using the grid as a guide, set out the length and width of the wheat field along two sides of its periphery with dashes and dots, where a dash is 10 and a dot is 1.

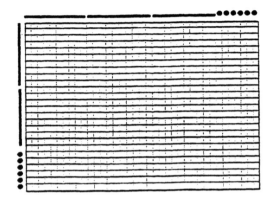

Then, in the array of squares, mark off 10 by 10 squares, dashes, and dots.

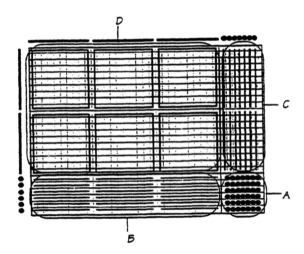

Finally, after labeling the sub-arrays, compute the products corresponding to each of them (called *partial products*) and add them up.

$$
\begin{array}{r}
37 \\
\times 26 \\
\hline
42 \\
180 \\
140 \\
600 \\
\hline
962
\end{array}
$$

42   Sub-array A (6×7)
180   Sub-array B $(6 \times 3) \times 10$
140   Sub-array C $(2 \times 7) \times 10$
600   Sub-array D $(2 \times 3) \times 100$

18. Use graph paper and organizing the array into sub-arrays of dots, dashes, and squares to find the product 45 × 32, as in the solution to the wheat field problem.

19. One way to make a model of a product is to use place value blocks. In a way similar to organizing an array into sub-arrays of dots, dashes, and squares, you make a rectangular layout with place value blocks, with unit cubes in place of dots, longs in place of dashes, and flats in place of squares. Use this method with place value blocks to find 27 × 34.

20. As in exercise 19, use base 5 place value blocks to make a model of the product ╪╪ × ╪╪ . Find the partial products as stick numerals and add them up to calculate the full product.

The Method of Sub-Arrays with Expanded Form, the Method of Partial Products with Zeros, and the Standard Method

The method of multiplying used in the solution to a harder problem used the following ideas and techniques.

■ Expanded form and the distributive property to establish sub-arrays
■ Calculation of the partial products corresponding to the sub-arrays
■ Adding up the partial products to get the final answer

A more abstract version of the solution, without using dots, dashes, and squares, might go like this. Break up the big array as before.

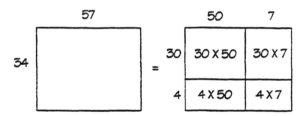

This time each partial product can be calculated using the associative and commutative properties of multiplication.

$$
\begin{aligned}
30 \times 50 &= (3 \times 5) \times 100 = 15 \times 100 = 1500 \\
30 \times 7\ &= (3 \times 7) \times 10\ = 21 \times 10\ = \ 210 \\
4 \times 50\ &= (4 \times 5) \times 10\ = 20 \times 10\ = \ 200 \\
4 \times 7\ & \hspace{4.5cm} = \ \ 28 \\
\hline
\text{Total} & \hspace{4.5cm} 1938
\end{aligned}
$$

Notice that each partial product is calculated by combining an elementary multiplication fact with multiplication by a power of 10.

An even more abstract version is like the one just completed but avoids the drawing of an array.

$$
\begin{array}{r}
57 \\
\times\ 34 \\
\hline
1500 \\
210 \\
200 \\
28 \\
\hline
1938
\end{array}
$$

It is called the method of *partial products with zeros.*

The thinking for a streamlined version of the method of partial products with zeros might go this way: "Consider the array for 34 × 57.

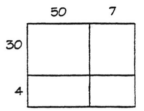

Instead of calculating the four partial products separately, we ought to be able to make some shortcuts. Let's calculate together the sum of the two lower partial products (the two bottom segments of the rectangle). This sum is actually the product 4 × 57. First, to calculate the partial product on the lower right, we multiply 4 times 7 and get 28. We write down the 8 and carry the 2 (tens). Then to calculate the partial product on the lower left, multiply 4 times 5 (tens) getting 20 (tens) and add on the carried 2 (tens) to make 22 (tens). Write 22 down just to the left of the 8 to get 228 (the sum of 22 tens plus 8). This is actually the product 4 × 57."

$$
\begin{array}{r}
57 \\
\times\ 34 \\
\hline
228
\end{array}
$$

(Notice that there is no actual need to draw the array; you just need to keep an image of it in mind.) "Next let's calculate the sum of the two upper partial products (the two segments at the top of the drawing). This sum should be the product 30 × 57. This should be the same as (3 × 57) × 10. So put down a zero right under the 8 of the 228 (for the "10" of the product). Then we write down just to the left of this zero what we get from computing 3 × 57. We calculate 3 × 57 just as we calculated 4 × 57 and get 171."

$$
\begin{array}{r}
57 \\
\times\ 34 \\
\hline
228 \\
1710
\end{array}
$$

A final stage would be to "suppress" the zero we have written under the 8 of 228 and begin writing the product 3 × 57 one digit to the left.

$$
\begin{array}{r}
57 \\
\times\ 34 \\
\hline
228 \\
171 \\
\hline
1938
\end{array}
$$

This is the *standard method* for multiplication.

An Anatomy of a Multiplication Problem

A more difficult multiplication problem is 38 × 567. We will solve this problem first by organizing the array into sub-arrays, then by partial products with zeros, and finally by the standard method. In this anatomy we will point out the skills needed at each stage.

METHOD 1, ORGANIZING THE ARRAY INTO SUB-ARRAYS We organize the solution into three steps.

Step 1 Sketch the array and organize it into sub-arrays using expanded notation and the distributive law.

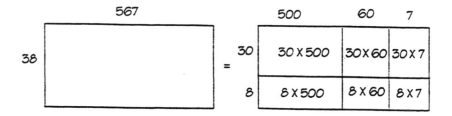

Step 2 Calculate each partial product using elementary multiplication facts, the associative property of multiplication, and the rule for multiplication of a decimal numeral by a power of 10.

F (3 X 5) X 1000	E (3 X 6) X 100	D (3 X 7) X 10
C (8 X 5) X 100	B (8 X 6) X 10	A 8 X 7

$$\begin{array}{r} 567 \\ \times\, 38 \end{array}$$

SUB-ARRAY	PARTIAL PRODUCTS		
A	8×7	$= 56$	$=\quad 56$
B	$(8 \times 6) \times 10$	$= 48 \times 10$	$=\quad 480$
C	$(8 \times 5) \times 100$	$= 40 \times 100$	$=\quad 4000$
D	$(3 \times 7) \times 10$	$= 21 \times 10$	$=\quad 210$
E	$(3 \times 6) \times 100$	$= 18 \times 100$	$=\quad 1800$
F	$(3 \times 5) \times 1000$	$= 15 \times 1000$	$= 15,000$

Add these.

$$21,546 \quad \text{Sum}$$

METHOD 2, PARTIAL PRODUCTS WITH ZEROS The method of partial products with zeros consists of writing down the set of partial products and adding them up. All the other steps of the method of organizing the array into sub-arrays are carried out mentally. Otherwise, method 2 is identical to method 1.

$$\begin{array}{r} 567 \\ \times\, 38 \\ \hline 56 \\ 480 \\ 4000 \\ 210 \\ 1800 \\ 15,000 \\ \hline 21,546 \end{array}$$

Add these.

Sum

METHOD 3, THE STANDARD METHOD

PARTIAL PRODUCTS WITH ZEROS		STANDARD METHOD

$$\begin{array}{r} 567 \\ \times\, 38 \\ \hline 56 \\ 480 \\ 4000 \end{array}$$ Add these. $\rightarrow$ 4536

$$\begin{array}{r} 210 \\ 1800 \\ 15,000 \end{array}$$ Add these. $\rightarrow$ 17,010 Suppress zeros. $\rightarrow$ 1701

$$\begin{array}{r} 567 \\ \times\, 38 \\ \hline \end{array}$$ $\rightarrow$ 4536

$$\begin{array}{r} 567 \\ \times\, 38 \\ \hline \end{array}$$ $\rightarrow$ 4536

21,546   21,546   21,546

EXERCISES

21. Solve the multiplication problem 476×53 using the three methods just shown.

22. Solve the stick numeral multiplication problem ╪╪╪ × ╪╪ using the three methods just shown. Remember that stick numerals are base 5 and that expanded form is an important part of the methods.

23. Solve the base 8 multiplication problems using the three methods just shown. Explain your steps carefully.

   (a) $45_{\text{eight}} \times 32_{\text{eight}}$ (b) $476_{\text{eight}} \times 53_{\text{eight}}$

Why Do We Need to Do All This?

Imagine the following fourth grade classroom scene.
"Ladies and gentlemen of the fourth grade, we want to find out how many seats are in this auditorium.

"You can see that the answer is the same as what you get when you add 38 together to itself 23 times. That is a lot of work. There's an easier way.

1. Write down 23 and 38:   23   38

2. Double 23, write it here.   →46   19   3. Halve 38; write it here.

4. Double 46, write it here.   →92   9   5. Halve 19, throw away the remainder, and write it here.

6. Keep doing this (doubling the numbers in the left-hand column and halving the numbers in the right-hand column) until you get a 1 in the right-hand column.
    184   4
    368   2
    736   1

7. Here is your work written out again. Look for the numbers in the right-hand column that are even. Cross out the numbers in those rows.
    -23----38-
    46   19
    92   9
    -184----4-

8. Add up the numbers in the left-hand column that haven't been crossed out. The resulting sum is your answer!
    -368----2-
    736   1
    ―――
    874

"There are 874 seats in the auditorium! It works! (It always works.) Check it out."

The Mathematical Idea: The Egyptian Method for Multiplication

Here is another multiplication problem (43 × 67) solved by the method just described.

$$
\begin{array}{rr}
43 & 67 \\
86 & 33 \\
\cancel{172} & \cancel{16} \\
\cancel{344} & \cancel{8} \\
\cancel{688} & \cancel{4} \\
\cancel{1376} & \cancel{2} \\
2752 & 1 \\
\hline
2881 &
\end{array}
$$

Talk about magic! If you had been taught to multiply this way with no other background (except learning how to double and how to halve), would you have been very happy with multiplication? I suspect that a fourth grader, taught the standard method without any background or explanation, would feel like you do right now, having been shown the method above. Things a person learns can and should make sense. Making sense takes time and care.

The method of multiplying by doubling and halving was used by the ancient Egyptians and is sometimes called the Egyptian method. It was also used in parts of Europe in the Middle Ages.

EXERCISE   24. Solve the multiplication problem 68 × 57 using the Egyptian method.

5.6 CALCULATORS AND COMPUTERS: MULTIPLICATION

It's easy to have a calculator or a computer calculate the product of two numbers. For example, if you want to multiply 74 times 87 with a calculator, you use the key sequence 74 [×] 87 [=]. For a microcomputer, you type PRINT 74*87.

Exactly how the calculator/computer finds the answer we are not told. (It probably uses a version of the standard method.) We know that 74 × 87 is what you get when you add 87 to itself 74 times. This is the basic meaning of 74*87, and the standard method is an alternative (shorter) way to find the number. We can get the calculator and the computer to obtain an answer using the basic meaning, the long way, and in such a way that we can see what is going on. This might be a useful thing to be able to do if you are trying to show young children that the standard method and the long way yield the same answer. You could also use the calculator or computer to multiply the long way *before* developing the standard method.

REPEATED ADDITION BY CALCULATOR   Take the problem 74 × 87. We can use the constant, or K, feature to add 87 repeatedly to itself 74 times. Here's how.

FOR A CALCULATOR WITH A [K] KEY		
KEYING SEQUENCE	DISPLAY	MATHEMATICAL EXPRESSION
87 [+] [K]	87	1×87
[=]	174	2×87
[=]	261	3×87
[=]	348	4×87
[=]	435	5×87

FOR MOST OTHER CALCULATORS		
KEYING SEQUENCE	DISPLAY	MATHEMATICAL EXPRESSION
87 [+]	87	1×87
[=]	174	2×87
[=]	261	3×87
[=]	348	4×87
[=]	435	5×87

(Your calculator may differ from both of these. If one of these key sequences doesn't work, check the manual for your calculator.) So, for both kinds of calculators, after having keyed [=] 73 times you will get 74×87, or 6438, and you will see all the intermediate additions as you go. Try it!

REPEATED ADDITION USING BASIC   The continual addition of 87 to an accumulating sum suggests that we use a loop. In BASIC this involves the use of the FOR . . . NEXT statements. In the program let's use the variable S for the accumulating sum; the value of S will change as the program progresses. To S we will keep adding 87 and we will do this 74 times. The LET command will enable us to change the value of S by adding 87 at each step of the loop:

```
LET S = S + 87
```

This statement says, "Take the present value of S and add 87 to it. The result is the new value of S." Here is a program, with loop, using this command.

```
10 FOR I = 1 TO 74
20 LET S = S + 87
30 NEXT I
100 END
```

We must assign a value to the variable S to begin the program. This is called *initializing*. We want S to begin with the value 0, so we type an additional line

```
5 LET S = 0
```

The full program is

```
5 LET S = 0
10 FOR I = 1 TO 74
20 LET S = S + 87
30 NEXT I
100 END
```

Type and run the program above. What happens?
Nothing happens that you can see. To see something happen, you have to tell the computer to print something on the screen. So you type

```
25 PRINT S
LIST
5 LET S = 0
10 FOR I = 1 TO 74
15 PRINT S
20 LET S = S + 87
30 NEXT I
100 END
```
Run this revised program. What happens?

31. Alter the program above so that in addition to multiplying 74 times 87, it will multiply any pair of numbers by repeated addition. This alteration will allow you to see what is happening when the program is run. You can do this by including two INPUT statements at the beginning of the program to assign values to the variables A and B; then the remainder of the program would multiply A times B using repeated addition.

5.7 SUMMARY OF IMPORTANT IDEAS AND TECHNIQUES

- The product of whole numbers A and B; the definition of *multiplication*
- An array as a rectangular arrangement of objects; the number of items in an array with A rows and B items is the product $A \times B$
- Items used to develop the standard method for multiplication

  The multiplication tables (or elementary multiplication facts): the products $A \times B$ for A and B between 1 and 10, inclusive

  The properties of multiplication: commutative, associative, and distributive over addition

  Multiplication by powers of 10

- Stages leading up to the standard method for multiplication of several-digit numbers

  (For two-digit numbers) an array with dots, dashes, and squares

  Sketch of an array using expanded form, the distributive law, and partial products

  The method of partial products with zeros

  The standard method

- The Egyptian method of multiplication
- New paradigms for multiplication: tree diagrams and cartesian product of sets
- Estimating products using the law relating multiplication with order
- Rules for the use of algebraic symbols; the cancellation law for multiplication; solving equations with unknowns
- Using calculators and computers to simulate repeated addition

PROBLEM SET

PRACTICING SKILLS

1. You are the catering manager for a large hotel and need to know how many tables can fit into the grand ballroom. A table is to be placed inside each little square in the picture of the grand ballroom shown on page 228. You know how to add three- and four-digit numbers, but you know nothing about multiplication. How would you solve this?

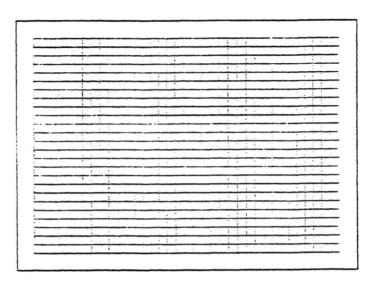

2. Without actually counting all the trees, figure out the number of trees in the orchard.

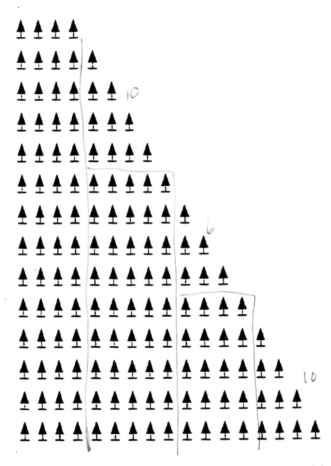

3. Joanna is in the third grade. Help her find the product 738 × 10 using (a) stones on a counting board and (b) place value blocks.

4. You know the associative property of multiplication, the multiplication tables, and how to multiply any number by 10. Use these to find the product 9 × 60.

5. Explain to Jaime how to multiply 1,000,000 × 879 so that he will know and understand how to multiply any number by 1,000,000. Why would Jaime want to be able to do this?

6. Find the product 73 × 86 by
   (a) Drawing a picture of the product as an array on graph paper using dots, dashes, and squares to organize the array.
   (b) Using partial products with zeros; show clearly how each partial product corresponds to a portion of the array in (a).

7. Find the product 675 × 49.
   (a) Sketch an array and organize it using expanded form and the distributive law.
   (b) Use the method of partial products with zeros. Show clearly how each partial product corresponds to a portion of the sketched array in (a).

8. Solve the problem using the doubling/halving Egyptian method: 94 × 87.

9. Use the rules for algebra to solve each of the following problems. Justify each step with a rule.
   (a) Find a whole number A such that $A + 8 = 20$.
   (b) Find a whole number B such that $4B + 3 = 31$.
   (c) Find a whole number C such that $5C = 4(C + 2)$.
   (d) Find a whole number D such that $3(2D + 5) = 7(D + 1)$.

10. The secretary of the school district needs to order paper for the office for the school year. Lower quality sulfite paper costs $6 per ream (500 sheets), while higher quality bond paper costs $9 per ream. The budget will allow her to spend $720 on paper. She knows from last year that she will need 90 reams and she wants as much bond paper as possible. How many reams of each kind should she buy?

11. Grant and Adam live 77 mi apart on opposite ends of a long country road. Both being avid bicyclists, they decide to bike toward each other and meet for lunch. Both will leave home at exactly 9 A.M. Grant bikes at an average pace of 15 mph, while Adam travels at an average pace of 18 mph. At what time will they meet for lunch? How far will each have traveled?

12. Use the law relating multiplication with order to estimate the products (by placing each product between two easily computable products).
   (a) 73 × 59   (b) 267 × 523   (c) 4577 × 6938

13. Sean and Sarah are buying a new condominium. They must choose colors for the living room carpet and the kitchen tile. They have six choices for the carpet: gray, beige, peach, blue, brown tweed, and off-white. There are five tile choices: yellow pattern, blue pattern, green pattern, solid tan, solid yellow. From how many color combinations do they have to choose? Solve this problem with (a) a tree diagram and (b) a table listing the elements of the cartesian product $C \times T$, where C is the set of carpet colors and T is the set of tile choices.

14. Help Mina complete the stick numeral multiplication table.

×	+	‡	≡	≣	⊣
+					
‡					
≡				‡‡	
≣					
⊣					

For each of the remaining problems, document your solution as clearly and completely as you can. Include in your documentation the steps you took, the problems and solutions that gave you ideas, and the problem-solving strategies that you used. You may want to organize all this before writing your final report.

15. Without actually counting all the seats, figure out the number of seats in the auditorium.

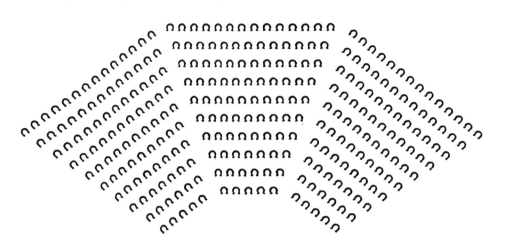

16. Without actually counting all the lots, figure out the number of lots in the housing development and explain how you did it.

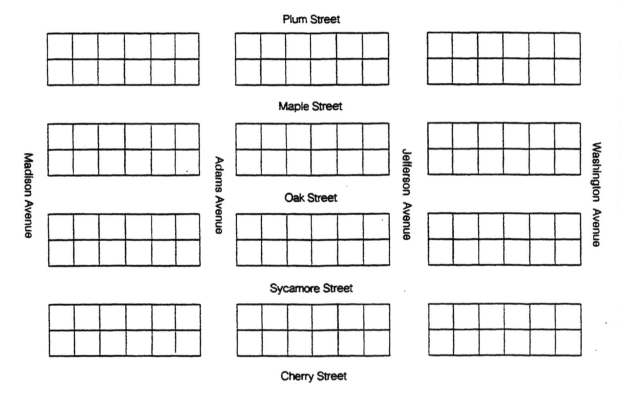

17. Consider the multiplication problem 453 × 57. Solve it three ways.
    (a) Sketch an array and organize it using expanded form and the distributive property.
    (b) Use the method of partial products with zeros. Show how each partial product corresponds to a portion of the array in (a).

(c)   Use the standard method. Show how the steps you take here correspond to those in (b) and point out which steps are shortcuts for those in (b).

18.   To figure out the product 34 × 256, you could sketch an array and organize it this way.

	200	50	6
30	30 X 200	30 X 50	30 X 6
4	4 X 200	4 X 50	4 X 6

It would be cumbersome to use just the units, flats, and longs from a set of place value blocks (or dots, dashes, and squares in a picture) to organize the array in the way shown on page 208 of the text. However, a collection of place value blocks has large cubes worth 1000 units in addition to the units, longs, and flats.

Figure out a way to organize the 34 × 256 array using this full set of place value blocks (or pictures of them) so that the partial products are clearly evident.

19.   Mina knows the stick numeral multiplication tables (see prob. 14). She knows the distributive property and she knows the connection between a product and an array. Use what she knows to find the product +⹋ × +≣.

20.   Mina must solve this stick numeral multiplication problem: +| × ≣ ≣ +. Use a base 5 counting board to show her how to figure out the answer.

21.   Mina knows her stick numeral multiplication table (see prob. 14); the commutative, associative, and distributive properties of multiplication; and how to multiply by +|. Help her figure out the number of trees in this orchard.

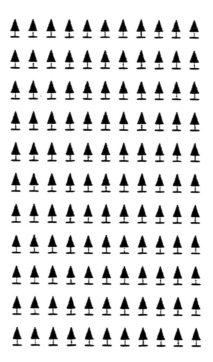

22. Using sticks, Mina organized an array of stones as shown.

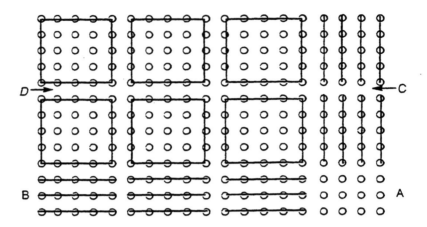

She was trying to figure out the product ⊤≡ × ≡≡. Each stick covers +| stones. Each arrangement of 4 sticks in a square fences in +|| stones. This organizes the big array into 4 sub-arrays. She calculated the number of stones in each array and added them up.

SUB-ARRARY	NUMBER OF STONES			
A	≡ × ≡		=	⊤⊤
B	(≡ × ≡) × +			=	+≡	
C	(⊤ × ≡) × +			=	+≡	
D	(⊤ × ≡) × +||		=	+ +		
			Total	+≡≡⊤

(a) Use this method to figure out the product ⊤≡ × ≡⊤ by drawing the array, organizing it into sub-arrays using sticks, calculating the product for each sub-array, and adding them up.

(b) Eventually, Mina has learned to calculate products using the method of partial products with zeros. For example, she now does the preceding problem this way:

$$
\begin{array}{r}
\text{⧚⧚} \\
\times \quad \text{⧚⧚} \\
\hline
\text{⧚⧚} \\
\text{⧚⧚⏐} \\
\text{⧚⧚⏐} \\
\text{⧚⧚⏐⏐} \\
\hline
\text{⧚⧚⧚⧚}
\end{array}
$$

Calculate the product of the next problem using the method of partial products with zeros.

$$
\begin{array}{r}
\text{⧚⧚} \\
\times \quad \text{⧚⧚}
\end{array}
$$

23. **Solve** the stick numeral multiplication problem ⧚⧚ × ⧚⧚ in three ways.

   (a) Draw a picture of the product as an array on graph paper. Use dots, dashes, and squares to organize the array.

   (b) Use the method of partial products with zeros (as in prob. 22); show clearly how each partial product corresponds to a portion of the array in (a).

   (c) Use the standard method adapted to stick numbers; point out the shortcuts being taken in the standard method that were not being made in (b).

24. **There** is a way of multiplying called front-end multiplication.

$$
\begin{array}{r}
325 \\
\times\, 421 \\
\hline
1400 \\
650 \\
325 \\
\hline
146{,}825
\end{array}
$$

Do the following multiplication problem using the same method.

$$
\begin{array}{r}
645 \\
\times\, 832
\end{array}
$$

Does it give you the right answer? Why or why not?

25. You discover this multiplication problem on a worn piece of paper at the bottom of an old trunk. Some of the digits are legible, but most are smudged. (A smudge is represented by a ◆.) Reconstruct the original problem.

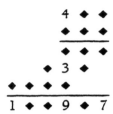

26. Café La Tour has a menu with 8 appetizers and 12 entrees.
    (a) Jacques, the proprietor, wants to know how many appetizer-entree meals are possible for a client. Draw an appropriate array and find the answer.
    (b) Café La Tour also has 5 dessert options. How many appetizer-entree-dessert meals are available at the restaurant? What appropriate geometric device (corresponding to the array for part [a]) could be used to display the meals and illustrate the answer?

27. A realtor claims that the house he is selling will double in price in a year and will triple in price in the two years after that. Thus he promises that the price in three years will be $2 \times 3 = 6$ times what it is now. How would you illustrate this situation in order to justify that 2×3 is the correct solution? (You could draw a 2 by 3 array. But an array of what?)

28. The Furniture Company makes one type of chair and one type of table. The owner wants to know how many chairs and how many tables she should produce each day. She has two workers, Able and Baker. They each have different skills and tools. To complete a finished chair, Able works on it for 2 hrs and Baker for 1. To complete a finished table, Able works on it for 1 hr and Baker for 2. Neither Able nor Baker will work more than 12 hr a day. There is a ready market for all that The Furniture Company produces. The owner wants to have as large a profit as she can. She makes a profit of $16 on each table and a profit of $12 on each chair. (Hint: Make a chart.)

29. We were off on our first trip ever to Europe. Our plane left at noon, but the travel agent told us to be at the airport an hour ahead of time. So we all left the house at 10 A.M. to drive the 40 mi to the airport. However, for some reason, there was very heavy traffic, and my father could only average 20 mph for the first 30 min. Both of my parents were getting more and more nervous before we got onto the freeway and the traffic cleared out. My mother asked me how fast we would have to go to get to the airport on time. What should my reply have been?*

30. Consider the base 8 multiplication problem $43_{eight} \times 57_{eight}$. Solve it three ways in the base 8 system.
    (a) Sketch an array and organize it using expanded notation (in the base 8 system) and the distributive property.
    (b) Use the method of partial products with zeros as adapted to the base 8 system. Show how each partial product corresponds to a portion of the array in (a).
    (c) Use the standard method as adapted to the base 8 system. Show how the steps you take here correspond to those in (b) and point out which steps are shortcuts for those in (b).

* From Carol Meyer and Tom Sallee, Make It Simpler, Addison-Wesley, Reading, Mass., 1983, p. 261.

31. A popular method for multiplying whole numbers in the Renaissance was called the *jalousie method*. You do your calculations on a grating, or jalousie. The two numbers to be multiplied—for example, 4672 and 83—are written at the top and right side of the grating.

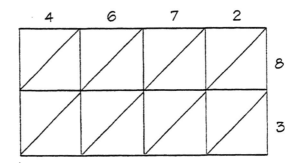

The products of pairs of digits in the two numbers are written in the squares of the grating. The numbers are added along the diagonals (upper right to lower left) to form the product of the two numbers. The product is written along the left and bottom of the grating.

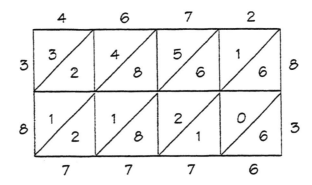

Draw a jalousie and find the product 643 × 895 using the jalousie method.

32. Why does the Egyptian method for multiplication work? (*Hints:* Think about the method for converting a number to a standard base 2 numeral. Think about the standard method of multiplication adapted to base 2 numerals.)

33. (a) To calculate 367,189 × 982,478, sketch an array and organize it as follows.

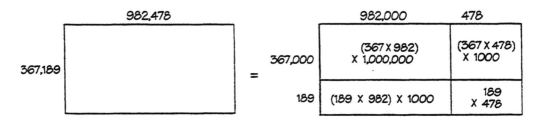

Then use a calculator to calculate the products 189 × 478, 189 × 982, 367 × 478, 367 × 982. Finally, use what you get to calculate the partial products and add them all up to get the answer to the original problem.

(b) Use the same method to calculate 470,987 × 872,395.

DIVISION OF WHOLE NUMBERS

In this chapter we will introduce division of whole numbers and discuss the evolution of a method for carrying out the operation when the numbers involved are "large." We will begin with several simple problems the solutions of which are, for us, clearly obtained by division. To somebody who hasn't had experience with division, it takes work to show that all these problems can be solved using the same technique.

We shall show, at a basic level, how solutions to these problems can be connected. At the same time, just as with addition, subtraction, and multiplication, the methods for dividing will evolve from the solutions to simple problems. As it turns out, the methods for division of "small" numbers versus "large" numbers are closely connected with different types of simple problems.

A donor has given 63 rose bushes to Monroe School. The students in the third grade want to plant the bushes in a garden having 7 rows, with the same number of bushes in each row. They want to know how many bushes will be in each row. The students have had no experience with division. How would they solve this?

A Solution to the Rose Garden Problem

The students draw a picture of the 7 rows:

_____

_____

_____

_____

_____

_____

_____

"If we were to fill in all the bushes in these rows, we'd have an array of 63 bushes with 7 rows, so that 7 times the number of items in each row would equal 63. The problem will be solved if we can find a number Q such that $7 \times Q = 63$. Seven times what number equals 63? We know from the multiplication tables that $7 \times 9 = 63$. The answer is 9; there will be 9 items in each row; there will be 9 rose bushes planted in each of the 7 rows."

The Mathematical Idea: Division as the Solution to a Missing Factor Problem

To solve the rose garden problem, the students found a number Q so that $7 \times Q = 63$. They found a *missing factor* in a multiplication problem. At some point after doing a number of missing factor problems, a third grader will be told that finding the missing factor is called *division*. Thus, finding Q such that $6 \times Q = 48$ is gotten by "dividing 48 by 6," and the answer is written as $48 \div 6 = 8$. Similarly, the answer to the rose garden problem is $63 \div 7 = 9$. This gives rise to a definition of division.

DIVISION

Given two whole numbers A and B, with $B \neq 0$, if there is a whole number Q such that $B \times Q = A$, then Q is the result of *division* of A by B, and we write $A \div B = Q$.

Notice that if $B = 0$ and $A \neq 0$, there is no solution to $B \times Q = A$. If $B = 0$ and $A = 0$, then any Q is a solution to $B \times Q = A$. Thus division by 0 is not considered.

A third or fourth grader can solve the division problems

$35 \div 5$
$56 \div 7$
$2350 \div 10$

by solving the respective missing factor problems

$5 \times Q = 35$
$7 \times Q = 56$
$10 \times Q = 2350.$

He can solve the first two without too much trouble because he knows the multiplication tables. He shouldn't have too much trouble with the third one, either, provided he knows that multiplication by 10 appends a zero. After a while, he will begin to remember directly the solutions to simple division problems closely related to the multiplication tables, such as $35 \div 5 = 7$ and $56 \div 7 = 8$. Such simple statements are the *elementary division facts.*

EXERCISES

1. Use the multiplication tables and other basic multiplication facts about stick numerals to solve these division problems.

(a) ╪╪ ÷ ╪   (b) ☰ ÷ ╪   (c) ╪╋ ÷ ☰

2. Use multiplication tables and other base 8 multiplication facts to solve the problems.
   (a) $52_{eight} \div 6_{eight}$ (b) $20_{eight} \div 4_{eight}$ (c) $5470_{eight} \div 10_{eight}$
   (d) $123,000_{eight} \div 1000_{eight}$

THE SCIENCE BOOK
PROBLEM

Try this yourself.

The third grade at Monroe Elementary has been given $63 to replace some of the science books, which are in poor condition. Each new replacement costs $7. The students want to know how many new books they can buy. The third graders have had limited experience with division. Help them solve this.

A First Solution to the Science
Book Problem

One third grader suggests, "Take the $63 in separate dollar bills. Put them into piles of 7 each, one pile for each book, until we use up all the 63 bills. Then we count the number of piles we get. This will be the number of books we can buy."

A Second Solution to the
Science Book Problem

A second third grader says, "I could put the 63 dollars into piles of 7 dollars each— one pile for each book. That would take a lot of work. Instead I *imagine* putting them into piles. For the first pile I would take $7 from the $63. I would have $63 − $7 = $56 left. I would take away $7 from that to make the second pile and have $56 − $7 = $49 left. Each time I form a pile, I would subtract $7 from what's left. The number of books we can buy is the same as the number of times I can subtract 7 from 63. Here goes.

$$
\begin{array}{r}
63 \\
-7 \\
\hline
56 \\
-7 \\
\hline
49 \\
-7 \\
\hline
42 \\
-7 \\
\hline
35 \\
-7 \\
\hline
28 \\
-7 \\
\hline
21 \\
-7 \\
\hline
14 \\
-7 \\
\hline
7 \\
-7 \\
\hline
0
\end{array}
$$

I was able to subtract 7 from 63 nine times. We can buy 9 books."

A Third Solution to the Science Book Problem   A third offers, "You don't have to do all that subtraction! Just *suppose* you subtracted 7 from 63 a certain number of times. What that would mean is that if you added 7 to itself that certain number of times

$$7 + 7 + 7 + \cdots$$

you would get 63. That means that $7 \times$ that certain number $= 63$. In other words, you want to find a number Q so that $7 \times Q = 63$. From the 7s multiplication table, $7 \times 9 = 63$. So the answer is 9."

The Mathematical Idea: Division as Repeated Subtraction

The second third grader was clever to notice that the science book problem could be solved by *repeated subtraction* of 7 from 63. The third student was equally clever to notice that a repeated subtraction problem could be turned into a missing factor problem, that is, into a division problem, a type of problem that he had had a lot of experience with. We have, then,

---

DIVISION AND REPEATED SUBTRACTION

Given whole numbers A and B, with $A \geq B > 0$, if Q is a whole number such that $B \times Q = A$, then Q is also the number of times that B can be subtracted repeatedly from A.

To calculate $A \times B$ you *add* B repeatedly A times and to calculate $A \div B$, you count the number of times you can *subtract* B repeatedly from A.

EXERCISE

3. Sarah is in the third grade and has been selling boxes of saltwater taffy for her class trip in the spring. She has sold $42 worth of the taffy, but she can't remember how many boxes she sold. She does know that each box sells for $6. How would she figure out how many boxes she sold?

THE CABBAGE PATCH
PROBLEM

Try this yourself.

Carlos is planting cabbages in his garden. He has purchased 60 plants and plans to plant them in 8 rows, with the same number of cabbages in each row. He wants to know how many plants he should plant in each row. How can he solve this problem? (Carlos is in the third grade. He knows his multiplication tables. He has solved many missing factor division problems.)

A Solution to the Cabbage
Patch Problem

Here is Carlos's solution: "Let me *draw a picture* of what my cabbage patch should look like.

```
✻ ✻ ✻ ✻ ✻ ✻ ...
✻ ✻ ✻ ✻ ✻ ✻ ...
✻ ✻ ✻ ✻ ✻ ✻ ...
✻ ✻ ✻ ✻ ✻ ✻ ...
✻ ✻ ✻ ✻ ✻ ✻ ...
✻ ✻ ✻ ✻ ✻ ✻ ...
✻ ✻ ✻ ✻ ✻ ✻ ...
✻ ✻ ✻ ✻ ✻ ✻ ...
```

It should be a rectangular array of cabbage plants with 8 rows. Every row should have the same number Q of cabbage plants. So 8 times Q should equal 60: $8 \times Q = 60$, or $60 \div 8 = Q$. I know from the multiplication tables that $8 \times 7 = 56$ and $8 \times 8 = 64$ and that any other numbers would give me a product smaller than 56 or larger than 64. There's no answer! Wait, I have cabbage plants to plant. I don't have enough to plant 8 in each row. But I could plant 7 plants in each row, use up 56 of the plants, and have $60 - 56 = 4$ plants left over. I'll figure out something to do with the 4 extra plants ..."

The Mathematical Idea: Division with Quotient and Remainder

For a given pair of whole numbers A and B there is not always a whole number Q such that $B \times Q = A$. However, as in the solution to the cabbage patch problem, we may still want to find a whole number Q so that $B \times Q$ is *close* to A. In fact, we will write $60 \div 8 = 7$ with a remainder of 4, to mean that 7 is the largest whole number Q such that $8 \times Q$ is no bigger than 60 and that $60 - 8 \times 7 = 4$. In other words, $60 = 8 \times 7 + 4$.

Similarly, $25 \div 3 = 8$ with a remainder of 1 means that 3 can be subtracted from 25 no more than 8 times and that when you do this, you will have 1 left over. In other words, $25 = 8 \times 3 + 1$. In general,

---

DIVISION WITH REMAINDER

Suppose that A and B are whole numbers with $B \neq 0$. If there are whole numbers Q and R such that $A = B \times Q + R$ and $0 \leq R < B$, then we write $A \div B = Q$ with a remainder R. Q is called the *quotient*, B the *divisor*, A the *dividend*, and R the *remainder*.

Notice that this definition includes the possibility that R, the remainder, be zero. When $R = 0$, then there is a whole number Q such that $A = B \times Q$. Thus, this definition includes the one given earlier.

Having remainders makes division different from addition, subtraction, and multiplication. Given two whole numbers, for each of those three operations there is associated a single third number—the sum, the difference, and the product, respectively. For division, given two whole numbers (the divisor and the dividend), there are associated two whole numbers—the quotient and the remainder. (Sometimes, when the remainder is zero, it is not mentioned.)

EXERCISES

4. Julie is having a birthday party. She and her mom have decided to give each friend who comes to the party a special favor. Her mom says: "Julie, here is $25 to buy the favors." Julie knows that each favor costs $3. She wonders how many favors she can buy because that will tell her how many friends she can invite. How can Julie solve this problem?

5. Solve the problems using only basic multiplication facts.
   (a) $1234 \div 10$ (b) $143{,}628 \div 100$

6. Using only the base 8 multiplication tables and basic multiplication facts, solve the problems.
   (a) $47_{\text{eight}} \div 6_{\text{eight}}$ (b) $50_{\text{eight}} \div 7_{\text{eight}}$ (c) $1234_{\text{eight}} \div 10_{\text{eight}}$
   (d) $143{,}627_{\text{eight}} \div 100_{\text{eight}}$

6.2   THE STANDARD METHOD OF LONG DIVISION

THE LOAVES OF BREAD PROBLEM

You have 65 loaves of bread, which you intend to share equally with 7 families. You want to know how many loaves each family will get. You have not had much experience with division; however, you have solved the rose garden problem and the science book problem. Here's the solution you come up with.

You line up the 7 families and begin handing out the loaves of bread 1 at a time: a loaf to the first family, a loaf to the second family, and so on, until you give a loaf to the seventh family. Then you make another pass through the families giving a second loaf to the first family, a second loaf to the second family, and so on, to the 7 families. You make as many passes through the families as you can until you can't make a complete pass. There may be some loaves left over. You keep track of the number of complete passes you make through all the families. The number of complete passes is the number of loaves each family has.

The Mathematical Idea: Division as Equal Distribution

We know that the loaves of bread problem can be solved by dividing 65 by 7. But, at first glance, the problem does not appear to be a missing factor problem or a repeated subtraction problem. After some thought, you can see that each pass in the solution corresponds to subtracting 7 from 65 and the number of passes you make is equal to the number of times you can subtract 7 from 65. In this way you turn the solution into the solution to a repeated subtraction problem. The loaves of bread problem is an *equal distribution* problem.

EQUAL DISTRIBUTION PROBLEM

Suppose that A and B are whole numbers such that $B \neq 0$. A problem in which A objects are to be distributed equally into B piles is called an *equal distribution* problem.

EXERCISES

7. Carlos has invited 8 friends to his birthday party. His mother has given him 70 pieces of candy to distribute equally among his friends as favors. Carlos wants to know how many pieces of candy each of his friends will get. Show that this is an equal distribution problem.

8. You have 43_{six} bottles of soda that you want to divide up equally among 7 friends coming to a party. How many bottles will each friend get? (A nice way of thinking of 43_{six} bottles of soda is 4 six-packs and 3 loose bottles.)

The Standard Method of Long Division with Single-Digit Divisor

Most versions of the standard method of long division are based on thinking of division as the solution to an equal distribution problem. We will show this using a single-digit divisor.

Consider the division problem 928 ÷ 7. First we *make a model* of 928 using place value blocks.

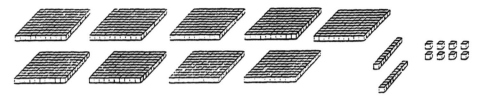

We want to put 928 items into 7 equal piles. Start with the flats. Distribute the 9 flats into 7 equal piles. Each pile gets 1 flat, and there are 2 left over: 9 ÷ 7 = 1 with remainder 2.

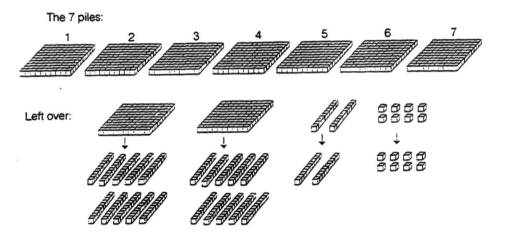

Trade the 2 leftover flats for longs, making 22 longs in all. Then, distribute the 22 longs equally into the 7 piles. Each pile gets 3 longs, and there is 1 left over: 22 ÷ 7 = 3 with remainder 1.

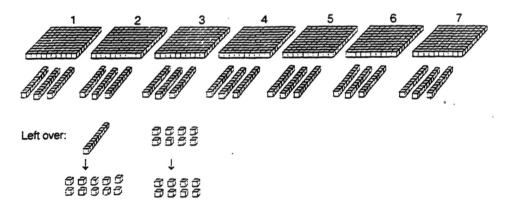

Trade the 1 leftover long for units, making 18 units in all. Finally, distribute the 18 units equally into the 7 piles. Each pile gets 2 units with 4 left over: 18 ÷ 7 = 2 with remainder 4.

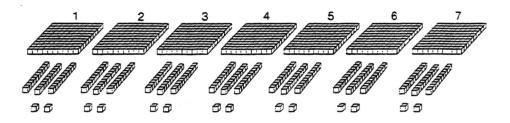

Left over: ⊟ ⊟ ⊟ ⊟

We have finished; as many as possible of the place value blocks have been used. Each of the 7 piles has 1 flat, 3 longs, and 2 units; there are 4 units left over. Thus, $928 \div 7 = 132$ with remainder 4.

Let's consider a second example. This time we will show the pencil and paper work for the standard method along with maneuvering place value blocks. The problem is $4371 \div 8$.

4371

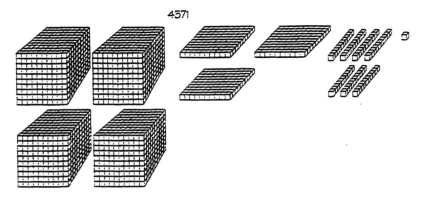

Since $4 \div 8 = 0$ with remainder 4, we trade the cubes for flats obtaining 43 flats in all.

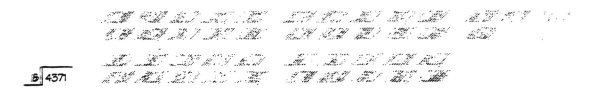

$8 \overline{)4371}$

Then we distribute the 43 flats equally into 8 piles. Each pile gets 5 flats, with 3 flats left over: $43 \div 8 = 5$ with remainder 3.

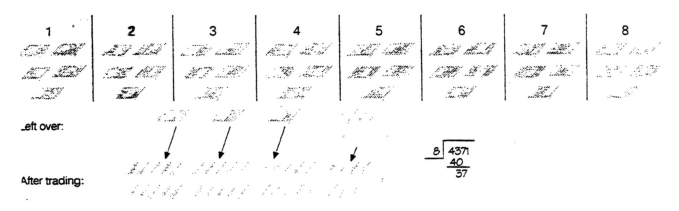

1	2	3	4	5	6	7	8

Left over:

After trading:

$$8 \overline{)\begin{array}{l}4371 \\ 40 \\ \hline 37\end{array}}$$

Trade the 3 flats for longs, getting $30 + 7 = 37$ longs in all. Distribute the 37 longs equally into the 8 piles. Each pile gets 4 longs, with 5 left over: $37 \div 8 = 4$ with remainder 5.

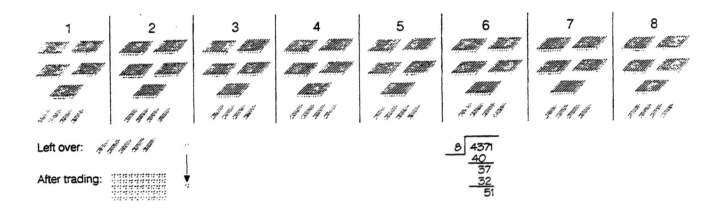

Left over:

After trading:

$$\begin{array}{r} 8\overline{)4371} \\ 40 \\ \hline 37 \\ 32 \\ \hline 51 \end{array}$$

Trade the 5 longs for units getting $50 + 1 = 51$ units in all. Distribute the 51 units equally into the 8 piles. Each pile gets 6 units, with 3 left over: $51 \div 8 = 6$ with remainder 3.

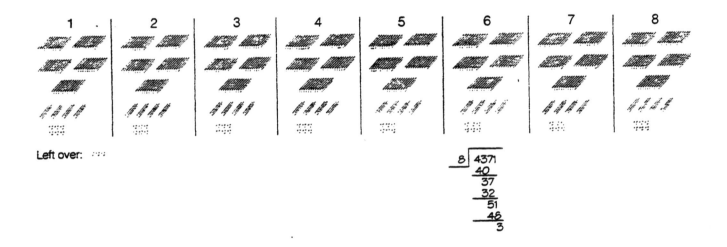

Left over:

$$\begin{array}{r} 8\overline{)4371} \\ 40 \\ \hline 37 \\ 32 \\ \hline 51 \\ 48 \\ \hline 3 \end{array}$$

We're finished. All the blocks have been accounted for. There are 5 flats, 4 longs, and 6 units in each of the piles with 3 left over: $4371 \div 8 = 546$ with remainder 3.

EXERCISES

9. Use the method just demonstrated with place value blocks (or pictures of them) to solve the division problems.
   (a) $1542 \div 5$ (b) $2364 \div 5$
   Draw in the steps of the standard method in parallel.

10. Use base 8 place value blocks (or pictures of them) to solve $542_{eight} \div 6_{eight}$ in the same way.

11. Solve $6072_{eight} \div 5_{eight}$ using the standard method adapted to base 8 numerals.

Now we turn to division problems in which the divisor has two digits.

THE SCIENCE EXPERIMENT KIT PROBLEM

Please try this yourself.

The principal of Elena's school has given $742 to her third grade class for the year's science supplies. The class decides to use the money to buy a Science Experiment Kit for each member of the class. Each kit costs $35. Elena has been put in charge of purchasing these kits and wants to know how many kits she can buy with $742. How would Elena solve this problem? (She has solved division problems as missing factor problems using the multiplication tables; she has also solved division problems in which the remainders are not zero and in which quotients can be gotten from the multiplication tables.)

A Solution to the Science Experiment Kit Problem

Elena thinks, "If I bought 1 kit, it would cost $35. I'd have this much left:

$$\begin{array}{r} 742 \\ -\ 35 \\ \hline 707 \end{array}$$

Then I can buy another one and have this much left:

$$\begin{array}{r} 707 \\ -\ 35 \\ \hline 672 \end{array}$$

I just keep subtracting 35 from whatever I have left. The number of times I can do this will be the number of kits we can buy. That's a repeated subtraction problem, so that it's also the division problem $742 \div 35 = Q$ with remainder R, or $35 \times Q + R = 742$.

"But I don't know the 35s multiplication table. I could try multiplying 35 times a lot of numbers to see if I could get 742. That sounds a little hit or miss. Let me go back to subtracting 35s.

$$\begin{array}{r} 742 \\ -\ 35 \\ \hline 707 \\ -\ 35 \\ \hline 672 \\ -\ 35 \\ \hline 637 \\ -\ 35 \\ \hline 602 \end{array}$$

"Maybe there's an easier way. Every time I subtract 35 twice, it's the same as subtracting $35 + 35 = 70$. Why don't I just subtract 70s from what I have left? I could also subtract 140s from what's left. That's two 70s, or four 35s. Let me try that and at the same time let me *organize what I have* by making a column on the right to keep track of the number of 35s I subtract.

NO. OF
35s SUBTRACTED

602	
− 140	4
462	
− 140	4
322	
− 140	4
182	
− 140	4
42	

I can't subtract any more 140s. But I can subtract one more 35.

NO. OF
35s SUBTRACTED

42	
− 35	1
7	

"Now let me figure out how many 35s I subtracted in all.

NO. OF
35s SUBTRACTED:

742		
− 35	1	
707		
− 35	1	
672		
− 35	1	4 times here
637		
− 35	1	
602		
− 140	4	
462		
− 140	4	
322		16 times here
− 140	4	
182		
− 140	4	
42		
− 35	1	1 time here
7		

"Let's see. That's $4 + 16 + 1 = 21$ times. That means we could buy 21 kits, and there would be $7 left over! I should check this answer. I was able to subtract 35 from 742 exactly 21 times, and there was 7 left over. Let me multiply 35 by 21.

$$
\begin{array}{r}
35 \\
\times\, 21 \\
\hline
35 \\
70 \\
\hline
735 \\
+7 \\
\hline
742
\end{array}
$$

and then add 7

It checks."

EXERCISES

12. You are in the third grade. You have had no experience with division except where the multiplication tables apply. You discover that you have $137 in your savings account. You want to know how many $17 Cabbage Patch Dolls you can buy with this amount. How would you find out?

13. Solve the problem in the base 8 system using only what you know about base 8 addition, subtraction, and division and the base 8 multiplication tables: $253_{eight} \div 32_{eight}$

14. Solve the stick numeral problem using only what you know about base 5 stick numeral addition, subtraction, and division and the stick numeral multiplication tables: 十丰十 ÷ 十丰.

THE ORPHANAGE PROBLEM   John's third grade class has raised $4762 from a raffle to buy clothing and school supplies for the children in a local orphanage. The class wants to divide the proceeds equally among the 29 children, and it wants John to figure out how much each child will get. John has had no experience with division except for problems solved by elementary division facts and with Elena, helping her solve the Science Experiment Kit problem. He knows how to multiply a number by a power of 10.

Here is John's solution to this problem: "If I give every child $1, that would use up $29, and I would have

$$
\begin{array}{r}
\$4762 \\
-\, \$\ \ 29 \\
\hline
\$4733
\end{array}
$$

left. If I give every child another dollar, that would use up $29 again, and then I'd have

$$
\begin{array}{r}
\$4733 \\
-\, \$\ \ 29 \\
\hline
\$4704
\end{array}
$$

left. It's like the *solution to a similar problem*, the Science Experiment Kit problem: You deal out dollars to the kids. Each time you deal out a dollar to everybody, you subtract 29 from what you have left. The number of times you can subtract 29 from

$4762 will be the number of dollars each child gets. But if I keep subtracting like this, it's going to take a long time. Let me give each child a bunch of dollars each time, like maybe $4. That would be $4 × 29 = $116 in all that I would have to subtract. That still wouldn't make much of a dent. Let me think of something bigger to give the kids and something easier to multiply times 29. How about $10 for each child? That's a bigger number and also easy to multiply with: $10 × 29 = $290. Multiplication by 10 is easy; so is multiplication by 100. Let me try that. It might be too big, but it's worth a try. $100 × 29 = $2900. It's not too big at all. Starting from the beginning with $4762, we'd have

$$\begin{array}{r} \$4762 \\ - \$2900 \\ \hline \$1862 \end{array}$$

left. Can I subtract another 100 × 29? No, but I could subtract 10 × 29 = 290. Let me *organize what I have* to keep track of the number of times I subtract 29 from 4762.

	NO. OF SUBTRACTIONS OF 29
4762	
− 2900	100
1862	
− 290	10
1572	
− 290	10
1282	
− 290	10
992	

I can keep subtracting 10 × 29 until I can't do it any more. But 290 is a little less than 300 and 3 × 300 = 900. So I ought to be able to subtract 3 × 290 (or 30 × 29) from what's left.

992	
− 870	30
122	

Now I can't subtract any 10 × 29s. Since 29 is close to 30 and 3 × 30 = 90, it looks as if I could subtract three 29s.

122	
− 87	3
35	
− 29	1
6	

I'm finished. Let me count the number of 29s I subtracted.

```
   4762
 − 2900          100
 ──────
   1862
 −  290           10
 ──────
   1572
 −  290           10
 ──────
   1282
 −  290           10
 ──────
    992
 −  870           30
 ──────
    122
 −   87            3
 ──────
     35
 −   29            1
 ──────
      6 (remainder)    164 (total no. of 29s subtracted)
```

"So each child will be given $164 worth of clothing and school supplies, and there will be $6 left over."

The Mathematical Idea: The Scaffold Method of Division

The solutions to the orphanage and science experiment kit problems took a long time. (Someone who knows the "standard" way of doing long division could do these problems more quickly.) However, they are accessible to people having little experience with division, and we can turn the solutions to these two problems into a method very close to the "standard" way of dividing called the *scaffold method*.

We will illustrate the method with the following problem: divide 79,783 by 24. To solve this, we will not think of the problem as a missing factor problem but as a repeated subtraction problem: How many times can we subtract 24 from 79,783? And how much will be left after subtracting 24 as much as we can?

We think of the *similar problems* we have just solved: From the original number 79,783 we want to subtract multiples of 24 that are easy to calculate. In fact, an important part of the method is to find the largest of 10×24 or 100×24 or 1000×24 or . . . that can be subtracted. Since $10,000 \times 24 = 240,000$ is larger than 79,783, and $1000 \times 24 = 24,000$ is smaller than 79,783, the latter must be the largest we can subtract. So we start by subtracting $1000 \times 24 = 24,000$.

Another feature of the scaffold method is the way we *organize our work.*

We keep track of the number of 24s subtracted in this column.

```
We write down the dividend
and divisor here, as usual.        24 │ 79,783
We subtract 1000 × 24 here. ──→      − 24,000         1000

Here is what is left after ──→        55,783
subtracting 1000 × 24.
```

We have 55,783 left. Now we want to know how many more 24s we can subtract from 55,783. Starting with the latter number, we think the same way as before: What's the largest of 10 × 24, 100 × 24, 1000 × 24, . . . that we can subtract from 55,783? We can see by now that we can subtract another 1000 × 24. We do that and continue on in this fashion. Here's our work and our thinking along the way.

COLUMN FOR KEEPING
TRACK OF THE
NUMBER OF 24s
SUBTRACTED

24	79,783		
	− 24,000	1000	
	55,783		
	− 24,000	1000	
	31,783		
	− 24,000	1000	
Can't subtract 1000 × 24 but can subtract 100 × 24.	7783		
	− 2400	100	
	5383		
	− 2400	100	Subtract another 100.
	2983		
	− 2400	100	And another 100.
Can't subtract 100 × 24 but can subtract 10 × 24.	583		
	− 240	10	
	343		
	− 240	10	And another 10.
Can't subtract 10 × 24 but can subtract 1 × 24.	103		
	− 24	1	
	79		We'll be bold and
	− 48	2	subtract two 24s at
	31		once.
	− 24	1	
We can't subtract any more 24s. This must be the remainder!	7	3324	

This is the sum of all the numbers in the column above it. It is the total number of times 24 can be subtracted from 79,783.

Thus, 79,783 ÷ 24 = 3324 with a remainder of 7.

As you experience using it, you learn to make shortcuts; you begin to replace two or more steps by one step. For example, at the first step, you might have thought, "I know I can subtract 1000 × 24 from 79,783; but I can do more: I can subtract

3000 × 24 from 79,783." So the beginning of your work might look like

$$
\begin{array}{r}
24\overline{\smash{\big)}\,79{,}783} \\
-\,72{,}000 \qquad 3000 \\
\hline
7783
\end{array}
$$

instead of

$$
\begin{array}{r}
24\overline{\smash{\big)}\,79{,}783} \\
-\,24{,}000 \qquad 1000 \\
\hline
55{,}783 \\
-\,24{,}000 \qquad 1000 \\
\hline
31{,}783 \\
-\,24{,}000 \qquad 1000 \\
\hline
7783
\end{array}
$$

When all the calculations for the problem have been shortened in this way, then the method looks a lot like the "standard" method of long division. Here they are side by side.

$$
\begin{array}{r}
24\overline{\smash{\big)}\,79{,}783} \\
-\,72{,}000 \qquad 3000 \\
\hline
7783 \\
-\quad 7200 \qquad 300 \\
\hline
583 \\
-\quad 480 \qquad 20 \\
\hline
103 \\
-\quad\ 96 \qquad\ 4 \\
\hline
7 \qquad 3324
\end{array}
\qquad
\begin{array}{r}
3324 \\
24\overline{\smash{\big)}\,79{,}783} \\
72 \\
\hline
77 \\
72 \\
\hline
58 \\
48 \\
\hline
103 \\
96 \\
\hline
7
\end{array}
$$

For someone learning how to divide, the scaffold method may have some advantages over the standard method. With the scaffold method you can be leisurely and make conservative guesses; with the standard method each "guess" must be exact (unless you want to do a lot of erasing of "poor" guesses). With the scaffold method it should be clear what you are doing at each step: You are always subtracting the divisor a certain number of times from what is left after previous subtracting. When you are finished, it is obvious that your answer is equal to the number of times you have subtracted the divisor.

EXERCISES

15. Solve the division problems using the scaffold method.
   (a) $60{,}983 \div 87$ (b) $57{,}041 \div 263$
   In solving these problems, take advantage of the features of the scaffold method. Don't try to mimic either the steps or the thinking associated with the standard method.

16. Solve the division problems using the scaffold method as adapted to base 8 numerals.
   (a) $653_{\text{eight}} \div 7_{\text{eight}}$ (b) $3054_{\text{eight}} \div 41_{\text{eight}}$

6.4

LOOKING BACK: DIVISION—ITS DEFINITION, WAYS OF THINKING ABOUT IT, AND METHODS FOR CARRYING IT OUT

The Definition of *Division*

Let's summarize the information given in this chapter in a formal definition of *division.*

DEFINITION OF *DIVISION*

Suppose that A and B are whole numbers such that $B \neq 0$. If whole numbers Q and R are such that $A = B \times Q + R$ and $0 \leq R < B$, then Q is called the *quotient* and R is called the *remainder* of A *on division by B*, and we write $A \div B = Q$ with remainder R.

It is worth having a look at this definition for several specific cases.

Case 1 Suppose that A is any whole number and that $B = 1$. What do you get when you divide A by 1? You get a quotient of A and a remainder of 0: $A = 1 \times A + 0$. If you think of $A \div 1$ as the solution Q to the missing factor problem $1 \times Q = A$, then $Q = A$ works. If you think of $A \div 1$ as the number of times you can subtract 1 from A, then $Q = A$ is the answer—and the remainder is 0.

Case 2 Suppose that A and B are whole numbers and that $A < B$. What happens when you divide A by B? Some might say "You can't divide A by B when B is bigger than A!" However, in the definition of division of whole numbers, the number 0 can play the role of quotient, and the number A the role of remainder: $A = B \times 0 + A$. If you think of $A \div B$ as the number of times you can subtract B from A, then 0 is the answer—with a remainder of A.

Case 3 Suppose $A = 0$ and that B is any nonzero whole number. What happens when you divide 0 by B? This is a special instance of case 2. You divide 0 by B and get a quotient of 0 with a remainder of 0: $0 = B \times 0 + 0$, or $0 \div B = 0$.

Case 4 We have already seen that $B = 0$ in the definition is either impossible ($A \neq 0$) or undesirable ($A = 0$). Thus, the possibility $B = 0$ is left out of the definition entirely.

Finally, the following theorem summarizes what the methods we have developed in this chapter do for us, something that we all have known (deep down); namely, in a division problem where the divisor is not zero, there always is a quotient and a remainder.

DIVISION THEOREM

Suppose that A and B are whole numbers and $B \neq 0$. Then there are whole numbers Q and R such that $A = QB + R$, $0 \leq R < B$.

Ways of Thinking about Division and Methods for Dividing

The formal definition of division evolved from several real problems, in the solutions of which division is used. From some of these solutions evolved the methods for actually finding the quotient and remainder, given the divisor and dividend. We can summarize the ways of thinking about division that these solutions suggest and how they relate to the methods for division.

MISSING FACTOR WAY OF THINKING ABOUT DIVISION

Suppose that A and B are whole numbers such that $B \neq 0$. If there is a whole number Q such that $B \times Q = A$, then Q is called A *divided by* B and is written $Q = A \div B$.

A person learning division for the first time thinks of it this way. Since there is not always a whole number Q such that $B \times Q = A$, the person next learns another way of thinking about division.

MISSING FACTOR WITH REMAINDER

Suppose that A and B are whole numbers such that $B \neq 0$. The largest whole number Q such that $B \times Q \leq A$ is called the *quotient of A divided by B*. If $R = A - B \times Q$, then we write $A \div B = Q$ with *remainder R*.

For $B \leq 10$ and most $A \leq 100$, the method of finding $A \div B$ is based on the missing factor way of thinking about division: To find the largest number Q such that $B \times Q \leq A$, look in the B's multiplication table for the Q that works; the remainder R is what's left over ($R = A - B \times Q$). This way of thinking is also useful when solving a problem in which the divisor B is a power of 10.

EQUAL DISTRIBUTION WAY OF THINKING ABOUT DIVISION

Suppose that A and B are whole numbers such that $B \neq 0$. Let S be a set with $n(S) = A$. Distribute the elements of S equally into B piles. The number of elements in each of the B piles is Q, the *quotient*. The number of items left over (i.e., not placed in one of the piles) is R, the *remainder*.

The standard method for dividing is based on this way of thinking about division. We developed this method in case the divisor B is a single-digit number.

REPEATED SUBTRACTION WAY OF THINKING ABOUT DIVISION

Suppose that A and B are whole numbers such that $B \neq 0$. Suppose that Q is the number of times that B can be subtracted from A; that is, $A - \underbrace{(B + B + \cdots + B)}_{Q \text{ times}} < B$. Then Q is the *quotient of A divided by B*. If

$R = A - Q \times B$, then $A \div B = Q$ with *remainder R*.

The repeated subtraction way of thinking about division was the basis for the scaffold method of division normally used when the missing factor way of thinking isn't appropriate.

Division by Organizing an Array Using Place Value Blocks

There is a way of carrying out division using the missing factor way of thinking together with the way of organizing an array using place value blocks (or dots, dashes, and squares) from chapter 5. Consider the problem $524 \div 46$. Think: In a 46-row array, how many items should be in each row in order that the array have 524 items in all (or as nearly close to 524 items as possible)?

To solve this problem, *make a model* of 46 as ///// ░░░ (Recall that 1 long / is worth 10 units ░.) Then arrange these blocks in a vertical column, making the left-hand border of an array that is yet to be filled in.

Next, *make a model* of 524 as

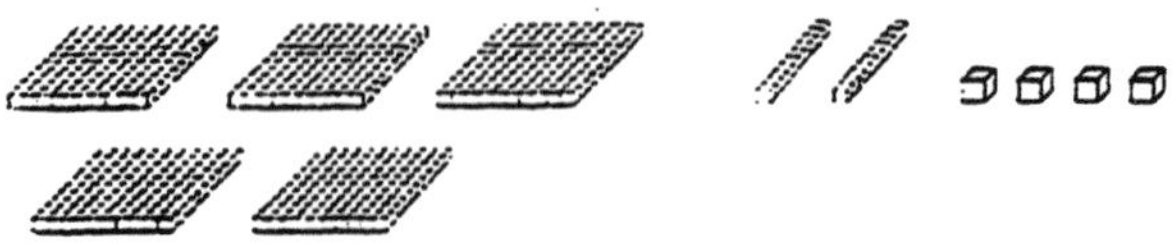

We want to arrange the latter blocks or their equivalent into the array drawn above having 46 on one side. When we finish, the array should look like the organized array for a multiplication problem; the answer to the division problem should appear horizontally on the top border of the array.

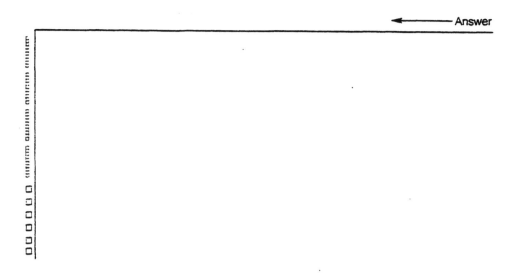

Let's start with the flats first. Four of them will go into an organized array.

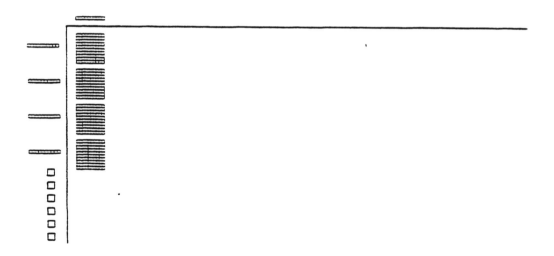

Now what do we put under the flats in order to complete the column and still have it look like an organized array? First, place a long at the top as part of the horizontal border and a long beside each unit in the vertical border.

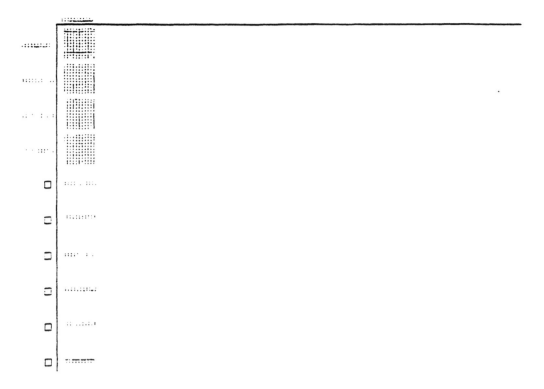

The 6 longs placed inside the array must come from the blocks for 524. How can this be? After using up 4 squares in 524, we have the following blocks left over.

To get the 6 longs for the array, we must exchange the last square in the leftover 524 pile for 10 longs, getting

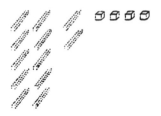

in the leftover 524 pile.

After putting 6 longs in the array, we have a new leftover pile consisting of

Now the array looks like the last array picture above. What should we do next? We know that we won't be able to put another long along the top border, because there are no flats in the most recent leftover pile. Let's put a unit on the top border so that we have the array shown on the left and the leftover pile shown on the right.

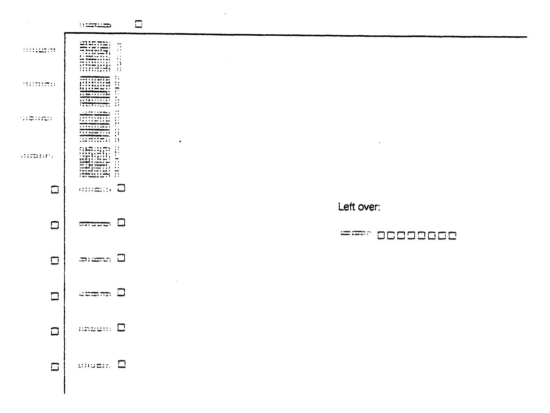

Left over:

Since the leftover pile has blocks worth less than 46, we're finished. The answer to the division problem 524 ÷ 46 is ▨▨ ▱ (11) with remainder ▨▨ ▱▱▱▱▱▱▱▱ (18).

EXERCISE 17. Use this method to solve the division problem 823 ÷ 37.

6.6 CALCULATORS AND COMPUTERS IN DIVISION

FINDING QUOTIENT AND REMAINDER USING A CALCULATOR   To divide 478 by 56 using a calculator, you use the keying sequence 478 [÷] 56 [=]. The calculator display will then read 8.535714286. The latter is an approximation of the fraction $\frac{478}{56}$ by a decimal fraction. Now $\frac{478}{56} = 8\frac{30}{56}$ so that $\frac{30}{56}$ is approximately equal to the decimal fraction .535714286. Also the whole number part of the display—8—is the quotient of 478 when divided by 56. (There will be more about fractions and division in chap. 8 and about approximating fractions by decimal fractions in chap. 10.)

How do you figure out the remainder from the calculator display? Since 8 is the quotient, we know that $478 = 8 \times 56 +$ remainder. Thus, to find the remainder, you multiply 8 by 56 and subtract what you get from 478: $478 - 8 \times 56 = 478 - 448 = 30$. The remainder is 30. In general,

---

HOW TO FIND QUOTIENT AND REMAINDER
WHEN DIVIDING WITH A CALCULATOR

To divide A by B, use the keying sequence A [÷] B [=]. The whole number part of the calculator display is the quotient Q. To find the remainder R, multiply Q by B and subtract the product from A: $A - Q \times B = R$.

For example, to find $943 \div 47$, use the keying sequence 943 [÷] 47 [=], after which the calculator will display 20.06382979. So the quotient is 20. To find the remainder, multiply 20 by 47 to get 940 and subtract the latter from 943 to get a remainder of 3. Thus $943 \div 47 = 20$ with remainder 3.

SIMULATING DIVISION ON A COMPUTER   In chapter 5 we showed how a computer could multiply directly by repeatedly adding one of the factors. We can also get a computer to divide by repeatedly subtracting the divisor from the dividend. Consider the division problem encountered earlier: $478 \div 56$. We want to get the computer to subtract 56 repeatedly from 478 and count the number of times this can be done. To get the computer to subtract 56 repeatedly, a loop would be just the thing. However, with multiplication we add one of the factors to itself and the number of times we do this is equal to the other factor; with division we subtract the divisor from the dividend but we don't know how many times ahead of time—in fact, the number of times we subtract is what we are trying to find out. It will be convenient to use a new command— GOTO—in place of a FOR ... NEXT loop. In BASIC, the GOTO command is always followed by a number, such as GOTO 30. When GOTO 30 is encountered in a program, the computer is instructed to "go to" line 30 and follow the program from there on. The following program carries out the division $478 \div 56$ using the GOTO command.

```
20 LET Q = 0 Initialization of Q
30 LET R = 478 Initialization of R
40 PRINT R, Q
50 LET R = R - 56
60 LET Q = Q + 1
70 GOTO 40
100 END
```

The variable R starts out having the value 478, then its value is $478 - 56$, then its value is what is left after another 56 is subtracted, and so on. The value of R changes and is what is left after successively subtracting 56. In line 50, after each subtracting of 56, you add 1 to the value of Q. Thus the variable Q "counts" the number of times 56 has been subtracted from 478.

There is a problem with this program. (It can be fixed!) Type it into your microcomputer and run it. What happens? It keeps going on and on and on and ... To stop the computer, hold down the CONTROL key and push C; or if your computer has a

BREAK key, push that. (Consult your BASIC manual or your computer expert if neither works.)

Your screen should look something like this.

RUN

478	0
422	1
366	2
310	3
254	4
198	5
142	6
86	7
30	8
-26	9
-82	10
-138	11

BREAK

The computer has negative numbers, and the computer doesn't hesitate to subtract whole number B from whole number A, even though B is larger than A. However, we want the computer to stop when R "gets too small." To get the computer to stop, we add the new line

```
45 IF R < 56 THEN GOTO 100
```

Line 45 involves the IF ... THEN ... command, which has two parts. The first part—what is typed between the IF and the THEN—is a statement involving one or more of the variables in use in the program. (In the example, the statement is R < 56.) The second part is typed after the THEN and is another command in BASIC. (In the example, the command is GOTO 100.)

Here is how IF ... THEN ... works: If the statement between IF and THEN is true, the computer carries out the command following THEN. If the statement is not true, the computer passes to the next line of the program.

In the example, if R < 56 is true (no more 56s can be subtracted), the command GOTO 100 is carried out (the computer "skips over" lines 50 through 70). If R < 56 is false (i.e., $R \geq 56$ and at least one more 56 can be subtracted), the computer moves on to line 50, and the "loop" continues.

We now type LIST to obtain the complete, revised program.

LIST

```
20 LET Q = 0
30 LET R = 478
40 PRINT R, Q
45 IF R < 56 THEN GOTO 100
50 LET R = R - 56
60 LET Q = Q + 1
70 GOTO 40
100 END
```

22. Run the preceding program. How does the printout tell you what the quotient and remainder are when 478 is divided by 56?

23. Revise the preceding program, which starts with the pair 478 and 56 and repeatedly subtracts the latter from the former, so that it will accept any pair of whole numbers A and B (via INPUT commands) with A bigger than B, then repeatedly subtract B from A and determine the quotient and remainder when A is divided by B. (*Hint:* Look at exercise 31 in chap. 5.)

6.7   SUMMARY OF IMPORTANT IDEAS AND TECHNIQUES

■ Division as the solution to a missing factor problem; introduction of terms *quotient*, *divisor*, and *dividend*

■ Using the multiplication tables and facts about multiplication by powers of 10 for solving many missing factor problems

■ Division as the solution to a repeated subtraction problem

■ Division with quotient and remainder

■ Division by zero not allowed

■ Division as the solution to an equal distribution problem

■ Division as the solution to equal distribution problems leading to the standard method

■ Division as the solution to a repeated subtraction problem leading to the scaffold method of division

■ The division property of equality as a rule for working with algebraic symbols

PROBLEM SET

PRACTICING
SKILLS
Problems 1 and 2 below are "primitive" division problems. To solve them, use the pairing of elements in two sets; do not count or use standard numerals in any way. Identify each as either a missing factor problem, a repeated subtraction problem, or an equal distribution problem.

1. The stones on the left represent the horses Ugboo would like to sell. The stones on the right represent the sheep Lagor would like to use for buying horses from Ugboo. The price is O O O O O sheep for each horse.

Horses

Sheep

Lagor will buy as many horses as he can with the sheep that he has. Show diagrammatically (for example, with arrows and circles) the horses Lagor is able to buy and the sheep he uses to buy them. Label clearly the sheep Lagor has left over after buying as many horses as he can; similarly, label the horses he is unable to buy.

2. Ugboo has loaves of bread represented by the stones on the left. The village warriors are represented by the stones on the right. Ugboo wants to distribute as many of the loaves as he can to the warriors so that all the warriors have the same amount. The loaves that are left over he will give to the chief and his family. Show how Ugboo would distribute the loaves. Indicate clearly the loaves the chief and his family get.

Loaves   Warriors

keep adding 9¢ til get to 72¢ which equals 8 drinks

3. Charlie returns to his lemonade stand, where Lucy has been taking care of things. She won't tell him how many glasses of lemonade she has sold in his absence, but she has made 72¢. Each glass of lemonade sells for 9¢. Charlie, who has no experience with division, wants to figure out how many glasses Lucy has sold. Help Charlie do this.

4. A new subdivision is to have four small neighborhood parks planted by the developer. Luis's father, who is in charge of planning these parks, has purchased 31 trees to be planted in the parks. Luis has no experience with division yet wants to help his father figure out how many trees should be planted in each park. Help Luis do this.

5. Joanna's third grade class has been given $1585 to spend on furniture for their classroom. The class decides they need new chairs. Each chair costs $56. How can Joanna find out how many chairs they can buy? She understands repeated subtraction.

6. Solve the following division problems as missing factor problems; do not carry out the long division.
   (a) $51 \div 8$ (b) $67 \div 7$ (c) $247 \div 10$ (d) $3562 \div 100$ (e) $81,704 \div 1000$

7. Solve the division problems using the scaffold method.
   (a) $6862 \div 78$ (b) $57,290 \div 59$ (c) $1,873,402 \div 428$

8. Solve the division problems using place value blocks (or pictures of them) and thinking of division as the solution to an equal distribution problem.
   (a) $472 \div 6$ (b) $3702 \div 8$ (c) $9064 \div 7$

9. Jill and her friends are going to the Burger Boy for Jill's eighth birthday. Including Jill, there will be 9 children in the party. Jill's father tells her she can spend up to $50 at the Burger Boy. Help Jill determine how much each child can spend by thinking of it as an equal distribution problem.

10. Monica leaves home at 6 A.M. for a long walk. At 7 A.M. Monica's husband, Robert, leaves home for a run. He follows the exact same route as Monica. Monica walks at 4 mph; Robert runs at 8 mph. At what time will Robert catch up to Monica?

11. You are in charge of a tutoring center. Your budget for this year is $15,700. You will need $2500 to cover nonpersonnel costs (paper, photocopying, telephone, etc.). Each tutor will be paid $1200. How many tutors can you hire?

12. **The** gardener has 392 flowers to plant. He selects 32 of the best plants to be placed in a circular planter in the center of the garden. How many flowers can be placed in each of the remaining 15 planters so that each planter has the same number of flowers?

13. **Use** the rules for algebra to solve the following problems. Justify each step of your solution with a rule.
    (a) Find a whole number A such that $8A + 5 = 37$.
    (b) Find a whole number B such that $12B - 7 = 5B$.
    (c) Find a whole number C such that $15C + 4 = 9C + 22$.
    (d) Find a whole number D such that $12D + 20 = 19D - 22$.
    (e) Find a whole number E such that $21E - 21 = 17E - 9$.

14. Use a calculator to find the quotient and remainder for each division problem.
    (a) $123,456 \div 406$ (b) $809,372 \div 7451$ (c) $1,298,347 \div 4572$

USING IDEAS   *For each problem remaining, document as clearly and completely as you can your solution to the problem. Include the steps you took to solve the problem, mention the problems or solutions from the text that gave you ideas, and include the problem-solving strategies you used. You might want to outline and organize these details before assembling your final report in the form of an essay.*

15. Ugboo wants to trade as many blankets as he can for Lagor's sheep. They agree to trade | | | blankets for O O O O sheep.

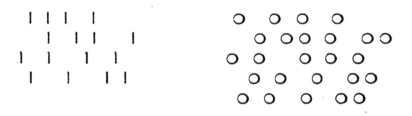

Ugboo's blankets   Lagor's sheep

Without counting or using standard numerals, figure out what will be left after all the trading has taken place.

16. Here are the single-digit multiplication tables for stick numerals.

	✚	✚	✚
✚	✚	✚✚	✚✚
✚	✚✚	✚✚	✚✚
✚	✚✚	✚✚	✚✚

Working entirely within the stick numeral system, solve the stick numeral division problems as missing factor problems.

(a) ┼≢ ÷ ≢   (b) ≢≢ ÷ ≢   (c) ┼≢| ÷ ┼|

(d) ≢|≢|| ÷ ┼|| (e) ≢≢ ÷ ≢   (f) ┼≢ ÷ ≢

(g) ≢≢┼ ÷ ┼| (h) ≣┼≢≢ ÷ ┼||

17. Solve the division problems in two ways: (1) use place value blocks while thinking of division as a solution to an equal distribution problem (use pictures to describe your solution) and (2) use the standard method. Show how each step of the solution in (1) is related to a step in the solution to (2).
    (a)   584 ÷ 9   (b)   908 ÷ 7   (c)   7603 ÷ 8

18. Solve the stick numeral division problems in two ways: (i) use base 5 place value blocks and the equal distribution way of thinking; and (ii) the standard method as adapted to stick numerals. Show how each step of the solution in (i) is related to a step in the solution to (ii). (Compare prob. 17.)

    (a) ≣≢┼ ÷ ≢   (b) ≢≢┼ ÷ ≢   (c) ┼|≢┼ ÷ ≢

19. Here is an example of a stick numeral division problem worked by the scaffold method.

Solve the stick numeral division problems using the scaffold method.

(a) ╪╪|╪ ÷ ╪╪   (b) ╪╪|╪╪ ÷ ╪╪

20. Use the method of division by organizing an array (using place value blocks) to solve $1521 \div 43$.

21. Solve the division problem $784 \div 37$ in two ways.

    (a) Use the missing factor approach to division together with our way of organizing an array using place value blocks. As in problem 20, set up an array with 37 rows that must be filled in with as close to 784 items as possible. Make a model of 37 in place value blocks, arrange along the left-hand border of the array, and go from there.

    (b) Use the scaffold method.

    Show how each stage of the scaffold method corresponds to what you do with the place value blocks in (a).

22. Below are two decimal division problems completed using the standard method. However, some of the digits have been erased (these are indicated by *s). Reconstruct the erased digits.

```
            * *                    9 * *
(a)  5 * ) 1 * * *      (b)  3 * ) * 4 * 9 *
         * 5 *                      * 1 *
         -----                      -----
         * * *                      * * *
         4 0 0                      * 1 *
         -----                      -----
                                    2 * 5
                                    2 * 5
```

23. You are the owner of Downtown Café. You want to serve a different soup-and-sandwich combination for each of the weekdays in the year. You want to know how many different kinds of sandwiches you will have to make in order to do this. Here are some clues:

    There are 261 weekdays in the year.
    You have a repertoire of 14 different soups.

24. The cost of janitorial supplies over an 8-month period has been $943.80. Projected over an entire year, what should the cost be?

25. An express train leaves Green City at 3 P.M. and arrives in Brownville at 6 P.M. In the same afternoon a slow train leaves Brownville at 1 P.M. and arrives in Green City at 6 P.M. The engineers of the two trains need to know within a minute when the two trains will be passing. Help them find out. Each train travels at a constant speed.

26. Here is another division problem solved by the standard method. Practically all the digits are missing. Find them.

```
                    * * 8 * *
      * * * ) * * * * * * * *
                * * *
                -----
                * * * *
                * * *
                -----
                  * * * *
                  * * * *
                  -------
```

27. Captain Spydyk was worried. A stray meteor had hit the *Star Quest* and severely damaged most of the air recycling system so that the carbon dioxide that the crew exhaled was slowly building up instead of being converted back into oxygen. Usually the equipment could convert 900 liters per hour of carbon dioxide back to oxygen, but now it was only possible to provide 150 liters of fresh oxygen per hr, while the crew needed almost 500 liters.

    Captain Spydyk knew there were 6500 liters of oxygen in reserve tanks and probably another 500 just now in the interior of the ship. He also knew that if the total oxygen inside the ship were less than 200 liters, there would not be enough to breathe. According to his computer, the nearest planet with breathable air was 17 hr away. Could he get there safely?*

28. Consider the following base 8 division problems. Some of them can be solved treating them as missing factor problems and using base 8 multiplication tables and other basic multiplication facts; others can be solved using the scaffold method adapted to base 8 numerals. Decide which method is appropriate and solve each of these completely within the standard base 8 numeral system. Justify the method you use.

    (a) $64_{eight} \div 7_{eight}$ (b) $573_{eight} \div 26_{eight}$
    (c) $4372_{eight} \div 100_{eight}$ (d) $4035_{eight} \div 6_{eight}$

29. Consider the division problem $753_{eight} \div 6_{eight}$. Make a model of 753 using place value blocks and solve the problem while thinking of division as the solution to an equal distribution problem.

30. The digits in a base twelve numeral system are 0,1,2,3,4,5,6,7,8,9,A,B. $A_{twelve} = 10$ and $B_{twelve} = 11$. Solve the following division problem completely within the base 12 system: $40A1B_{twelve} \div 5A_{twelve}$. Describe the method you use.

---

* From Carol Meyer and Tom Sallee, *Make It Simpler*, Addison-Wesley, Reading, Mass., 1983, p. 263.

REVIEW TEST FOR CHAPTERS 4, 5, AND 6

For each multiple-choice question several possible answers are given. Circle the letter just to the left of the item that best answers the problem.

1. Here is the beginning of the solution to a division problem using the scaffold method.

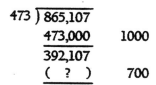

$$473 \overline{)865,107}$$
$$\underline{473,000} \qquad 1000$$
$$392,107$$
$$(\ ? \ ) \qquad 700$$

   The number where the ? is written should be
   (a) 61,007 **(b)** 3311 **(c)** 331,100 **(d)** 3784 **(e)** 378,400

2. The solution to the following stick numeral missing factor problem  ╪||| × ? = ╪╪|╪╪ is

   (a) ╪ with remainder ╪|╪   **(b)** ╪+╪ with remainder ╪╪

   (c) ╪ with remainder ╪+╪   **(d)** ╪╪ with remainder +╪

   (e) ╪╪| with remainder +╪

3. Roga has coconuts and Norum has blankets and have agreed to trade as much as possible according to the following scheme ○○○○○ coconuts will be traded for ||| blankets. After all the trading has taken place, what will be left over?

Roga's coconuts   Norum's blankets

   (a) ○○○| **(b)** ○○○○||| **(c)** ○○ |||
   (d) ○○○○○○ | **(e)** ○○○○○| i|

4. Consider the two following collections of base 4 place value blocks:

Their sum is

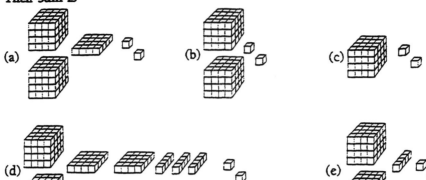

(a)   (b)   (c)

(d)   (e)

5. Here is a subtraction problem using expanded notation on a counting board.

8	3	4
3	7	8

$$\begin{array}{r} 834 \\ -\ 378 \\ \hline \end{array}$$

A next step using the method of equal additions might be

(a)

8	2	14
3	7	8

(b)

7	12	4
3	7	8

(c)

8	3	14
3	17	8

(d)

8	13	4
3	7	18

(e)

8	3	14
3	8	8

6. The merchant Neevil sold three rugs for ┼│╪, ╪╪╪, and ╪┼, respectively. His total earnings from the three rugs were

   (a) ┼│╪╪   (b) ╪╪╪   (c) ╪╪┼   (d) ╪┼╪   (e) ┼╪╪

7. Septipolis has the following coinage system

   ⓎⓎⓎⓎⓎⓎ = Ⓡ

   ⓇⓇⓇⓇⓇⓇ = Ⓖ

   You want to buy a chariot and give the merchant the coin Ⓖ. The chariot costs Ⓡ ⓎⓎⓎⓎⓎ. Your change will be

   (a) ⓎⓎ ⓇⓇⓇⓇⓇ   (b) Ⓖ Ⓡ ⓎⓎⓎⓎⓎ   (c) ⓎⓎ ⓇⓇⓇⓇⓇⓇ
   (d) Ⓨ ⓇⓇⓇⓇⓇ   (e) Ⓨ ⓇⓇⓇⓇⓇⓇ

8. The diagram illustrates an instance of which property of multiplication of whole numbers?

   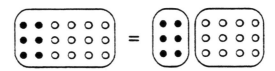

   (a) associative   (b) commutative
   (c) distributive over addition   (d) multiplication by a power of 10

9. To illustrate the product ╪╪ × ╪╪ of stick numerals, you draw the following array using dots, dashes, and squares:

   The partial product ╪│ × ╪ corresponds to which part of this array?
   (a) A   (b) B   (c) C   (d) D

10. In the stick numeral subtraction problem some of the digits have been replaced by the letters P, Q, and R

$$┼│\ P\ ┼$$
$$-\ Q\ ╪╪$$
$$\overline{┼\ R}$$

   What should the digit P be in order to make a correct solution?
   (a) │   (b) ┼   (c) ╪   (d) ╪   (e) ╪

For each of the remaining problems, document your solution carefully in the form of an essay.

11. Use the scaffold method to solve the following division problem. Explain all your steps in such a way that it is evident that you are subtracting the divisor from the dividend a lot of times, that the quotient is the number of times you can subtract the divisor from the dividend, and that the remainder is what is left over after doing all of the subtracting.

$$87 \overline{)\ 25,701}$$

12. Consider the multiplication problem 35×42. Solve it in three ways.
    (i) Think of the product as the number of items in a 35 by 42 array. Organize the array using dots, dashes, and squares.
    (ii) Use the method of partial products with zeros.
    (iii) Use the standard method.

    With these solutions, (a) show clearly how each of the partial products of (ii) correspond to portions of the array in (i), and (b) explain clearly how and where the standard method of (iii) is a shortcut to (ii).

13. The land of Octavia uses base 8 place value blocks for its monetary system. You are visiting Octavia and purchase two items.

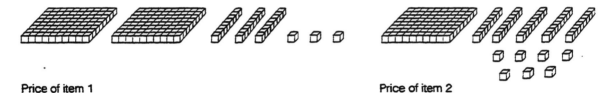

Price of item 1   Price of item 2

You have in Octavian currency:

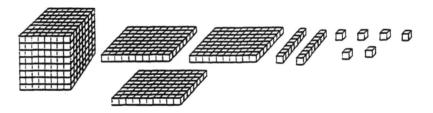

    You want to know how much you will have left over after you make your purchase. Show how you figure this out. What you have left over should involve the fewest possible coins.

14. Consider the division problem $852 \div 34$. Solve it (a) using the scaffold method, (b) using the standard method, and (c) using the missing factor method with place value blocks as in the problem set. Compare these methods and show how they relate.

INTRODUCTION TO
FRACTIONS AND RATIOS

CHAPTER **8**

ı this chapter we will show that · ıere is a need to provide names for ıuantities that are parts of whole ıings, thereby introducing the idea f fraction. We will discuss how to ompare fractions, what adding and ıbtracting fractions mean, and how) attach a fraction to the result. .long the way we will deal with a ariety of issues: mixed numbers, nproper fractions, and the connec- .on of fractions with the division of ʰole numbers. We will introduce quality of fractions: two fractions re equal when they represent the same quantity. This notion will enable us to reduce problems of comparing, adding, and subtracting fractions to corresponding whole number problems.

We will also introduce the notion of ratio, discuss some of the connections between the notions of ratio and fraction, and point out some areas of possible confusion. Finally, we will reintroduce the number line, a convenient device with which to visualize the relative sizes of fractions.

8.1

WHAT ARE FRACTIONS AND
WHAT ARE THEY GOOD FOR?

THE APPLE PROBLEM

Try solving this problem.

The fourth grade teacher bought two bags of apples for a picnic for his class. He gives one bag to one group of eight students to divide up equally among the members of the group, and the other bag to another group to do the same. The first group opens its bag and counts the apples to find that there are 29 apples for the eight of them. Help them figure out how many apples each person will get. (They don't know much about fractions.)

A Solution to the Apple Problem

Here's how the students might tackle the problem. Sue says: "Let's see. This is a division problem. Divide 29 by 8 to figure out how many apples each of us will get."

John adds: "Yes, you're right. 29 divided by 8 is 3 with a remainder of 5. Everybody gets 3 apples."

Olivia: "Well, that's fine; but what do we do with the 5 apples left over?"

Luis: "Cut them up into pieces."

Marie: "How do we do that so everybody gets the same amount?"

Sam: "I know. There are 8 of us, right? Cut up every one of the 5 apples into 8 equal pieces. Then everybody take 1 of the 8 pieces from each apple."

Alice: "Since you cut each apple into 8 *equal* pieces, each piece must be an eighth of an apple. Everybody takes 5 of the pieces. That makes 5 eighths of an apple for everybody. So everybody gets 3 whole apples plus 5 eighths of an apple."

EXERCISE

1. There are six people in the other group going on the picnic. This group's bag of apples contains 22 apples. The 22 apples are to be divided equally among the six. Help the group figure out how many apples each person will get.

The Mathematical Idea: Concept of Fraction

You have a set whose elements you want to distribute equally among so many persons. You carry out the division and you get a quotient and a remainder. What do you do with the remainder? The apple problem is such a situation. And the idea of a fraction of an apple is one solution. The idea is this: You cut up an apple into 8 equal pieces. You call one of these pieces *an eighth* of an apple. It is then natural to call 5 of these pieces *five-eighths* of an apple. The idea is so useful in other situations as well that the phrase "five eighths" is frequently replaced by the symbol $\frac{5}{8}$. The quantity of apple is called a *fractional quantity* and the name—$\frac{5}{8}$—for the quantity is called a *fraction.*

What is a fraction made up of? There is a *unit,* a set or an item or a whole thing, a portion of which will be named by the fraction. The unit is divided into a nonzero whole number B of equal parts. The portion of the unit in question consists of A of the B equal parts. The whole number A is called the *numerator* and B is called the *denominator.*

For example, for the fraction $\frac{5}{8}$, the unit is an apple, 8 is the denominator, and 5 is the numerator. Let's look at some other fractions with various numerators, denominators, and units.

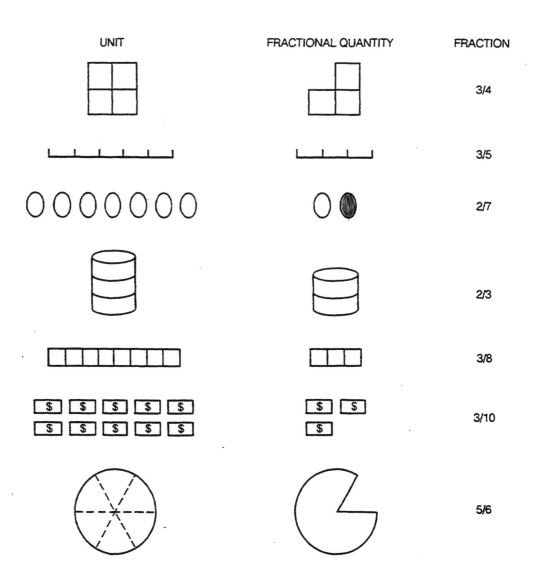

UNIT	FRACTIONAL QUANTITY	FRACTION
		3/4
		3/5
		2/7
		2/3
		3/8
		3/10
		5/6

The Mathematical Idea: Mixed Numbers

The answer to the first apple problem was 3 whole apples plus $\frac{5}{8}$ of an apple. This is usually written $3\frac{5}{8}$ apples and said as "three and five-eighths apples"; it is called a *mixed number.*

Paul, another member of the group of eight, kept quiet while the others were discussing how to divide up the apples. Now, as they are about to cut the apples, he speaks up: "Wait! I get another answer! Cut each of the extra 5 apples into halves.

That gives you 10 halves. Then give each of the eight people a half. Now everybody would have 3 apples plus $\frac{1}{2}$ an apple. Take the remaining 2 halves and cut each one into 4 equal pieces.

That would give you 8 little pieces all the same size. Give everybody one of those. Then everybody would have 3 whole apples plus half an apple plus one of those little pieces.

See? Isn't that right?"

Alice: "Yes, you are right—and so are the others. I'm going to draw a picture of your solution, Paul, and the solution the others came up with. I'll show only the part beyond 3 whole apples.

Earlier solution

Paul's solution

These two are the same quantity of apple."

Paul: "How could that be? My solution has 2 pieces; theirs has 5 pieces."

Alice: "It's not the number of pieces that counts; it's the amount of apple that's important. Look, if I gave John this whole apple and you these 2 halves, who would have more apple?"

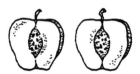

Paul: "Well, we'd both have the same amount of apple. But we wouldn't have the same thing. I mean having 2 halves is not the same thing as having a whole apple."

Alice: "I agree. But the real issue is whether the two *amounts* of apple are the same. You agree that 2 halves is the same amount of apple as a whole apple. So we could write $1 = \frac{2}{2}$. Now, let me cut each of the halves in half. That would give me 4 quarters of an apple. Then we would have $1 = \frac{4}{4}$ and $\frac{1}{2} = \frac{2}{4}$. We're almost done. Next, I want to cut each of the quarters in half giving me 8 eighths of an apple. We would have

$$1 = \frac{8}{8} \qquad \frac{1}{2} = \frac{4}{8} \qquad \frac{1}{4} = \frac{2}{8}.$$

Let's go back to your solution. You had $\frac{1}{2}$ plus $\frac{1}{8}$. That's the same amount as $\frac{4}{8}$ plus $\frac{1}{8}$, or $\frac{5}{8}$."

Paul: "You're right."

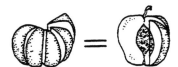

The Mathematical Idea: Equal Fractions

If we have a whole thing cut up into 5 equal pieces and we take 3 of them, then we have $\frac{3}{5}$. But, if each of the 5 equal pieces is in turn cut up into 4 smaller, equal pieces, then this would cut up the whole thing into $4 \times 5 = 20$ equal pieces. Originally we took 3 of the 5 pieces; to take the same amount now, we'd have to take $4 \times 3 = 12$ pieces or $\frac{12}{20}$ of the whole thing.

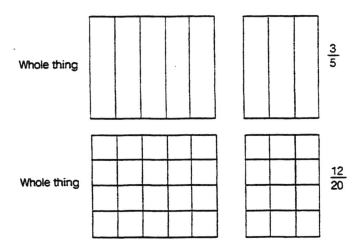

The fractions $\frac{3}{5}$ and $\frac{12}{20}$ represent the same quantity of apple. We call $\frac{3}{5}$ and $\frac{12}{20}$ *equal fractions* and write

$$\frac{3}{5} = \frac{4 \times 3}{4 \times 5} = \frac{12}{20}.$$

In reconciling the two solutions to the apple problem we encountered the pairs of equal fractions so that we can write

$$\frac{1}{2} = \frac{2 \times 1}{2 \times 2} = \frac{2}{4}$$

$$\frac{1}{2} = \frac{4 \times 1}{4 \times 2} = \frac{4}{8}$$

$$\frac{1}{4} = \frac{2 \times 1}{2 \times 4} = \frac{2}{8}.$$

More examples of equal fractions follow.

1. $\dfrac{5}{6} = \dfrac{3 \times 5}{3 \times 6} = \dfrac{15}{18}.$

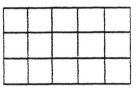

2. $\frac{3}{5} = \frac{21}{35}$

because $\dfrac{3}{5} = \dfrac{7 \times 3}{7 \times 5} = \dfrac{21}{35}.$

3. $\frac{21}{35} = \frac{12}{20}$

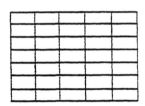

because $\dfrac{21}{35} = \dfrac{7 \times 3}{7 \times 5} = \dfrac{3}{5} = \dfrac{4 \times 3}{4 \times 5} = \dfrac{12}{20}.$

(This one is trickier!)

FIRST DEFINITION OF EQUAL FRACTIONS

That two fractions A/B and C/D are *equal* means that they represent the same quantity and we write $A/B = C/D$.

How do we decide when two fractions represent the same quantity? The examples we have seen suggest that A/B and MA/MB are equal fractions for any nonzero whole number M.

$$\frac{A}{B} = \frac{MA}{MB}.$$

What if we want to know whether $A/B = C/D$ and C is not a multiple of A (as in example 3 above)? Let's replace the two fractions by equal fractions with the same denominator. One denominator that will work is BD. Since $\dfrac{A}{B} = \dfrac{AD}{BD}$ and $\dfrac{C}{D} = \dfrac{CB}{DB}$, then $\dfrac{A}{B} = \dfrac{C}{D}$ means that $\dfrac{AD}{BD} = \dfrac{CB}{DB}$, which (since the two latter fractions have the same denominator) in turn means $AD = CB$, and vice versa. This gives us a more operational definition of equal fractions.

> ## SECOND DEFINITION OF *EQUAL FRACTIONS*
>
> Suppose that A/B and C/D are fractions. Then $\dfrac{A}{B} = \dfrac{C}{D}$ if and only if $AD = CB$.

In the second definition of equal fractions the phrase "if and only if" between the two statements $\dfrac{A}{B} = \dfrac{C}{D}$ and $AD = CB$ means that both the following statements must be true:

1. From $\dfrac{A}{B} = \dfrac{C}{D}$ it follows that $AD = CB$.

2. From $AD = CB$ it follows that $\dfrac{A}{B} = \dfrac{C}{D}$.

EXERCISE   2. Decide which of the following pairs of fractions are equal:

(a) $\frac{1}{5}$ and $\frac{1}{6}$ (b) $\frac{3}{4}$ and $\frac{15}{20}$ (c) $\frac{10}{12}$ and $\frac{15}{18}$

8.2   COMPARING THE SIZES OF FRACTIONS

THE APPLE COMPARISON PROBLEM

Solve this yourself, first.

The other group going on the picnic has six people and 22 apples. This group divided the 22 apples equally among 6 people and got $3\frac{2}{3}$ apples per person. The first group, hearing of this, wanted to know which was the bigger quantity $3\frac{5}{8}$ or $3\frac{2}{3}$. How will they decide? (The students all know what fractions are by now and what equal fractions are. But that's all.)

A Solution to the Apple Comparison Problem

The group figures out that the question boils down to: Which is the larger amount of apple, $\frac{5}{8}$ or $\frac{2}{3}$? The members of the group realize that if they were comparing $\frac{5}{8}$ apple with $\frac{7}{8}$ apple their job would be easy: $\frac{7}{8}$ is larger than $\frac{5}{8}$. The denominators of $\frac{5}{8}$ and $\frac{7}{8}$ are the same.

"How do you compare $\frac{1}{8}$ with $\frac{1}{3}$?" they ask. The eight students with the 29 apples think of how they reconciled the two solutions to their problem by replacing the fraction $\frac{1}{2}$ by an equal fraction $\frac{4}{8}$. Can they do something similar here? They realize that there is no way to turn eighths into thirds or vice versa; to carry out the program they must turn both into something else. They must change both $\frac{5}{8}$ and $\frac{2}{3}$ into two other fractions with the same denominator. They know that a fraction equal to $\frac{5}{8}$ must be of the form

$$\frac{5}{8} = \frac{5Q}{8Q}$$

and similarly for $\frac{2}{3}$:

$$\frac{2}{3} = \frac{2P}{3P}.$$

They wonder how to find numbers Q and P so that the two denominators 8Q and 3P would be equal, $8Q = 3P$. They aren't sure how they could do this, but they notice that such a denominator would be a common multiple of 8 and 3.

Sue: "I know. 24 is a common multiple of 8 and 3."

John: "And then

$$\frac{5}{8} = \frac{5 \times 3}{8 \times 3} = \frac{15}{24} \quad \text{and} \quad \frac{2}{3} = \frac{2 \times 8}{3 \times 8} = \frac{16}{24}.$$

The numerator 16 is larger than the numerator 15 so the fraction $\frac{16}{24}$ is larger than $\frac{15}{24}$. Thus $\frac{2}{3}$ is larger than $\frac{5}{8}$. Each of them gets a little bit more apple than we do!"

The Mathematical Idea: Finding Common Denominators in Order to Compare Fractions

A solution to the apple comparison problem was found by replacing the given fractions by equal fractions having the same denominator and then comparing the numerators. Let's summarize what we did.

ORDER FOR FRACTIONS

1. For fractions with the same denominator:
   A/B is *less than* C/B, written $A/B < C/B$, if and only if $A < C$.

2. For fractions with different denominators:
   Take fractions D/E and F/G and replace them by equal fractions having the same denominator. Then use 1.

   Fractions D/E and F/G always have the common denominator EG, in which case the equal fractions are

   $$\frac{DG}{EG} \quad \text{and} \quad \frac{FE}{GE}$$

   Thus, $D/E < F/G$ if and only if $DG < FE$.

What we know about equal fractions and order on fractions gives us the following useful and general method for deciding whether two fractions are equal and if not which is greater.

GENERAL METHOD FOR DECIDING ORDER AND EQUALITY OF FRACTIONS

1. $A/B = C/D$ if and only if $AD = CB$.
2. $A/B < C/D$ if and only if $AD < CB$.
3. $A/B > C/D$ if and only if $AD > CB$.

The problem of comparing fractions has been reduced to a problem of comparing whole numbers.

EXERCISE 3. For each of the following pairs of fractions, decide which of the two is greater.

(a) $\frac{2}{3}$ or $\frac{5}{7}$ (b) $\frac{2}{3}$ or $\frac{7}{11}$ (c) $\frac{7}{12}$ or $\frac{5}{8}$

8.3   ADDING AND SUBTRACTING FRACTIONS

THE RECIPE PROBLEM

Try this yourself, first.

John is cooking. One dish he is making calls for $\frac{2}{3}$ of a cup of milk; another dish calls for $\frac{1}{4}$ of a cup of milk. He wants to know how much milk he will need in all for both dishes. John is in the fifth grade, knows about equal fractions and has had experience comparing fractional quantities. How would he solve this?

A Solution to the Recipe Problem

John might think like this: "Let me *solve a simpler, similar problem.* If one dish used $\frac{3}{8}$ of a cup of milk and the other used $\frac{1}{8}$ of a cup, then the two dishes together would use $\frac{1}{8} + \frac{3}{8} = \frac{4}{8}$ of a cup. The problem is easy to solve when the two fractions have the same denominators. Can I turn the original problem into an easier one where the denominators are the same? When we were trying to decide whether $\frac{5}{8}$ apples or $\frac{2}{3}$ apples was larger, we asked the same question. We solved it by replacing that problem by an easier one in which the fractions had the same denominators; we used equal fractions to do it. Let's try that here: Replace both $\frac{1}{4}$ and $\frac{2}{3}$ by equal fractions having the same denominator. We can use $4 \times 3 = 12$ as a common denominator.

$$\frac{1}{4} = \frac{1 \times 3}{4 \times 3} = \frac{3}{12} \quad \text{and} \quad \frac{2}{3} = \frac{2 \times 4}{3 \times 4} = \frac{8}{12}.$$

It's easy to add now.

$$\frac{1}{4} + \frac{2}{3} = \frac{3}{12} + \frac{8}{12} = \frac{11}{12}.$$

I will need $\frac{11}{12}$ of a cup of milk. That's a little less than a cup."

The Mathematical Idea: Adding and Subtracting Fractions

Given two quantities that are fractions of some unit, how much do you have when you put the two together? The answer is called the *sum* of the two fractions.

THE SUM OF TWO FRACTIONS

The *sum* of A/B and C/D is written A/B + C/D. A/B and C/D are called the *addends.*

Finding a fraction equal to the sum is called *addition* of fractions. If the two addends have the same denominator, then the sum is a fraction having the same denominator and having a numerator equal to the sum of the two original numerators. For example,

$$\frac{3}{11} + \frac{5}{11} = \frac{8}{11}.$$

In general, we arrive at a method.

HOW TO ADD FRACTIONS

1. For fractions with the same denominator:

$$\frac{E}{F} + \frac{G}{F} = \frac{E+G}{F}.$$

2. For fractions with different denominators: Replace fractions A/B and C/D by equal fractions having the same denominator and use method 1 to add the two equal fractions.

As before, a common denominator that always works for fractions A/B and C/D is BD, in which case the equal fractions are

$$\frac{AD}{BD} \quad \text{and} \quad \frac{CB}{DB}$$

and the sum is

$$\frac{A}{B} + \frac{C}{D} = \frac{AD}{BD} + \frac{CB}{DB} = \frac{AD + CB}{BD}.$$

Similarly, if you have a fraction A/B of a unit and you remove from that a smaller fraction C/D of the same unit, you want to know what you have left. The answer is written $A/B - C/D$ and called the *difference* of A/B and C/D. Just as for whole numbers, the difference of A/B and C/D is the solution X to the missing addend problem $C/D + X = A/B$. Finding a fraction equal to $A/B - C/D$ is called *subtraction*. The method for doing this is similar to that for addition of fractions.

DEFINITION OF SUBTRACTION OF FRACTIONS

If $C/D < A/B$, then finding the missing addend X in $C/D + X = A/B$ is called *subtraction*, and we write $X = A/B - C/D$.

HOW TO SUBTRACT FRACTIONS

1. For fractions with same denominator:

$$\frac{E}{F} - \frac{G}{F} = \frac{E - G}{F}.$$

2. For fractions with different denominators: Replace fractions A/B and C/D by equal fractions having the same denominator and use method 1 to subtract the two equal fractions. Using the common denominator BD for these two fractions, you find that the equal fractions are

$$\frac{AD}{BD} \quad \text{and} \quad \frac{CB}{DB}$$

and the difference is

$$\frac{A}{B} - \frac{C}{D} = \frac{AD}{BD} - \frac{CB}{DB} = \frac{AD - CB}{BD}.$$

Just as the problem of comparing two fractions was reduced to the problem of comparing two whole numbers, so also the problems of finding the sum and difference of two fractions have been reduced to finding the sum and difference of two whole numbers.

EXERCISE   4. Given the two fractions $\frac{7}{15}$ and $\frac{9}{20}$, compare them, add them, and find their difference.

8.4   IMPROPER FRACTIONS

THE CREPE PROBLEM   John is cooking again. He wants to make 20 crepes and has a recipe for 10 crepes. He will have to double the amount of each ingredient called for by the recipe. The recipe calls for $\frac{3}{4}$ cup of flour. How much flour will he need for 20 crepes?

Please try this.

A Solution to the   John realizes that he will need $\frac{3}{4} + \frac{3}{4}$ cups of flour. He also knows that, since the two
Crepe Problem   fractions have the same denominator, the sum is easy: $\frac{3}{4} + \frac{3}{4} = \frac{6}{4}$. He is puzzled by the fraction $\frac{6}{4}$, since the numerator is larger than the denominator. "How can you divide something up into 4 equal pieces and take 6 of them?" He thinks a bit. "I know. If I had 2 cups of flour and divided each one of them up into 4 equal portions, it

would make sense to call each one of the 8 portions $\frac{1}{4}$ of a cup. Then I take 6 of those portions. That would make $\frac{6}{4}$ of a cup. That's one full cup plus $\frac{1}{2}$ of a cup.

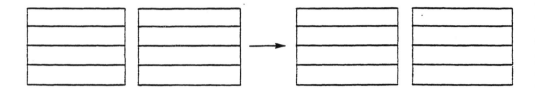

In other words, $1 + \frac{1}{2} = \frac{4}{4} + \frac{2}{4} = \frac{6}{4}$."

The Mathematical Idea: Improper Fractions

In the solution to the crepe problem, a fraction of the form A/B where A is larger than B arose naturally, and John was able to make sense of it. Such a fraction is called an *improper fraction*. (The choice of language is historical and is not meant to suggest the occurrence of some impropriety.) In the solution to the problem we also saw that $\frac{6}{4} = 1\frac{1}{2} = 1 + \frac{1}{2}$. As we have noted before, the fraction $1\frac{1}{2}$ is called a *mixed number*.

THE PIE PROBLEM John's family is having a picnic, and his mother plans to serve pie for dessert. She wants to know how much pie to order. She assumes that each pie will be cut into 8 equal pieces

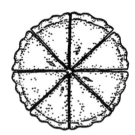

and that each person will get one of these pieces. Twenty-nine people including the members of John's family will be at the picnic. John has been given the job of solving the problem of how much pie to order. Help him solve the problem.

A Solution to the John has been studying fractions in school and thinks, "Each pie will be divided up
Pie Problem into 8 equal pieces.... Each person will get 1 of these pieces.... Each person will get $\frac{1}{8}$ of a pie! So the amount of pie that we'll need is $\frac{1}{8}$ added up 29 times: $\frac{1}{8} + \frac{1}{8} + \frac{1}{8} + \cdots$. All those fractions have the same denominator so the sum must be $\frac{29}{8}$. That's $\frac{29}{8}$ of a pie. To figure out how many whole pies Mom will have to buy, I know that $\frac{8}{8}$ is 1 whole pie. Divide 29 by 8: $29 \div 8 = 3$ with remainder 5, or $29 = 3 \times 8 + 5$. So I have

$$\frac{29}{8} = \frac{3 \times 8 + 5}{8} = \frac{3 \times 8}{8} + \frac{5}{8} = \frac{3}{1} + \frac{5}{8} = 3\frac{5}{8}.$$

We need $3\frac{5}{8}$ pies. We'll have to buy 4 whole pies. We'll use up 3 whole ones and 5 pieces from the fourth one. That will leave us with $\frac{8}{8} - \frac{5}{8} = \frac{3}{8}$ of a pie left over."

The Mathematical Idea: A Fraction as an Answer
to a Whole Number Division Problem

The fraction $\frac{29}{8}$ is an improper fraction equal to the mixed number $3\frac{5}{8}$. Seeing the two equations

$$\frac{29}{8} = 3\frac{5}{8} \quad \text{and} \quad 29 \div 8 = 3 \text{ with a remainder of } 5$$

suggests a strong connection of fractions with division of whole numbers. In certain cases one can think of the fraction A/B as an answer to the whole number division problem $A \div B$.

■ Twenty-nine apples divided equally among 8 people is $\frac{29}{8} = 3\frac{5}{8}$ apples. Compare this with: $29 \div 8 = 3$ with remainder 5. (The answer is either "$3\frac{5}{8}$" or "3 with remainder 5," depending on whether you want to cut up the remainder of 5 apples.)

■ Twenty-two apples divided equally among six people is $\frac{22}{6} = 3\frac{4}{6}$ apples. Compare this with: $22 \div 6 = 3$ with remainder 4.

■ Thirty-seven pencils are distributed equally among five children. How many pencils does each child get? This is a division problem: $37 \div 5 = 7$ pencils with 2 pencils left over. Is $\frac{37}{5} = 7\frac{2}{5}$ pencils also an answer? What does $\frac{2}{5}$ of a pencil mean? Here a division problem interpreted as a fraction doesn't make much sense, because a fraction of a pencil doesn't make much sense for this problem.

■ One hundred dollars has been allocated to buy math books for the third grade. Each math book costs \$7. How many books can be purchased? Again, this is a division problem: $100 \div 7 = 14$ books with \$2 left over. The corresponding fraction is $\frac{100}{7}$, which equals $14\frac{2}{7}$. Again, the fraction form of the division doesn't make sense—and for the same reason: A fraction of a book doesn't make sense for this problem.

WHOLE NUMBER DIVISION AND FRACTIONS

If A and B are whole numbers, $B \neq 0$, and $A \div B = Q$ with remainder R, then the fraction A/B is equal to the

$$\text{Mixed number } Q\frac{R}{B}$$

In some cases it is useful to write $A \div B = \dfrac{A}{B}$.

EXERCISES 5. Twelve pints of milk are to be evenly distributed to seven children. How much should each child get? Does it matter whether the answer is a fraction or a quotient with remainder? How would you measure out how much each child should get?

6. Fifty microcomputers are to be distributed equally to the eight elementary schools in the district. How many microcomputers should each school get? Does it matter whether the answer is a fraction or a quotient with remainder?

In describing its strength in Green City the Republican party has found out that the city has roughly 600,000 voters, among whom 200,000 are registered as Republicans. One way to describe the party's strength is as a fraction: The fraction of all registered voters consisting of Republicans is 200,000/600,000. Of course, this is equal to $\frac{1}{3}$, a fraction easier to understand.

The Republican party wants to compare its strength directly with the Democratic party, which has roughly 300,000 registered voters in Green City. (The remaining 100,000 registered voters are independents.) How can the party compare 200,000 directly with 300,000? The fraction 200,000/300,000 (equal to $\frac{2}{3}$) doesn't make sense because the 200,000 Republicans are not a part of the 300,000 Democrats. A way out is to say that the *ratio* of registered Republicans to Democrats in Green City is 200,000 to 300,000.

The benefits of this new language will become obvious when we figure out a way to compare ratios.

THE RATIO COMPARISON PROBLEM

The national Republican party has determined that the ratio of Republicans to Democrats in Green City is 200,000 to 300,000 and that the ratio of Republicans to Democrats in Brownsville is 150,000 to 250,000. Party officials would like to compare the strength of the Republicans versus Democrats in Green City against the strength in Brownsville; that is, they would like some way to compare ratios.

Someone points out that $200,000 = 2 \times 100,000$, $300,000 = 3 \times 100,000$ and that registered Republicans and Democrats in Green City can be arranged in an array like this:

```
R R    D D D
R R    D D D
R R    D D D      (100,000 rows)
: :    : : :
```

Suppose a smaller group of voters could be arranged in the array

```
R R    D D D    (11 rows)
R R    D D D
R R    D D D
R R    D D D
R R    D D D
R R    D D D
R R    D D D
R R    D D D
R R    D D D
R R    D D D
R R    D D D
```

Then you would say that this small group has the same strength of Republicans versus Democrats that Green City has. This group also has the same strength as

    R R   D D D
    R R   D D D
    R R   D D D

as does this little group

    R R   D D D.

We agree that the ratio of Republicans to Democrats is the same for all of these groups. The ratio of the last one is 2 to 3. For each of the groups there is a number N so that the number of Republicans is $2 \times N$ and the number of Democrats is $3 \times N$. Thus, we have agreed that a ratio of $2 \times N$ to $3 \times N$ is the same as a ratio of 2 to 3.

Using this agreement, we can simplify the ratio of 150,000 to 250,000. Since $150,000 = 15 \times 10,000$ and $250,000 = 25 \times 10,000$, the ratio of 150,000 to 250,000 is the same as the ratio of 15 to 25. Since $15 = 3 \times 5$ and $25 = 5 \times 5$, the ratio of 15 to 25 is the same as the ratio of 3 to 5. Thus the ratio of Republicans to Democrats in Brownsville is also 3 to 5. The Republicans and Democrats in Brownsville can be arranged in an array:

    R R R   D D D D D   (50,000 rows)
    R R R   D D D D D
    R R R   D D D D D
    ⋮ ⋮ ⋮   ⋮ ⋮ ⋮ ⋮ ⋮

The relative strength of Republicans is the same for Brownsville as it is for this little group of voters:

    R R R   D D D D D.

The Mathematical Idea: When Two Ratios Are the Same

Here is our agreement regarding the equality of ratios.

FIRST DEFINITION OF *EQUALITY FOR RATIOS*

The ratio of AN to BN is *equal* to the ratio of A to B.

THE RATIO COMPARISON PROBLEM, CONTINUED   The ratio of Republicans to Democrats in Green City is 2 to 3 and the ratio of Republicans to Democrats in Brownsville is 3 to 5. How can we compare these? Let's look at a simpler situation. If we were comparing a ratio of 2 to 5 to a ratio of 3 to 5, then we'd be comparing two groups that could be arranged in arrays as shown.

```
R R    D D D D D        R R R    D D D D D
R R    D D D D D        R R R    D D D D D
R R    D D D D D        R R R    D D D D D
: :    : : : : :        : : :    : : : : :
```

Certainly the strength of the Republican party is greater for the group on the right. So we agree that a ratio of 3 to 5 is *larger than* a ratio of 2 to 5.

In general,

FIRST DEFINITION OF ORDER FOR RATIOS

If A is larger than B, then the ratio of A to P ($\neq 0$) is *larger than* the ratio of B to P.

Returning to the harder problem of comparing the ratio of 2 to 3 with the ratio of 3 to 5, we could solve it if we were able to get the second of each pair of numbers to be the same. We know that the ratio of 2 to 3 is the same as a ratio of $2N$ to $3N$ (for any whole number N). And we know that the ratio of 3 to 5 is the same as a ratio of $3M$ to $5M$. Can we find whole numbers N and M so that $3N = 5M$? Whole numbers $N = 5$ and $M = 3$ will work. That means that a ratio of 2 to 3 is the same as a ratio of 2×5 to 3×5 (or 10 to 15), and a ratio of 3 to 5 is the same as a ratio of 3×3 to 5×3 (or 9 to 15). We've agreed that a ratio of 10 to 15 is larger than a ratio of 9 to 15 and that means that the strength of the Republican party relative to the Democrats is greater in Green City than in Brownsville.

The Mathematical Idea: Comparing Ratios; Ratios and Fractions

Suppose we want to compare two ratios A to B and C to D. We know that the ratio of AD to BD is equal to the ratio of A to B, and we know that the ratio of CB to DB is equal to the ratio of C to D. Thus, to compare ratio A to B with C to D is the same as comparing ratio AD to BD with CB to DB. Hence, to compare them, all we have to do is compare whole number AD with whole number CB. We can summarize.

SECOND DEFINITION OF *EQUALITY* AND ORDER FOR RATIOS

Suppose that $B \neq 0$ and $D \neq 0$.

1. Ratio A to B is *equal to* ratio C to D if and only if $AD = BC$.
2. Ratio A to B is *larger than* ratio C to D if and only if $AD > BC$.

Notice that the ratio A to B is equal to (respectively, larger than) the ratio C to D exactly when $A/B = C/D$ (respectively, $A/B > C/D$). To compare ratios, you compare fractions.

The connection of ratios with fractions is also apparent in the language used to talk about ratios. For example, the numbered statements all mean the same thing.

1. The ratio of Republicans to Democrats is 2 to 3.
2. For every 2 Republicans there are 3 Democrats.
3. The ratio of Republicans to Democrats is $\frac{2}{3}$.
4. There are $\frac{2}{3}$ as many Republicans as Democrats.

Ratios are frequently replaced by fractions and vice versa. For example, in Green City there are 200,000 registered Republicans among 600,000 registered voters. As we noted earlier, that means that the set of Republicans is $\frac{1}{3}$ of the set of all of the registered voters. One can use the language of ratios here and also say that the ratio of registered Republicans to all registered voters is 1 to 3. Thus, all the numbered statements mean the same thing.

1. The ratio of Republicans to all registered voters is 1 to 3.
2. One out of every three registered voters is a Republican.
3. The ratio of Republicans to all registered voters is $\frac{1}{3}$.
4. The fraction of Republicans among all registered voters is $\frac{1}{3}$.

The connection of ratios with fractions enlarges the number of situations in which fractions can be used. The reading contest problem points out that there are situations when this connection leads to confusion. You have to be careful!

THE READING CONTEST PROBLEM   The fourth grade students at Fort Lowell Elementary School were excited. The results of the current fourth grade reading contest had just been posted.

CLASS	NO. OF STUDENTS READING MORE THAN 25 BOOKS	TOTAL NO. IN CLASS
Mr. Jones	13	26
Ms. Eby	14	35
Ms. Ballentine	8	24

For each class they figured out the fraction of good readers out of the whole class.

Mr. Jones: $\frac{13}{26} = \frac{1}{2}$
Ms. Eby: $\frac{14}{35} = \frac{2}{5}$
Ms. Ballentine: $\frac{8}{24} = \frac{1}{3}$

They compared these fractions and found that $\frac{1}{2}$ was biggest so that Mr. Jones's class was the fourth grade winner for Fort Lowell as far as reading went. They also knew that, since the classes were of different sizes, they were comparing these fractions as if they were comparing ratios, not as if they were comparing fractions as "amount of class." Now they are interested in another question: Knowing that $\frac{1}{2}$ of Mr. Jones's class consists of good readers and that $\frac{1}{3}$ of Ms. Ballentine's class consists of good readers, what fraction of the *combined* two classes consists of good readers? How can they solve this?

Three students in the fourth grade offer solutions.

Fritz offers this solution: "The fraction of Mr. Jones's class that consists of good readers is $\frac{1}{2}$. The fraction of Ms. Ballentine's class that consists of good readers is $\frac{1}{3}$. The fraction of the combined classes that consists of good readers should be $\frac{1}{2} + \frac{1}{3}$

and, using equal fractions, I get $\frac{1}{2} + \frac{1}{3} = \frac{3}{6} + \frac{2}{6} = \frac{5}{6}$. So $\frac{5}{6}$ of the combined classes should consist of good readers."

Jane puts her hand in, saying: "No, that's all wrong. The unit is the set of students in the *two* classes, not the set of students in one class. The $\frac{1}{2}$ of Mr. Jones's class is really $\frac{1}{4}$ of the two classes and the $\frac{1}{3}$ of Ms. Ballentine's class is really $\frac{1}{6}$ of the two classes. Let me draw you a picture.

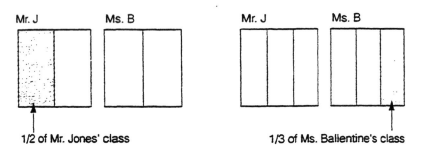

1/2 of Mr. Jones' class   1/3 of Ms. Ballentine's class

"So, to find out what fraction of the *two* classes consists of good readers, I add $\frac{1}{4}$ and $\frac{1}{6}$. Using equal fractions, I get $\frac{1}{4} + \frac{1}{6} = \frac{3}{12} + \frac{2}{12} = \frac{5}{12}$. That means that $\frac{5}{12}$ of the combined classes consists of good readers."

Antonio offers this solution: "If you don't mind my saying so, neither of you is right. You're treating all those ratios as if they were fractions, and you're getting some wrong answers. You're adding peaches to oranges and getting nonsense. Let's look at the data.

CLASS	NO. OF GOOD READERS	NO. IN CLASS
Jones	13	26
Ballentine	8	24
Total	21	50

As I see it, the combined class would have 50 students in it. Of those, 21 are good readers. Right? That means that the ratio of good readers to total number of students is 21 to 50, or $\frac{21}{50}$ of the students are good readers. Let's compare this with the fractions gotten by the other two methods.

$$\frac{21}{50} \text{ versus } \frac{5}{6}$$

$$\frac{21}{50} = \frac{21 \times 3}{50 \times 3} = \frac{63}{150} \qquad \text{versus} \qquad \frac{5}{6} = \frac{5 \times 25}{6 \times 25} = \frac{125}{150}$$

The two fractions $\frac{21}{50}$ and $\frac{5}{6}$ are not equal.

$$\frac{21}{50} \text{ versus } \frac{5}{12}$$

$$\frac{21}{50} = \frac{21 \times 6}{50 \times 6} = \frac{126}{300} \qquad \text{versus} \qquad \frac{5}{12} = \frac{5 \times 25}{12 \times 25} = \frac{125}{300}$$

The two fractions $\frac{21}{50}$ and $\frac{5}{12}$ aren't equal either. They're close, though!"

The Mathematical Idea: You Can't Add Ratios
in the Same Way You Add Fractions

Which of the three solutions above is correct? Fritz made an error about the unit for the fraction. He assumed that the unit was one class rather than two. Jane was a bit more subtle, but she assumed (erroneously) that all classes are the same size and wound up adding fractions of two different units. Antonio calculated the fraction directly, and his solution must be correct. The clue is that the fractions in question are fractions of different kinds. To compare them, you must compare them as ratios. Adding these ratios (as if they were fractions) doesn't make sense, as we have seen.

EXERCISE

7. Recall from earlier in the chapter that there are $\frac{2}{3}$ as many registered Republicans as Democrats in Green City and $\frac{3}{5}$ as many registered Republicans as Democrats in Brownsville. Figure out the ratio of registered Republicans to Democrats in the two cities combined. (To solve this, you may need to use information given in the ratio comparison problem.)

8.6   VISUALIZING FRACTIONS ON A NUMBER LINE

THE CITY-WIDE READING CONTEST PROBLEM

The fourth grade students at Fort Lowell Elementary have just seen the city-wide results for the fourth grade reading contest. Results for each class have been expressed as the fraction of the whole class consisting of good readers. Here are the fractions for the nine participating classes:

Fort Lowell: Jones $\frac{1}{2}$, Eby $\frac{1}{3}$, Ballentine $\frac{2}{5}$
Washington: Smith $\frac{4}{15}$, Garcia $\frac{3}{4}$, Hasselhoff $\frac{11}{30}$
Hughes: Thomas $\frac{3}{10}$, Schwartz $\frac{5}{12}$, Kopsky $\frac{3}{5}$

The students were trying to make sense of these scores. Each wanted to know how his or her class compared to all the other classes: How many were better? How many worse? The students in Mr. Jones's class—which did quite well city-wide—wanted to know how close their class was to its nearest competitors. The students in Ms. Ballentine's class—which didn't do well city-wide—wanted to know how close their score was to the lowest scores. They wanted a way to look at all the city scores so that they could answer these and similar questions easily. Can they find one?

One of the students *thought of a similar problem:* "A while ago, we were looking at the distances of the planets from the Sun and wanted to get some feeling for how everything was placed in the solar system. We *drew a picture,* a number line with the Sun at zero and each planet at the point on the line corresponding to its distance from the Sun. Those distances were all whole numbers. Now, we have fractions, but perhaps we could find a way to picture them on a number line."

Second student: "Let's draw a line. Since all of our fractions are less than 1, we can label one end 0 and the other 1.

|_____|

0   1

Let's start with the fraction $\frac{3}{4}$ (Garcia's score). Divide the unit length (between the points 0 and 1) into four equal lengths.

|_____|_____|_____|_____|
0   1

Each of the four equal lengths is $\frac{1}{4}$ of the unit length. If you start at 0 and measure off $\frac{1}{4}$, you get the first point. Label that point with $\frac{1}{4}$. Measure off a second $\frac{1}{4}$ from the first, getting a second point, which you label with $\frac{2}{4}$. Then measure off a third $\frac{1}{4}$ from the second point, getting a third point that you label with $\frac{3}{4}$.

|_____|_____|_____|_____|
0               $\frac{1}{4}$ $\frac{2}{4}$ $\frac{3}{4}$ 1

                                                                 $\frac{4}{4}$

If you measure off a fourth $\frac{1}{4}$ from the third point, you get the point that is already labeled 1."

Third student: "The same idea will work with any fraction. Take $\frac{3}{5}$. Divide the unit length into 5 equal pieces. You'll get 4 points between 0 and 1. The third one from the left is the one corresponding to $\frac{3}{5}$.

|_____|_____|_____|_____|_____|
0           $\frac{1}{5}$ $\frac{2}{5}$ $\frac{3}{5}$ $\frac{4}{5}$ 1

                                                                 $\frac{5}{5}$

Here's what it would look like on top of the picture with the $\frac{1}{4}$s."

|_____|__|_____|____|_____|____|__|_____|
0           $\frac{1}{5}$ $\frac{1}{4}$ $\frac{2}{5}$ $\frac{2}{4}$ $\frac{3}{5}$ $\frac{3}{4}$ $\frac{4}{5}$ 1

                                                                 $\frac{5}{5}$

                                                                 $\frac{4}{4}$

Fourth student: "It's beginning to look complicated. Is there a way to take what we have and add points for fractions without putting separate pictures together?"

Fifth student: "When we compare $\frac{3}{4}$ with $\frac{3}{5}$, we find a common multiple of 4 and 5—for example, 20. Then we convert $\frac{3}{4}$ and $\frac{3}{5}$ to $\frac{1}{20}$ths using equal fractions: $\frac{3}{4} = (3 \times 5)/(4 \times 5) = \frac{15}{20}, \frac{3}{5} = (3 \times 4)/(5 \times 4) = \frac{12}{20}$. Going from $\frac{1}{5}$s to $\frac{1}{20}$s amounts to dividing up each of the $\frac{1}{5}$s into 5 equal pieces. Let's do that and see what we get.

|_|_|_|_|_|_|_|_|_|_|_|_|_|_|_|_|_|_|_|_|
0 $\frac{1}{20}$ $\frac{2}{20}$ $\frac{3}{20}$ $\frac{4}{20}$ $\frac{5}{20}$ $\frac{6}{20}$ $\frac{7}{20}$ $\frac{8}{20}$ $\frac{9}{20}$ $\frac{10}{20}$ $\frac{11}{20}$ $\frac{12}{20}$ $\frac{13}{20}$ $\frac{14}{20}$ $\frac{15}{20}$ $\frac{16}{20}$ $\frac{17}{20}$ $\frac{18}{20}$ $\frac{19}{20}$ 1

                                                                 $\frac{20}{20}$

          $\frac{1}{5}$ $\frac{1}{4}$ $\frac{2}{5}$ $\frac{2}{4}$ $\frac{3}{5}$ $\frac{3}{4}$ $\frac{4}{5}$ $\frac{4}{4}$

                                                                 $\frac{5}{5}$

You get different labels for the same point. See, $\frac{15}{20}$ and $\frac{3}{4}$ label the same point. The reason is that they are equal fractions."

Sixth student: "Now take $\frac{1}{3}$. A common denominator of $\frac{1}{3}$ and $\frac{1}{20}$ is 60. Using equal fractions, we have $\frac{1}{3} = (1 \times 20)/(3 \times 20) = \frac{20}{60}$. To add the $\frac{1}{60}$ths to the picture, we will have to divide each of the $\frac{1}{20}$ths into 3 equal pieces, dividing the unit length into 60 equal pieces. Here's the picture."

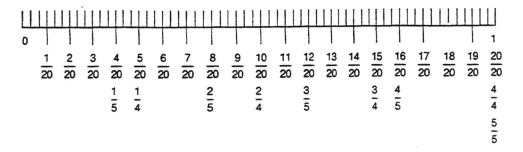

Seventh student: "I just noticed that it's easy to put the other fractions in the picture because they're all equal to fractions with the denominator 60. When all the fractions have the same denominator, then to picture them on the number line, all you have to do is line up the numerators as whole numbers."

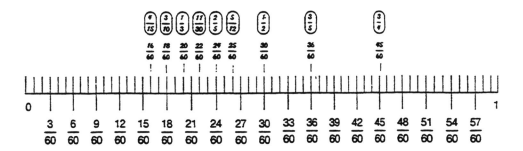

Eighth student: "Let's see how the various classes in the city did in the reading contest. The scores are spread between $\frac{4}{15}$ and $\frac{3}{4}$. Also, the winners did a lot better than Mr. Jones's class did—even though his class was third in the city. A lot of the scores are clustered very close to the score of Ms. Ballentine's class and those that are close are below it, so her kids shouldn't feel too bad."

The Mathematical Idea: Fractions on a Number Line

As you can see from the solution to the city-wide reading contest problem, it is useful to be able to associate a fraction with a point on a number line. It is especially useful when you have a set of fractions the relative sizes of which you want to compare: You do this by comparing their relative *positions* on the line. There is a conceptual bonus in associating fractions with points: You can observe that different labels for a point correspond to a fraction's different disguises amounting to equal fractions.

The use of the number line in the solution to the city-wide reading contest problem involved fractions between 0 and 1 only—so-called proper fractions. There is no difficulty in associating improper fractions with points on the number line; the idea is the same.

| ⌐___|___|___|___|___|___|___|___|___|___|___|___| |

| 0 | $\frac{1}{4}$ | $\frac{1}{2}$ | $\frac{3}{4}$ | 1 | $\frac{5}{4}$ | $\frac{3}{2}$ | $\frac{7}{4}$ | 2 | $\frac{9}{4}$ | $\frac{5}{2}$ | $\frac{11}{4}$ |

In a later chapter, we will use the number line a lot in working with decimal fractions.

EXERCISE

8. Here are some fictitious ratios—treated as fractions—of registered Republicans to Democrats in several southwestern states: Arizona: $\frac{2}{3}$; New Mexico: $\frac{2}{5}$; California: $\frac{5}{4}$; Nevada: $\frac{4}{5}$; Utah: $\frac{3}{2}$; Colorado: $\frac{5}{6}$. Place these fractions on a number line. On your line indicate the strongest and weakest Republican states in this group of states.

8.7   LOOKING BACK: GCDs, LCMs, AND FRACTIONS

From what we know about equal fractions, a given fractional quantity has several names. For example, $\frac{2}{3}$, $\frac{4}{6}$, $\frac{6}{9}$, $\frac{22}{33}$, $\frac{106}{159}$, and 10,000/15,000 are all names for the same quantity. Of all these names, $\frac{2}{3}$ is the most familiar, perhaps because its denominator is the smallest of all the fractions shown. There is no fraction equal to $\frac{2}{3}$ with a denominator smaller than 3. The reason for this is that the GCD of 2 and 3 is equal to 1. Indeed, if A/B is a fraction equal to $\frac{2}{3}$, i.e., $A/B = \frac{2}{3}$, then you know that $3A = 2B$. By the fundamental theorem of arithmetic you know that A must be a multiple of 2 and B must be a multiple of 3: $A = 2M$, $B = 3P$. In fact, $M = P$ and $A = 2M$, $B = 3M$. Any fraction equal to $\frac{2}{3}$ must have a denominator bigger than or equal to 3.

The same argument works for any fraction C/D that has the property that the GCD of C and D is equal to 1. (Two nonzero whole numbers the GCD of which is 1 are called *relatively prime*.)

A FRACTION IN LOWEST TERMS

Suppose that the GCD of C and D is 1. Then of all fractions equal to C/D, the fraction C/D has the smallest denominator. We call the fraction C/D a fraction in *lowest terms*.

Consider the fraction $\frac{54}{72}$. One reason it is not in lowest terms is because both 54 and 72 have a common divisor bigger than 1. In fact, $54 = 3 \cdot 18$, and $72 = 4 \cdot 18$, so that

$$\frac{54}{72} = \frac{3 \cdot 18}{4 \cdot 18} = \frac{3}{4}.$$

Since the GCD of 3 and 4 is 1, the fraction $\frac{3}{4}$ is in lowest terms. Since the number 18 is the GCD of 54 and 72, this suggests a general method, given a fraction E/F, for finding a fraction equal to E/F and in lowest terms.

REDUCING A FRACTION TO LOWEST TERMS

If E/F is a fraction, one method for finding a fraction equal to it that is in lowest terms is as follows. If E and F are relatively prime, then you are finished: E/F is in lowest terms. Otherwise, E and F have a common divisor $G > 1$. Then there are whole numbers J and K such that $E = JG$ and $F = KG$. Thus,

$$\frac{E}{F} = \frac{JG}{KG} = \frac{J}{K}.$$

If J and K are relatively prime, then you are finished. Otherwise, J and K have a common divisor bigger than 1, and you proceed as before. Eventually you will wind up with an equal fraction in lowest terms.

For example, to reduce $\frac{48}{72}$ to lowest terms, you notice that the 48 and 72 have 2 as a common divisor so

$$\frac{48}{72} = \frac{2 \times 24}{2 \times 36} = \frac{24}{36}.$$

But then 24 and 36 also have 2 as a common divisor.

$$\frac{24}{36} = \frac{2 \times 12}{2 \times 18} = \frac{12}{18}.$$

This time the numerator and denominator have 6 as a common divisor.

$$\frac{12}{18} = \frac{6 \times 2}{6 \times 3} = \frac{2}{3}.$$

You are finished, because 2 and 3 have no common divisor bigger than 1. Thus $\frac{48}{72} = \frac{2}{3}$.

EXERCISE 9. Reduce the fractions to lowest terms.

    (a) $\frac{4}{18}$ (b) $\frac{21}{35}$ (c) $\frac{16}{88}$ (d) $\frac{96}{168}$ (e) 50,000/150,000

LCMs and Common Denominators

To add (or subtract or compare) $\frac{5}{6}$ with $\frac{3}{4}$, you replace each of $\frac{5}{6}$ and $\frac{3}{4}$ by an equal fraction, so that both of the replacements have the same denominator. This *common denominator* is a common multiple of the two initial denominators, in this case a common multiple of 6 and 4. To keep the common denominator small, a good choice is the LCM (least common multiple) of the two initial denominators. In the example, the LCM of 6 and 4 is 12.

$$\frac{5}{6} = \frac{5 \times 2}{6 \times 2} = \frac{10}{12} \qquad \text{and} \qquad \frac{3}{4} = \frac{3 \times 3}{4 \times 3} = \frac{9}{12}.$$

This LCM is the smallest possible common denominator, sometimes called the *least common denominator*. Using the LCM may help you keep fractions from getting too unwieldy. Here is a summary of the method.

FINDING COMMON DENOMINATORS USING THE LCM

Suppose that A/B and C/D are fractions and that you want to replace them by equal fractions having the *least common denominator*. Find the LCM of B and D and denote it by L. Find whole numbers N and M so that $L = BN = DM$. Then

$$\frac{AN}{BN} \quad \text{and} \quad \frac{CM}{DM}$$

are the two equal fractions having the least common denominator.

For example, to find fractions equal to $\frac{11}{15}$ and $\frac{7}{12}$ and having the least common denominator, you find that the LCM of 15 and 12 is 60. You also know that $15 \times 4 = 60$ and $12 \times 5 = 60$ (4 and 5 are the N and M in the description of finding common denominators using the LCM). Thus,

$$\frac{11}{15} = \frac{11 \times 4}{15 \times 4} = \frac{44}{60} \quad \text{and} \quad \frac{7}{12} = \frac{7 \times 5}{12 \times 5} = \frac{35}{60}.$$

The least common denominator is 60, and the two fractions are $\frac{44}{60}$ and $\frac{35}{60}$.

EXERCISE 10. For each pair find the least common denominator and replace each fraction by an equal fraction with that denominator.

(a) $\frac{7}{9}$ and $\frac{5}{12}$ (b) $\frac{3}{20}$ and $\frac{7}{8}$ (c) $\frac{4}{25}$ and $\frac{8}{15}$ (d) $\frac{16}{45}$ and $\frac{73}{150}$

_8.10_ SUMMARY OF IMPORTANT IDEAS AND TECHNIQUES

- That two fractions representing the same quantity are called *equal*
- Of all fractions equal to a given fraction, how to find the one with the smallest denominator by reducing it to lowest terms
- Addition and subtraction of fractions
- The ease of comparing, adding, and subtracting fractions when they have common denominators
- Methods for finding fractions A/B and C/D equal to these and having common denominators:
  Using BD as common denominator
  Using LCM of B and D as common denominator
- Special types of fractions: improper fractions and mixed numbers; special fractions: zero fraction; whole numbers as fractions

- The utility of expressing the answer to a whole number division problem as a fraction:
$$A \div B = A/B$$
- Commutative and associative properties of addition of fractions; 0 as an additive identity
- How ratio and fractions are related
- When two ratios are equal
- When one ratio is larger than another
- Alternate expressions for the same ratio
- That ratios can't always be added as if they were fractional quantities
- Visualizing fractions on the number line
- Visualization of order relation between fractions
- Visualization of addition and subtraction of fractions using add-subtract slide rule
- Formal order properties of fractions with respect to addition and subtraction
- A way in which the set of fractions and the set of whole numbers differ: density of fractions on the number line

PROBLEM SET

PRACTICING SKILLS

1. Which of the following pairs of fractions are equal?
   (a) $\frac{5}{6}$ and $\frac{15}{18}$ (b) $\frac{15}{20}$ and $\frac{24}{32}$ (c) $\frac{0}{3}$ and $\frac{0}{1}$ (d) $\frac{3}{4}$ and $\frac{3}{5}$

2. Which of the two fractions in each pair is larger?
   (a) $\frac{3}{4}$ or $\frac{5}{7}$ (b) $\frac{2}{9}$ or $\frac{3}{11}$ (c) $\frac{5}{6}$ or $\frac{8}{9}$ (d) $\frac{17}{30}$ or $\frac{13}{24}$

3. Convert the following improper fractions to mixed fractions.
   (a) $\frac{57}{3}$ (b) $\frac{12}{2}$ (c) $\frac{5721}{1000}$ (d) $\frac{5721}{100}$

4. Convert the following mixed fractions to improper fractions.
   (a) $2\frac{3}{4}$ (b) $5\frac{1}{3}$ (c) $3\frac{7}{10}$ (d) $5\frac{721}{1000}$

5. Add the following fractions.
   (a) $\frac{1}{5} + \frac{1}{6}$ (b) $\frac{1}{6} + \frac{11}{18}$ (c) $\frac{5}{9} + \frac{8}{15}$ (d) $\frac{5}{28} + \frac{5}{24}$ (e) $\frac{3}{11} + \frac{0}{8}$

6. Subtract the following fractions.
   (a) $\frac{2}{5} - \frac{1}{3}$ (b) $\frac{13}{24} - \frac{3}{8}$ (c) $\frac{7}{12} - \frac{7}{18}$ (d) $\frac{5}{36} - \frac{4}{45}$

7. You know that you have $1\frac{1}{2}$ rolls of high quality white paper in stock. You have three printing jobs today that will require you to use this paper. One job requires $\frac{1}{4}$ roll, the second requires $\frac{2}{5}$ of a roll, and the third requires $\frac{2}{3}$ of a roll. Will you have enough paper for the three jobs? If you do, how much paper will be left? If you don't, how much more paper will you need?

8. You take a metal strip 45 in long from inventory. From this you cut three smaller strips having lengths $12\frac{3}{4}$ in, $15\frac{1}{8}$ in, and $11\frac{2}{3}$ in. You waste $\frac{1}{8}$ in of the strip for each cut. You return what is left to inventory. You must record on an inventory form the length of the strip that you return. What do you record?

9. (a) You are going to give 56 turkeys equally to 6 shelters. How many turkeys should each shelter receive?

(b) The third grade class has collected $9.00 to purchase pumpkins to decorate their classroom for Halloween. Pumpkins cost $ .70 apiece. How many pumpkins can they buy?

(c) The Gonzales family purchased 12 small rosewood bushes to plant along a straight stretch of the southern boundary of the family's property. The stretch is 75 ft. They plan to plant them so that they are equally spaced and with a bush at each extreme end of the row. The family wants to know how many feet should be between each bush. What is it?

10. A current flu strain seems to be particularly prevalent among young grade school children. The health department is comparing the strength of the epidemic among first graders in two schools at opposite ends of town. Here are the results.

SCHOOL	INFECTED	HEALTHY
Northside	54	99
Southside	44	110

(a) Find the ratio of infected to healthy for each school.

(b) Which school has the greater ratio of infected to healthy?

(c) Find the ratio of infected to healthy for the two schools combined.

11. In the first month of the season, Joe was at bat 20 times and made 11 hits, so his batting average for that month was $\frac{11}{20}$. In the second month he was at bat 15 times and made 7 hits, so his average for the second month was $\frac{7}{15}$. Which was his better month? What was his batting average for the two months?

12. (a) If there are $\frac{3}{4}$ as many boys as girls in a class, and there are 12 boys, how many children are in the class?

(b) At a concert, there are $\frac{2}{3}$ as many boys as girls and $\frac{3}{4}$ as many girls as adults. If 48 adults are at the concert, how many children are there?

(c) Ms. Jones reports that there are $\frac{4}{5}$ as many girls as boys in the school choir, and she requests that 8 more girls be added to equalize the sexes. How large will the equalized choir be?

13. For nine Midwestern schools suppose that the following are ratios of the number of students enrolled in a undergraduate liberal arts program, such as mathematics or French, to the number enrolled in a nonliberal arts undergraduate program, such as engineering or nursing:

Ohio State: $\frac{5}{4}$; University of Wisconsin: $\frac{2}{1}$; Indiana University: $\frac{2}{3}$; University of Illinois: $\frac{2}{6}$; University of Iowa: $\frac{7}{6}$; University of Nebraska: $\frac{3}{5}$; University of Minnesota: $\frac{4}{5}$;

University of Michigan: $\frac{7}{3}$; Michigan State: $\frac{7}{12}$.

(a) Put these fractions (ratios) on a number line.

(b) What is the smallest ratio? The largest ratio?

(c) What school is closest to being evenly balanced in the liberal arts/nonliberal arts enrollment?

14. Reduce each fraction to its lowest terms.

(a) $\frac{21}{27}$ (b) $\frac{24}{56}$ (c) $\frac{84}{108}$ (d) $\frac{12,000}{32,000}$

15. Replace each pair of fractions by an equal pair having the least common denominator.

(a) $\frac{5}{12}$ and $\frac{8}{15}$ (b) $\frac{25}{42}$ and $\frac{7}{24}$ (c) $\frac{16}{33}$ and $\frac{30}{121}$ (d) $\frac{10}{21}$ and $\frac{19}{26}$

16. (a) Find a fraction between $\frac{1}{3}$ and $\frac{2}{9}$.

(b) Find a fraction between $\frac{31}{116}$ and $\frac{32}{115}$.

(c) Find three distinct fractions between $\frac{63}{32}$ and 2.

17. Each of the following is a sentence involving a fraction and pictures. Fill in the missing part to each sentence.

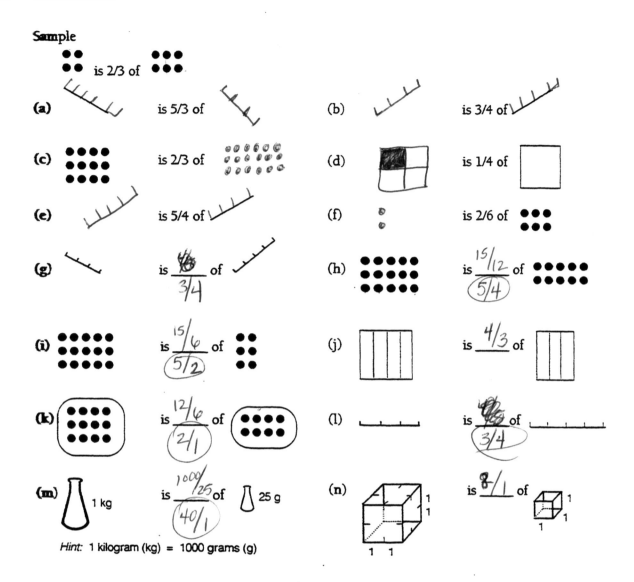

Sample

•• is 2/3 of •••
••   •••

(a) is 5/3 of

(b) is 3/4 of

(c) •••• is 2/3 of
    ••••
    ••••

(d) is 1/4 of

(e) is 5/4 of

(f) is 2/6 of •••
                •••

(g) is 4/8/3/4 of

(h) is 15/12 / 5/4 of •••••
                      •••••
                      •••••

(i) ••••• is 15/6 / 5/2 of ••
    •••••   ••
    •••••   ••

(j) is 4/3 of

(k) is 12/6 / 2/1 of

(l) is 4/8 / 3/4 of

(m) 1 kg is 1000/25 / 40/1 of 25 g

Hint: 1 kilogram (kg) = 1000 grams (g)

(n) is 8/1 of

USING IDEAS   For each of the remaining problems, describe as clearly and completely as you can your solution to the problem. Include the steps you took to solve the problem, mention the problems or solutions from the text that gave you ideas, and include the problem-solving strategies you used. You might want to outline and organize these details before assembling your final description in the form of an essay.

18. In each of the following a unit and a pair of fractions (of that unit) is given. For each, draw an appropriate picture showing why the two fractions (of that unit) are equal.
    (a) $\frac{3}{4}$, $\frac{9}{12}$, pie   (b) $\frac{10}{15}$, $\frac{8}{12}$, mile
    (c) $\frac{3}{8}$, $\frac{6}{16}$, cup of milk (d) $\frac{6}{10}$, $\frac{9}{15}$, square yard

19. A wheat farmer has 5 dairy cows to supply the family's needs for dairy products. Whatever is left over is sold to the local dairy. Here is last week's production: Cow 1 produced $6\frac{3}{4}$ gal of milk; 2 produced $5\frac{1}{3}$ gal; 3 produced $5\frac{2}{3}$ gal; 4 gave $5\frac{1}{4}$ gal; and 5 produced $3\frac{5}{6}$ gal. The farmer saves out 3 qt per day for her family. How much milk did she sell to the dairy last week?

20. In a load of 264 tons of ore there is only $\frac{3}{8}$ as much iron (by weight) as there is waste. How much iron is in the load?

21. A box of firecrackers is $\frac{1}{8}$ duds. There are 120 more good firecrackers than duds. How many duds are in the box?

22. Two-thirds of the people in Switzerland speak German, $\frac{7}{12}$ speak French, and $\frac{1}{4}$ speak Italian.
    (a) What is the smallest fraction of the population that could speak all three languages?
    (b) What is the largest fraction of the population that could speak all three languages?*

23. In a cross-country motorcycle race across Avra Valley, it is 70 mi to the flag and 70 mi back. Alice averages 80 mph going out, but then with clutch trouble can only manage 60 mph coming back. Sally can only manage 70 mph but maintains this for the entire race. Who wins the race?

24. A fishery biologist wants to estimate the number of bass fish in a lake. To do this, he takes a sample of 250 bass from the lake, marks them, and returns them to the lake. In 2 weeks' time, he assumes that the marked bass have pretty much evenly distributed themselves around the lake. He takes another sample of 160 bass and finds that 25 of them have been marked. His method of estimating the whole population is this: He assumes that the ratio of the total number of marked fish (250) to the whole population is the same as the ratio of marked fish in his sample (25) to the total number of fish in the sample (160). What is his estimate of the whole population of bass fish in the lake?

25. Wires carrying electricity are often placed in a protective steel pipe called *conduit*. A wiring job calls for 32 pieces of conduit $7\frac{1}{2}$ ft long, 3 pieces $7\frac{3}{4}$ in. long, 8 pieces $13\frac{1}{4}$ in long, and 6 pieces $9\frac{5}{8}$ in long.
    (a) Conduit comes in standard lengths of 10 ft. How many such lengths are needed for this job?
    (b) How should the 10-ft lengths in part (a) be cut in order that there be as little waste as possible? Pieces of less than 2 ft in length are considered waste. Try to cut the 10-ft lengths so that there are as few pieces left with length less than 2 ft as possible.†

26. Find the length of a bolt that will go through a piece of tubing with $\frac{1}{2}$ in outside diameter, a washer $\frac{1}{16}$ in thick, a piece of tubing with $\frac{3}{4}$ in outside diameter, another washer, and a nut $\frac{3}{16}$ in thick.

27. You want to frame a matted photograph measuring 16 by 20 inches, using framing material the cross section of which is as shown. You plan to add an additional $\frac{1}{16}$ inch to length and width to permit the photograph to fit easily into the frame.
    (a) What should the finished outside dimension of the frame be?

---

* From Deborah Hughes Hallett, *The Math Workshop: Algebra*, Norton, New York, prob. 41, p. 41.
† From D. Bushaw et al., *A Sourcebook of Applications of School Mathematics*, National Council of Teachers of Mathematics, Reston, Va., prob. 1. 17, p. 26.

(b)　Is an 80-in piece of frame material long enough? (Each cut your saw makes eats up $\frac{1}{8}$ in of the length.)

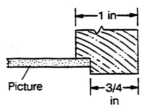

28.　To "push" Kodak Tri-X (ASA rating of 400) film to an ASA rating of 800, you can use 1 part AGFA Rodinal developer and 50 parts water. How much developer will you need to make 240 ml of working solution?

29.　A painter has formed a light pink by mixing 4 parts white with 1 part red. There are 2 liters of a darker pink that is half red and half white. How much white should be added to the darker pink to convert it to the lighter pink?

MULTIPLICATION AND DIVISION OF FRACTIONS

CHAPTER 9

In this chapter we will look at several problems in which fractions occur but which call for different types of solutions than those that appeared in the previous chapter. At first glance, the problems in this chapter seem to be unrelated. After a while some similarities appear—similarities in the ways the problems are solved. These similarities lead to the notions of multiplication and division of fractions. Since it is important to know how and when to use these concepts in solving problems, it is helpful to be aware of the problems that gave birth to the concepts in the first place. It is also important to remember that the concepts serve the problems rather than the other way around: The problems are not just examples of the uses of the concepts.

We will also continue the discussion of ratios begun in chapter 9, expanding on the situations in which the notion of ratio can be useful and connecting it with the multiplication and division of fractions discussed in the rest of the chapter.

THE BOOK PACK PROBLEM

Please try this first.

The students in the sixth grade are making simple packs out of lightweight canvas for carrying books and other school items. Each pack requires $\frac{3}{4}$ yd of the canvas material. The students have been given the problem of finding the total length of canvas material needed for making 27 packs, one for each person in the class. The students have had experience comparing, adding, and subtracting fractions. Help them solve this problem.

A Solution to the Book Pack Problem

The students quickly realize that the answer can be gotten by the repeated addition of $\frac{3}{4}$ twenty-seven times and that, since all the fractions being added are the same, they also have the same denominator. They deduce from this that the answer is a fraction the numerator of which is 3 added to itself 27 times and the denominator of which is 4; that is, the fraction is $(27 \times 3)/4$. From this they carry out the following computations to get the answer they want: $(27 \times 3)/4 = \frac{81}{4} = 20\frac{1}{4}$ (yd).

The Mathematical Idea: Repeated Addition of Fractions

The book pack problem was solved by repeated addition of the fraction $\frac{3}{4}$ twenty-seven times. The answer is $(27 \times 3)/4$. The general rule is the following.

REPEATED ADDITION OF FRACTIONS

If A/B is a fraction and N a whole number, then

$$\underbrace{\frac{A}{B} + \frac{A}{B} + \cdots + \frac{A}{B}}_{N \text{ times}} = \frac{NA}{B}.$$

Because repeated addition of whole numbers corresponds to multiplication of whole numbers, we can define the product of a whole number with a fraction.

MULTIPLICATION OF A FRACTION BY A WHOLE NUMBER

The *product* of whole number N with fraction A/B is written $N\left(\dfrac{A}{B}\right)$ and is equal to $\dfrac{NA}{B}$.

EXERCISE

1. A certain recipe for a single cake calls for $\frac{2}{3}$ cup of milk. You are organizing a banquet at which 16 cakes will be needed. How much milk will you need for all these cakes?

THE GRADUATION PREDICTION PROBLEM

Solve this yourself, first.

During an orientation program at the beginning of the school year, the seventh graders were told that of all seventh graders who had entered the school in the past only $\frac{8}{15}$ eventually graduated. The students were interested in answering this question: If that trend were to continue, how many of the 135 students present at the program would eventually graduate? Help them solve this problem.

A Solution to the Graduation Prediction Problem

To solve this, the students realize that they must divide the set of 135 students up into 15 (disjoint) subsets with the same number of students in each and then take the union of 8 of those 15 subsets. Dividing 135 by 15, they get 9. That means that $\frac{1}{15}$ of 135 is 9. Taking 8 of these $\frac{1}{15}$ths, they get $8 \times 9 = 72$. So 72 of the 135 would eventually graduate if the trend continues.

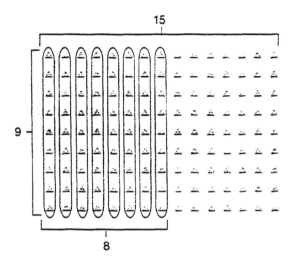

The Mathematical Idea: A Fraction of a Whole Number

The students solved this problem: If a set with 135 elements is the unit, what is $\frac{8}{15}$ of the unit? To solve it, you first find $135 \div 15$ and then you take 8 of what you get; that is, you repeatedly add $\frac{135}{15}$ eight times. The answer is $8 \times (\frac{135}{15})$.

A FRACTION OF A WHOLE NUMBER

If the unit is a whole number quantity N, then the fraction A/B of the unit is $N(A/B) = (NA)/B$.

EXERCISE

2. It is estimated that $\frac{2}{3}$ of the owners of your town's businesses are Republicans. In a certain service club there are 96 members. If the club's makeup reflects that of all business owners in the town, how many of its members should be Republicans?

THE GOLD LEAF PROBLEM

Try this yourself.

In the restoration of an antique picture frame a small rectangular area must be recovered with gold leaf. The cost of gold plating is $30 per square inch of surface. The rectangle measures $\frac{3}{4}$ by $\frac{2}{5}$ in. You want to know how much the gold leaf will cost you. You know about fractions, equivalent fractions, and how to add, subtract, and compare fractions. But that's all.

A Solution to the Gold Leaf Problem

You figure out that you must find the area of the rectangle. Toward this end you *draw a picture.*

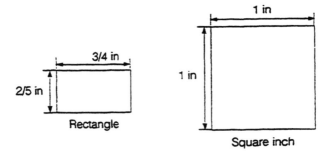

Your idea is to find out what fraction the area of the rectangle is of the square inch. You think "If the rectangle had half the area of the square inch, then the cost would be half as much, or $15; if the rectangle had the area of $\frac{1}{3}$ square inch, then the cost would be $\frac{1}{3}$ as much, or $10.

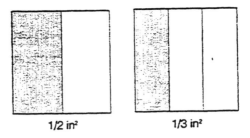

One of the sides of the rectangle is $\frac{3}{4}$ in. Let's divide a square inch up into $\frac{1}{4}$s like this

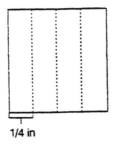

and then mark the width of the rectangle.

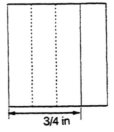

The other side of the rectangle is $\frac{2}{5}$ in. I can divide the square inch into $\frac{1}{5}$s in the other direction, then mark the length of the other side of the rectangle.

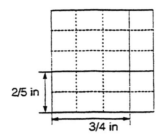

2/5 in

3/4 in

I can see the rectangle sitting inside the square inch. The lines I've drawn turn the square inch into a 5 by 4 array of little rectangles. All the little rectangles have the same area, and there are $5 \times 4 = 20$ of them, so each one must have an area of $\frac{1}{20}$ square inch. Now, all I have to do is count the number of little rectangles that appear in the rectangle. The lines divide the rectangle up into a 2 by 3 array of the same little rectangles, each one $\frac{1}{20}$ square inch. There are $2 \times 3 = 6$ of them in the rectangle. So the area of the rectangle is $\frac{6}{20}$ square inch."

EXERCISE

3. Complete the solution to the gold leaf problem by computing the cost of the gold leaf covering the rectangle.

THE ALCOHOL/TOBACCO CONSUMPTION PROBLEM

It is estimated that $\frac{2}{7}$ of the parents of school-age children smoke. It is also estimated that $\frac{4}{5}$ of those who smoke also consume alcohol. You want to know what fraction of the parents do both: smoke *and* consume alcohol. You know about fractions, equivalent fractions, and how to add, subtract, and compare fractions. You have also solved the gold leaf problem. But that's all. Can you solve this?

You think: "Maybe I can *use the solution to another problem.* I solved the gold leaf problem by showing how the rectangle fit into the square inch, the unit. Now the unit is the collection of all parents. Let me *draw a picture* of this unit—representing it by a square—and try to solve the problem as we did the gold leaf problem.

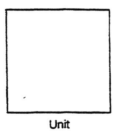

Unit

Some part of this square should represent the parents who smoke. I know that they amount to $\frac{2}{7}$ of the unit. Let me divide the unit into seven equal pieces, two of which represent the parents who smoke.

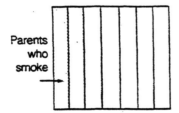

Parents who smoke →

I'm interested in $\frac{4}{5}$ of those folk. Just as in the solution to the gold leaf problem, let's divide up the unit horizontally into five equal strips.

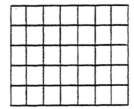

The horizontal lines also divide the smoking parents into five equal pieces. I'm interested in four of those. This represents a part of the unit corresponding to the parents who smoke *and* drink. That's the doubly shaded part of the picture.

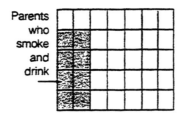

Now, to determine what fraction the doubly shaded part is of the whole square (the unit), I notice that the vertical and horizontal lines divide the unit into a 5 by 7 array of equal pieces. It divides the part representing parents who smoke *and* drink into a 4 by 2 array of those same equal pieces. Each one of those equal pieces is $1/(5 \times 7) = \frac{1}{35}$ of the unit. Parents who smoke *and* drink make up $2 \times 4 = 8$ of these $\frac{1}{35}$ths, or $\frac{8}{35}$ of all the parents (the unit)."

The Mathematical Idea: Multiplication of Fractions

Consider the two problems we have just worked:

- The gold leaf problem: The area of a rectangle of size $\frac{3}{4}$ by $\frac{2}{5}$ in equals $(3 \times 2)/(4 \times 5)$ square inch.
- The alcohol/tobacco consumption problem: $\frac{4}{5}$ of $\frac{2}{7}$ of a unit (that is, all the parents) equals $(4 \times 2)/(5 \times 7)$ of the unit.

What we observed were instances of two general rules:

1. The area of a rectangle of width A/B of an inch and length C/D of an inch is $\frac{AC}{BD}$ square inch:

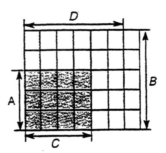

2. Given a fraction A/B of a unit, then the fraction C/D of A/B is the following fraction of the unit: $\dfrac{AC}{BD}$.

Because $(AC)/(BD)$ is the answer to so many problems that include the fractions A/B and C/D as part of their data, we make the following definition.

DEFINITION OF MULTIPLICATION OF FRACTIONS

$(AC)/(BD)$ is the *product* of A/B and C/D. We write

$$\frac{A}{B} \times \frac{C}{D} = \left(\frac{A}{B}\right)\left(\frac{C}{D}\right) = \frac{A}{B} \cdot \frac{C}{D} = \frac{AC}{BD}.$$

We also say that $(AC)/(BD)$ is the result of *multiplying* A/B times C/D.

This definition of multiplication is consistent with the multiplication of a fraction by a whole number, provided we make the following agreement. We have already included whole numbers as fractions: $1 = \frac{2}{2}$, $3 = \frac{12}{4}$, and so on. One can also think of a whole number N as the fraction $N/1$ so that, for example, $1 = \frac{1}{1}$ and $3 = \frac{3}{1}$. This is consistent with the fraction $N/1$ being the answer to the whole number division problem $N \div 1$. Agreeing to write $N = N/1$ enables us to rewrite the equation

$$N\left(\frac{A}{B}\right) = \frac{NA}{B}$$

as

$$\left(\frac{N}{1}\right)\left(\frac{A}{B}\right) = \frac{N \times A}{1 \times B}$$

and thus to see that multiplication of a fraction by a whole number is an instance of the multiplication of two fractions.

The book pack and the graduation prediction problems can be solved using multiplication of fractions, thusly:

■ The book pack problem: Repeated addition of $\frac{3}{4}$ twenty-seven times equals $(27 \times 3)/4 = (27 \times 3)/(1 \times 4) = \left(\frac{27}{1}\right)\left(\frac{3}{4}\right)$.

■ The graduation prediction problem: The unit is the set of 135 individual students; $\frac{8}{15}$ of the unit consists of $(8 \times 135)/15$ individual students. What is more, $(8 \times 135)/15 = (8 \times 135)/(15 \times 1) = \left(\frac{8}{15}\right)\left(\frac{135}{1}\right)$.

Here is another problem in which some of these ideas are used.

THE GAS TANK PROBLEM

Try this.

Your car gets $15\frac{2}{3}$ mi/gal. You have just put $5\frac{3}{4}$ gal of gasoline into an empty tank. You want to know how far you can go on that amount of gas. You know all about multiplication of fractions. How would you solve this?

A Solution to the
Gas Tank Problem

You think: "Each gallon will enable me to go $15\frac{2}{3}$ miles. So 5 gallons should enable me to go $5 \times 15\frac{2}{3}$ miles. I know how to figure that out:

$$5 \times 15\frac{2}{3} = 5 \times \frac{47}{3} = \frac{5 \times 47}{3} = \frac{235}{3} = 78\frac{1}{3} \text{ (miles)}.$$

"But what about that extra $\frac{3}{4}$ gallon? If I can go $15\frac{2}{3}$ miles with 1 gallon, then I should be able to go $\frac{3}{4}$ of $15\frac{2}{3}$ miles with $\frac{3}{4}$ gallon. How do I figure out $\frac{3}{4}$ of a unit when the unit is an improper fraction? Let me *draw a picture*.

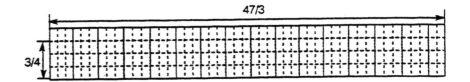

"Each teeny rectangle in the picture represents $\frac{1}{12}$ gallon. There are $3 \times 47 = 141$ of these teeny rectangles in the part of the picture that represents $\frac{3}{4}$ of $\frac{47}{3}$. Thus $\frac{3}{4}$ of $\frac{47}{3}$ equals $\frac{141}{12}$. Moreover,

$$\frac{141}{12} = \frac{3 \times 47}{4 \times 3} = \frac{3}{4} \times \frac{47}{3}.$$

Multiplication of fractions is appropriate even when the fractions are improper.
"The complete answer to the problem is this:

$$\frac{235}{3} + \frac{141}{12} = \frac{235 \times 4}{3 \times 4} + \frac{141}{12}$$

$$= \frac{940}{12} + \frac{141}{12}$$

$$= \frac{1081}{12}$$

$$= 90\frac{1}{12}$$

I can go $90\frac{1}{12}$ miles with $5\frac{3}{4}$ gallons of gasoline."

The Mathematical Idea: Some Properties of Multiplication of Fractions

The solution to the gas tank problem could have been solved directly this way: The answer is just the product of the fraction $15\frac{2}{3}$ and the fraction $5\frac{3}{4}$,

$$15\frac{2}{3} \times 5\frac{3}{4} = \frac{47}{3} \times \frac{23}{4} = \frac{47 \times 23}{3 \times 4} = \frac{1081}{12} = 90\frac{1}{12}.$$

Jim, who was the person solving the problem, may have hesitated to use this solution because he felt more comfortable *breaking the problem up into smaller ones* (not at all a bad strategy) or he was not sure that the rules for multiplication of fractions applied to mixed numbers. Indeed, the examples that led up to the definition of fraction multiplication involved factors neither of which were mixed numbers. In any case, Jim's solution shows that repeated addition of $15\frac{2}{3}$ five times is

$$5 \times \frac{47}{3} = \frac{5}{1} \times \frac{47}{3}$$

and that $\frac{3}{4}$ of $15\frac{2}{3}$ is the same as

$$\frac{3}{4} \times \frac{47}{3}.$$

Jim then added these two together to get the answer. We now know that the sum of these two is just $5\frac{3}{4} \times 15\frac{2}{3}$. In other words,

$$\left(5\frac{3}{4}\right)\left(15\frac{2}{3}\right) = \left(\frac{5}{1} + \frac{3}{4}\right)\frac{47}{3} = \left(\frac{5}{1}\right)\left(\frac{47}{3}\right) + \left(\frac{3}{4}\right)\left(\frac{47}{3}\right).$$

From the chapter on multiplication of whole numbers, you recognize that the latter equation is an instance of the distributive law for fractions.

MULTIPLICATION OF FRACTIONS DISTRIBUTES OVER ADDITION OF FRACTIONS

For all fractions A/B, C/D, and E/F,

$$\left(\frac{A}{B} + \frac{C}{D}\right)\frac{E}{F} = \left(\frac{A}{B}\right)\left(\frac{E}{F}\right) + \left(\frac{C}{D}\right)\left(\frac{E}{F}\right).$$

There are two more rules that are useful in working with fractions.

MULTIPLICATION OF FRACTIONS IS COMMUTATIVE

For all fractions A/B and C/D,

$$\frac{A}{B} \cdot \frac{C}{D} = \frac{C}{D} \cdot \frac{A}{B}.$$

MULTIPLICATION OF FRACTIONS IS ASSOCIATIVE

For all fractions A/B, C/D, and E/F,

$$\left(\frac{A}{B} \cdot \frac{C}{D}\right)\frac{E}{F} = \frac{A}{B}\left(\frac{C}{D} \cdot \frac{E}{F}\right).$$

EXERCISES

4. A certain kitchen counter-top material is sold by the square foot. How many square feet are there in a piece of material $1\frac{2}{3}$ by $3\frac{3}{4}$ ft?

5. Market researchers claim that $\frac{3}{8}$ of all adults use Fluorana regularly. Dental researchers claim that of all adults who use Fluorana regularly $\frac{2}{5}$ experience significant reduction in tooth decay. What fraction of the adult population experiences significant reduction in tooth decay while using Fluorana?

6. A woman who hikes at the rate of $2\frac{1}{3}$ mph has been hiking for $3\frac{5}{6}$ h (or 3 h and 50 min). How far has she hiked during that time?

9.2 DIVISION OF FRACTIONS

Four Partially Solved Missing Factor Problems

Each of the following four problems has an incomplete solution. To complete each, one must find a fraction (?) satisfying an equation of the form $\frac{A}{B} \times (?) = \frac{C}{D}$.

1. THE SHIRT PROBLEM

The Hathaway Shirt Company has $5\frac{2}{3}$ yd left of a special oxford cloth. The foreman in charge wants to know how many shirts the company can make with this material. Each shirt requires $\frac{3}{4}$ yd of the material. Help the foreman solve this problem.

A Partial Solution to the Shirt Problem

The foreman realizes that if N is the number of shirts that can be made, then N is the number of times that $\frac{3}{4}$ can be subtracted from $5\frac{2}{3}$. From this he concludes that $5\frac{2}{3} = \frac{3}{4} \times N$ plus whatever is left over (less than $\frac{3}{4}$ yd).

2. THE FENCE PROBLEM

The fence in your backyard needs to be painted. You have a gallon of fencing paint. The label on the can says 1 gal will paint 100 ft² of fence. Your fence is $5\frac{3}{4}$ ft high. How many feet along the fence can you paint with the 1 gal?

A Partial Solution to the Fence Problem

You *draw a picture* of your fence.

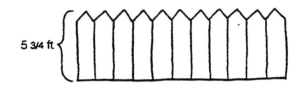

5 3/4 ft

You think: If I can paint (?) feet along the fence, then I know that the area I paint will be equal to 100 square feet. That means $5\frac{3}{4} \times (?) = 100$.

3. THE BILINGUAL PROBLEM   It is estimated that $\frac{3}{8}$ of the population of the city speak both Spanish and English. It is also estimated that $\frac{9}{10}$ of those who speak Spanish also speak English. You want to know what fraction of the population speaks Spanish.

A Partial Solution to the Bilingual Problem   You *draw a picture* (a square) of the unit, the entire population of the city.

Inside the square you draw a circle representing the fraction $\frac{3}{8}$ of the population.

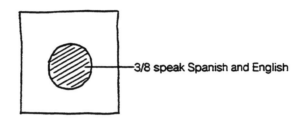

You want to indicate the fraction S of the population who speak Spanish. You know that this part must include the $\frac{3}{8}$ who speak *both* Spanish and English. You draw a larger circle inside the square that encloses the smaller one you have just drawn.

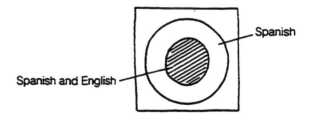

Now you look at the other piece of information that you have: $\frac{9}{10}$ of the Spanish-speaking population also speaks English. *That* would be the $\frac{3}{8}$ you've got drawn in. So if S is the fraction in the larger circle, then

$$\frac{9}{10} \text{ of } S = \frac{3}{8} \quad \text{or} \quad \frac{9}{10} \times S = \frac{3}{8}.$$

4. THE ARTICHOKE PROBLEM   You know that a $7\frac{3}{4}$-oz jar of marinated artichoke hearts costs $6\frac{1}{2}$. You are comparison shopping and you want to know how much 1 oz costs.

You figure out that if the answer were C dollars, then C times $7\frac{3}{4}$ would equal $6\frac{1}{2}$.

$$7\frac{3}{4} \times C = 6\frac{1}{2}.$$

The Mathematical Idea: Solving Missing Factor Problems

The solution to all four of these problems can be cast in this form: Given fractions A/B and C/D, find a fraction S such that

$$\frac{A}{B} \times S = \frac{C}{D}.$$

Such a problem is called a *missing factor* problem, in which the product and one of the factors of a multiplication problem are given. Such situations arise often enough that it would be nice to have a general technique for solving them. We have already seen the analogous problem for whole numbers: For whole numbers N and M find a whole number Y such that $NY = M$. We know that the solution to this equation (when it has a whole number solution) can be gotten by division: $Y = M \div N$. This suggests that, if the equation

$$\frac{A}{B} \times S = \frac{C}{D}$$

has a solution S, then perhaps it can be obtained by division of fractions:

$$S = \frac{C}{D} \div \frac{A}{B}.$$

This begs the question: What is

$$\frac{C}{D} \div \frac{A}{B}?$$

Now *we* know the answer to this. But how do we arrive at the answer using only the knowledge of fractions that has been developed so far? Let's try to solve the artichoke problem with what we have developed so far. We want to find a fraction S so that $7\frac{3}{4} \times S = 6\frac{1}{2}$ or, what is the same, $\frac{31}{4} \times S = \frac{13}{2}$.

To get a clue, let's try to *solve a simpler problem.* How about $\frac{31}{4} \times T = 1$? To solve this, replace T with A/B so that

$$\frac{31}{4} \times \frac{A}{B} = 1.$$

Then multiply it out:

$$\frac{31A}{4B} = 1.$$

In order that $(31A)/(4B) = 1$, the whole numbers $31A$ and $4B$ must be the same: $31A = 4B$. Numbers A and B that make this last equation work are $A = 4$ and $B = 31$: $31 \times 4 = 4 \times 31$. A solution to

$$\frac{31}{4} \times \frac{A}{B} = 1$$

is $A/B = \frac{4}{31}$ so that

$$\frac{31}{4} \times \frac{4}{31} = 1.$$

Will that help us with the original problem

$$\frac{31}{4} \times S = \frac{13}{2}?$$

Since

$$\frac{31}{4} \times \frac{4}{31} = 1 \qquad \text{and} \qquad 1 \times \frac{13}{2} = \frac{13}{2},$$

$$\left(\frac{31}{4} \times \frac{4}{31}\right) \times \frac{13}{2} = \frac{13}{2}.$$

Using the associative property to write the left-hand side of the last equation another way, we have

$$\frac{31}{4} \times \left(\frac{4}{31} \times \frac{13}{2}\right) = \frac{13}{2}.$$

The fraction

$$\frac{4}{31} \times \frac{13}{2} = \frac{52}{62} = S$$

is what we are looking for. This means 1 oz of marinated artichokes costs $\$\frac{52}{62}$!

Reciprocals and Division of Fractions

The general problem is: Given A/B and C/D, find a fraction S so that

$$\frac{A}{B} \times S = \frac{C}{D}.$$

The major breakthrough in solving $\frac{31}{4} \times S = \frac{13}{2}$ was in *solving a simpler problem* $\frac{31}{4} \times T = 1$ with $T = \frac{4}{31}$. To solve the general equation

$$\frac{A}{B} \times T = 1 \qquad \text{with } A \neq 0 \text{ and } B \neq 0,$$

we notice that

$$\frac{A}{B} \times \frac{B}{A} = 1$$

so that $T = B/A$. This solution is so important that we make the following definition.

DEFINITION OF RECIPROCAL

For $B \neq 0$ and $A \neq 0$ the fraction B/A is called the *reciprocal* of the fraction A/B. It has the property $A/B \times B/A = 1$.

So $\frac{4}{31}$ is the reciprocal of $\frac{31}{4}$. How do we go from knowing this, that

$$\frac{A}{B} \times \frac{B}{A} = 1$$

to solving

$$\frac{A}{B} \times S = \frac{C}{D}?$$

Since $1 \times \frac{C}{D} = \frac{C}{D}$, we have

$$\left(\frac{A}{B} \times \frac{B}{A}\right) \times \frac{C}{D} = \frac{C}{D},$$

which, using the associative property of multiplication, we can rewrite as

$$\frac{A}{B} \times \left(\frac{B}{A} \times \frac{C}{D}\right) = \frac{C}{D}.$$

The fraction $\frac{B}{A} \times \frac{C}{D}$ is our answer. Using the commutative property of multiplication we can also write the answer as

$$\frac{C}{D} \times \frac{B}{A}.$$

We can summarize this.

DIVISION OF FRACTIONS

If $A \neq 0$ and $B \neq 0$, the *division of* fraction C/D by fraction A/B is denoted by

$$\frac{C}{D} \div \frac{A}{B}$$

and is equal to

$$\frac{C}{D} \times \frac{B}{A}.$$

It is the solution S to

$$\frac{A}{B} \times S = \frac{C}{D}.$$

To check an answer to a fraction division problem, you remember that the answer is supposed to solve a missing factor problem—the last equation in the box. Plug your answer into the equation. If it works, you have the right answer. If not, you have a wrong answer.

We now know that the four problems with the partial solutions can be solved by division of fractions.

Something to Watch Out For in Division of Fractions

You recall that the solution to the shirt problem was reduced to: Find a whole number N and a fraction C/D such that $5\frac{2}{3} = \frac{3}{4} \times N + C/D$, where C/D is a fraction that is less than $\frac{3}{4}$.

Let's carry out the division of fractions to find the answer to the missing factor problem $5\frac{2}{3} = \frac{3}{4} \times$ [?].

$$5\frac{2}{3} \div \frac{3}{4} = \frac{17}{3} \div \frac{3}{4} = \frac{17}{3} \times \frac{4}{3} = \frac{68}{9} = 7\frac{5}{9}.$$

This means that, by the distributive law,

$$5\frac{2}{3} = \frac{3}{4} \times 7\frac{5}{9} = \frac{3}{4}\left(7 + \frac{5}{9}\right) = \frac{3}{4} \times 7 + \frac{3}{4} \times \frac{5}{9}.$$

Consequently, the company can make $N = 7$ shirts out of the $5\frac{2}{3}$ yd. The amount of material that will be left over (and wasted) is

$$\frac{3}{4} \times \frac{5}{9} = \frac{15}{36} = \frac{5}{12} \text{ yd.}$$

Notice that $C/D = \frac{5}{12}$. It is not $\frac{5}{9}$ yd that is left over but $\frac{5}{12}$ yd. (However, $\frac{5}{12}$ yd is $\frac{5}{9}$ the amount of material needed to make a whole shirt.) Division of fractions will find N, the whole number part of the answer but not the fractional leftover as was asked for in the original problem. You have to do a little additional work as we did in the preceding solution.

EXERCISES

7. A social worker has $15\frac{3}{4}$ lb of surplus cheese that he wants to divide equally among four families. He wants to know how much each family should get. Find out.

8. A garden row $15\frac{1}{2}$ m (meter, meters) long is to be planted with cabbage plants. The plants must be planted with a space of $\frac{2}{3}$ m between them. How many cabbage plants will be planted in the row?

9. You are an outdoor painter. One job you do is put protective coating on wooden fences. You estimate that you can coat about 75 ft^2 of fencing in an hour. A prospective customer has a fence that is $5\frac{2}{3}$ ft high. What length of this fencing can you coat in 1 hr?

10. If $\frac{5}{8}$ of the children in Norway are blue-eyed blonds, and $\frac{9}{10}$ of the blond children in Norway have blue eyes, what fraction of the children in Norway are blond?

11. You drove your car 153 mi and used $10\frac{3}{4}$ gal of gas. If this were typical driving for you, how many miles could you drive on 1 gal?

9.3   MORE ON RATIOS: SCALE DRAWINGS AND RATIOS OF LENGTHS

Here are two photographs.

A

B

Photo A is a *reduction* of photo B. Equivalently, photo B is an *enlargement* of photo A. One is a *scale drawing* of the other. This means that the ratio of the height of A to the height of B is the same as the ratio of the width of A to the width of B. It also means that the ratio of any other pair of corresponding lengths in the two photos is the same as the ratio of the height of A to the height of B. Let's see how all this works with some specific measurements.

A

B

In the case of these particular photos the ratio of the width of A to the width of B is 3 to 5. Here are some phrases that mean the same thing.

- The width of A is $\frac{3}{5}$ the width of B.
- The width of A is $\frac{3}{5}$ times the width of B.
- The ratio of the width of B to the width of A is 5 to 3.
- The width of B is $\frac{5}{3}$ the width of A.
- The width of B is $1\frac{2}{3}$ the width of A.
- The width of B is $1\frac{2}{3}$ times the width of A.

Let's look at a problem involving ratios and scale drawings.

Roberto lives in Santa Fe. He is in the sixth grade and is working on a project having to do with agricultural uses of land in New Mexico. He has a small copy of the map of the state but needs to make a much larger version on which he can record all his accumulated data. The map he wants to enlarge is shown below.

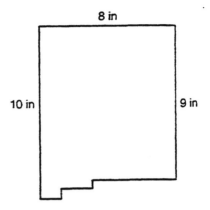

8 in

10 in   9 in

Solve this yourself, first.

He has decided that he wants the length of the northern boundary of the state for the larger version to be 20 in. He wants to know what the lengths of the other sides should be in order that the enlarged map be a scale drawing of the smaller one. He knows about ratios. Help him solve this.

A Solution to the Enlargement Problem

Roberto measures the northern boundary of the small map and finds that it is 8 in long. He thinks: "The northern boundary of the larger map is 20 in and that of the smaller map is 8 inches. That means that 20 in in the larger corresponds to 8 inches in the smaller map. That's a ratio of 20 to 8. So the length of the larger is $\frac{20}{8}$ of the smaller. But $\frac{20}{8} = \frac{5}{2} = 2\frac{1}{2}$. So the larger is $2\frac{1}{2}$ times the length of the smaller. That means that when I measure the western side of the smaller map, the length of the western side of the enlarged map should be $2\frac{1}{2}$ times as large. The ratio of the length of the western side of the large map to the length of the western side of the small map should be $\frac{5}{2}$ or 5 to 2. Let's see, the length of the western side of the small map is 10 inches.

"That means that the western side of the enlarged map should be 10 in $\times \frac{5}{2} = 25$ in. That solves the problem."

EXERCISE

12. What should the eastern boundary of the state in the large version be?

Scale Drawings: The Choice of the Unit Length

For the two photos we saw earlier, the ratio of the widths was easy to figure out. The width of A was marked off into 3 pieces of equal length and the width of B was marked off into 5 pieces of the same length. The ratio of the width of A to the width of B was 3 to 5.

In the case of the two maps, the ratio of lengths was also easy to figure out. The northern boundary of the large map was 20 in, and the northern boundary of the small map was 8 in. The ratio of the larger to the smaller was 20 to 8.

In both these situations a *unit of length* was found so that the two lengths in question were equal to a whole number of those units. In the case of the photos the unit of length was not given a name but was suggested by the markings in the picture.

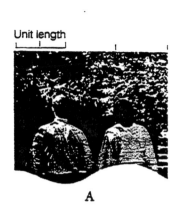

A

B

For the maps, the unit length was equal to an inch.

In the next problem the choice of unit length is not obvious.

A RATIO OF LENGTHS
PROBLEM

You know that the distance from A to B is $5\frac{3}{4}$ ft and that the distance from C to D is $9\frac{2}{3}$ ft.

A ———————————————————————————— B
C ———————————————————————————————————— D

You want to find the ratio of the length of *AB* to the length of *CD*. How can you solve this?

You know that if the distance from A to B were 4 ft and the distance from C to D were 10 ft, then the ratio of the length of *AB* to the length of *CD* would be 4 to 10 or $\frac{4}{10}$. The problem is to chop up the $5\frac{3}{4}$ and the $9\frac{2}{3}$ into lengths of equal size; the problem is to find a suitable unit of length. You think: "Let's look at those fractional lengths a little more closely: $5\frac{3}{4} = \frac{23}{4}$ and $9\frac{2}{3} = \frac{29}{3}$. If I had fractions $\frac{23}{4}$ and $\frac{29}{4}$ instead, then there would be no problem: a natural common unit would be $\frac{1}{4}$ foot and the ratio would be $\frac{23}{29}$.

"What I need to do is find a common denominator for the fractions $\frac{23}{4}$ and $\frac{29}{3}$, and use equal fractions. A common denominator is $4 \times 3 = 12$ and

$$\frac{23}{4} = \frac{23 \times 3}{4 \times 3} = \frac{69}{12} \quad \text{and} \quad \frac{29}{3} = \frac{29 \times 4}{3 \times 4} = \frac{116}{12}.$$

I can use $\frac{1}{12}$ of a foot as my unit of length. Then the ratio of the smaller to the longer of the two lengths is 69 to 116, or $\frac{69}{116}$."

The Mathematical Idea: Ratios of Lengths and Division of Fractions

Suppose you have two lengths: A/B units of length and C/D units of length. You are interested in the ratios of the first length to the second. The preceding solution suggests a general method for figuring out this ratio, namely, find a common denominator and use equal fractions. For these two fractions one common denominator is BD, so that

$$\frac{A}{B} = \frac{AD}{BD} \quad \text{and} \quad \frac{C}{D} = \frac{CB}{DB}.$$

A common unit of length is $1/BD$ and the ratio of the first length to the second is AD to CB or $(AD)/(CB)$. But the latter fraction is just $(AD)/(BC)$, which is equal to

$$\frac{A}{B} \div \frac{C}{D}.$$

We can make a statement about the situation.

RATIOS AND FRACTION DIVISION

The ratio of length A/B units to length C/D units is the fraction

$$\frac{A}{B} \div \frac{C}{D}.$$

EXERCISE   13. A photograph that is $5\frac{3}{4}$ by $8\frac{3}{8}$ in is to be reduced to a picture having its shorter side equal to $2\frac{1}{2}$ in. What is the ratio of the length of the reduced side to the length of the original? What should the other dimension of the reduced picture be?

We have labeled lots of points on the number line with fractions. Imagine labeling all the points of the number line that correspond to fractions (all infinity of them). Is there a point on the number line that is not labeled with a fraction?

We know what the answer would be if we replaced "fractions" by "whole numbers." Between any two consecutive whole numbers—such as 2000 and 2001 there is a "hole," a space between the two points labeled 2000 and 2001.

Points labeled by fractions differ from points labeled by whole numbers. In the last chapter we discussed the density property of fractions: Between any two different fractions there must be a third fraction, different from the other two. That means that between any two points corresponding to different fractions on the number line, *no matter how close the two fractions are*, there is always a third point strictly between the two corresponding to a fraction. In fact, we have seen that there are infinitely many fraction points between even very close fractions.

It seems reasonable that if you select any point on the number line, you will always find a fraction to which it corresponds. This is what the Pythagoreans, a Greek sect from around 500 B.C., assumed. Their worldview was built on the assumption that everything could be reduced to fractions (*ratio* was the term they used). Here is a story about the Pythagoreans and the difficulties this assumption about fractions and points on the number line brought them.

On the interval from 0 to 1 on the number line, the Pythagoreans built a square.

Then they cut the square into halves along a diagonal.

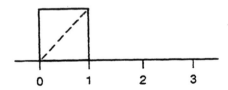

After that, they took one of the half squares and lay the diagonal side on the number line, with one end at 0, like this:

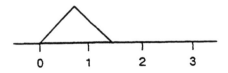

The other end of the diagonal side touches a point of the number line, and so corresponds to a fraction A/B.

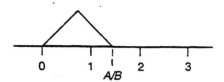

The Pythagoreans wanted to know what the fraction A/B was; they wanted to know its numerator and its denominator. To keep things specific, they decided that A/B should be a fraction reduced to lowest terms, that is, the GCD of A and B should be 1. Then they gathered some more information about A/B. First of all, they knew that A/B was the length of the diagonal of the original square. After some playing around, they took two copies of the original square, cut them along their diagonals, and arranged them like this.

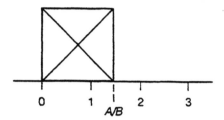

The four pieces formed a larger square! Immediately, the Pythagoreans sought to determine what new insight this fact would give them as to the identity of the fraction A/B. The first thing they noted was that the large square, having A/B for a side, had area equal to $(A/B)^2$ units. Next, they noted that the original smaller square, having a length of 1 for each side, had area 1 unit^2. Thus, two of the smaller squares put together would have 2 units^2. At the same time, the two smaller squares—cut up and the pieces rearranged—make the large square.

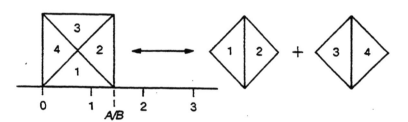

The large square has area 2 and also area $(A/B)^2$. Thus,

$$2 = \frac{A}{B} \times \frac{A}{B} = \frac{A^2}{B^2}.$$

They were excited. They were getting somewhere. They stared at the equation

$$2 = \frac{A^2}{B^2}$$

a bit and realized that they could multiply both sides by B^2 and arrive at the equation in whole numbers $2B^2 = A^2$.

At this point they realized they could use all they knew about multiples and divisors of whole numbers. First they recalled that the GCD of A and B is 1. Since $2|2B^2$, $2|A^2$ also. And, since $2|A^2$, it must also be that $2|A$ (how could it be otherwise?). So $A = 2C$, for some whole number C, and $2B^2 = (2C)(2C) = (2)(2)C^2$.

Consequently (the excitement was rising), $B^2 = 2C^2$.

Then, noticing that the latter equation is similar to the original equation in whole numbers $2B^2 = A^2$, they used the same argument to get that $B = 2D$. At this point they stopped dead in their tracks, horrified at what they saw. Here's what they had: GCD of A and B is 1; $2|A$; $2|B$.

"Something must be wrong!" someone shouted. "A and B can't both have 2 as a common divisor and at the same time have a GCD equal to 1." They went back and looked again at everything they had done. Everything was O.K. Every conclusion they had reached—assuming that the point on the number line corresponded to fraction A/B—was correct. The only thing that could be wrong was the initial assumption itself. They were forced to conclude that the point on the number line does not correspond to a fraction!

This discovery—that some points on the number line do not correspond to fractions, that labeling points on a number line with fractions leaves holes—shattered the worldview of some leaders of the Pythagoreans and threatened to challenge the influence of the religious sect. The story goes that people who breathed a word of this discovery would be put to death.

Of course, we know the story in the following shortened (and dull) form: "If X is the length of the diagonal of a square of side one, then $X^2 = 2$; that is, X is the square root of 2. The square root of 2 is known to be *irrational* (meaning, 'not a ratio,' 'not a fraction')."

Many other points on the number line do not correspond to fractions. Numbers that correspond to such points are called *irrational numbers*. The totality of all numbers corresponding to the points of our number line to the right of zero are called the *positive real numbers*. There will be more on the real numbers in a later chapter.

EXERCISES

21. Suppose length X is not a fraction. Show that length $X + 1$ is also not a fraction.

22. If length X is not a fraction, show that length $5X$ is not a fraction.

23. Use the ideas and results from exercises 21 and 22 to show that there are infinitely many irrational numbers.

24. Suppose that Y is a length such that $Y^2 = 3$. Is Y a fraction or isn't it? Why or why not?

25. Suppose that Z is a length such that $Z^2 = 4$. Is Z a fraction or isn't it? Why or why not?

9.7   SUMMARY OF IMPORTANT IDEAS AND TECHNIQUES

■ Multiplication of fractions: $\dfrac{A}{B} \times \dfrac{C}{D} = \dfrac{AC}{BD}$

■ Division of fractions: $\dfrac{A}{B} \div \dfrac{C}{D} = \dfrac{A}{B} \times \dfrac{D}{C}$

- Properties and ideas associated with operations with fractions: distributive, commutative, and associative properties satisfied by multiplication of fractions, 1 as multiplicative identity
- That a nonzero fraction A/B has a multiplicative inverse (or reciprocal) equal to B/A, enabling every missing factor problem involving fractions to have a solution that is also a fraction
- Similarity between multiplication of whole numbers and multiplication of fractions in satisfying a law relating it to the order of fractions
- Using the properties to solve equations involving unknown fractions and to estimate fraction products and quotients
- Use of operations with ratios
- Definitions of generalized and algebraic fractions, their properties
- Irrational numbers

PROBLEM SET

PRACTICING
SKILLS

1. A metal alloy company has received an order for 175 lb of an alloy that is $\frac{4}{7}$ aluminum. How much aluminum will be needed to make this much of the alloy?

2. A certain rug material costs \$15/yd^2. How much will a rug that measures $1\frac{3}{4}$ by $2\frac{2}{3}$ yd cost?

3. About $\frac{2}{5}$ of the student body smokes. Roughly $\frac{3}{4}$ of those who smoke also consume alcohol. What fraction of the student body smokes and drinks alcohol?

4. Sam runs at a rate of $9\frac{3}{5}$ mph. He has been running for 42 min. How far has he run?

5. A textile worker makes vests out of a manufactured leatherette fabric. She has $3\frac{1}{2}$ yd of the material on hand. Each vest uses $\frac{5}{8}$ yd of the leatherette. How many vests can she make? How much fabric will she have left over?

6. An electronics technician can assemble a microcomputer in $1\frac{2}{3}$ hr. How many can he assemble in a 35-hr work week?

7. The height of a row of bricks is $2\frac{5}{8}$ in. Mortar between each row is $\frac{3}{4}$ in. How many rows of bricks will be needed to build a wall 5 ft high?

8. The circumference of a circle (the distance around the circle) is about $\frac{22}{7}$ times its diameter. How big must the diameter of a circle be if the circumference is to be $5\frac{3}{4}$ ft?

9. A farmer raises chickens, geese, and goats. There are $\frac{2}{3}$ as many chickens as geese and $\frac{4}{5}$ as many chickens as goats. She raises 80 goats. How many chickens and geese does she raise?

10. A photograph that is $3\frac{1}{4}$ by $7\frac{5}{16}$ in is to be enlarged to a picture having its longer side equal to $15\frac{1}{2}$ in. What is the ratio of the length of the enlarged side to the length of the original? What should the other dimension of the enlarged picture be?

11. Solve the following equations. Express your answer in simplest terms.
    (a) $(\frac{3}{5})A + \frac{8}{15} = \frac{5}{6}$ (b) $(\frac{3}{16})B + \frac{3}{4} = \frac{6}{7}$ (c) $(\frac{2}{7})C + \frac{5}{8} = \frac{10}{9}$

12. Estimate the answers to the following fraction problems. Give upper and lower bounds for each.
    (a) $(11\frac{2}{9}) \times (6\frac{4}{5})$ (b) $(7\frac{8}{15}) \times (4\frac{12}{13})$ (c) $(53\frac{3}{4}) \div (10\frac{7}{12})$ (d) $(86\frac{6}{7}) \div (8\frac{1}{6})$

13. For each of the following expressions, find the fraction equal to it. Your answer should be in lowest terms.

(a) $\dfrac{\frac{5}{2}}{\frac{7}{6}} + \dfrac{\frac{1}{3}}{\frac{10}{9}}$

(b) $\dfrac{\frac{1}{8}}{\frac{3}{5}} + \dfrac{\frac{1}{6}}{\frac{5}{2}}$

(c) $\dfrac{(\frac{5}{2} \times \frac{1}{3})}{(\frac{7}{6} \times \frac{10}{9})}$

(d) $\dfrac{(\frac{3}{4} \times \frac{3}{8})}{(\frac{12}{5} \times \frac{3}{16})}$

14. Express each of the following algebraic fractions in simplest terms.

(a) $\dfrac{56a^3b}{64ab}$

(b) $\dfrac{25(c+d)^2}{5c+5d}$

(c) $\dfrac{x^3y^2}{x^2y}$

(d) $\dfrac{w+wy}{(1+y)^2}$

15. Solve for r_1 in terms of R and r_2 if

$$\frac{1}{R} = \frac{1}{r_1} + \frac{1}{r_2}.$$

USING IDEAS   *For each of the remaining problems, document as clearly and completely as you can your solution to the problem. Include the steps you took to solve the problem, mention the problems or solutions from the text that gave you ideas, and include the problem-solving strategies you used. You might want to outline and organize these details before assembling your final report in the form of an essay.*

16. Indicate which fraction product the doubly shaded portion of each picture illustrates.

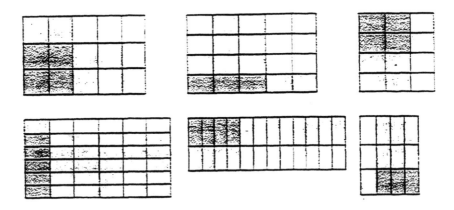

17. Draw a picture, similar to those in problem 16, illustrating each of the following fraction products.

(a) $\dfrac{2}{3} \times \dfrac{4}{7} = \dfrac{8}{21}$

(b) $\dfrac{3}{4} \times \dfrac{2}{5} = \dfrac{6}{20}$

(c) $\dfrac{1}{3} \times \dfrac{1}{3} = \dfrac{1}{9}$

18. A water purification plant works by passing the dirty water through two filters in turn. The first takes out all but $\frac{1}{4}$ of the dirt in the water and the second leaves $\frac{1}{3}$ of the dirt reaching it. What fraction of the dirt is left in the water after it has gone through the plant?

19. Four of five criminal cases are misdemeanors. The remainder are felonies. Two-thirds of all felony cases are solved, but $\frac{2}{3}$ of all misdemeanors are not solved. What is the fraction of all crimes that are solved?

20. You are building a cabinet that is to be 33 in high. It is to have a 4-in-thick base and a $2\frac{1}{2}$-in top. Four equally sized drawers must fit in the remaining space, with $1\frac{1}{4}$ in between drawers. You want to know what the height of each drawer should be.

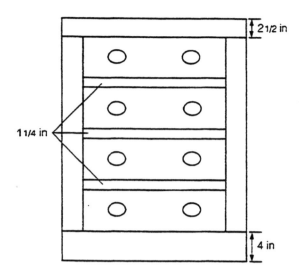

21. An old and very finicky natural gas compressor in an oil field burns a fuel mixture that must be precisely $\frac{2}{3}$ gasoline and $\frac{1}{3}$ oil. After the cranky machine failed to operate, the head roustabout took a look at the fuel tank and discovered that some of the gas had evaporated, leaving 4 gal of evenly mixed oil and gas. How much gas should the roustabout add to the tank to satisfy the compressor?[*]

22. The doctor prescribes a 1000-ml (milliliter, milliliters) intravenous bottle to be given to a patient over an 8-hr period. The nurse must set the drip rate of the bottle. Each milliliter contains 15 drops. How many drops per minute should there be?[†]

23. Before the active ingredient in a well-known nose drops medicine is sold over the counter, it is diluted with distilled water. One solution is made for children and another for adults. For children, the active ingredient is $\frac{1}{3}$ the solution. For adults, the active ingredient is $\frac{1}{2}$ the solution. A pharmacist is temporarily out of the solution for children and out of the pure active ingredient. He does have sufficient supplies of the adult solution, and he has lots of distilled water. He needs to dispense 100 ml of the child's solution. How can he do that?

24. A metallurgist has two tin-copper alloys. Alloy A is $\frac{1}{4}$ tin; alloy B is $\frac{1}{2}$ tin. He wants to make 40 lb of a tin-copper alloy that is $\frac{1}{3}$ tin by melting certain amounts of alloy A and B and mixing them together. How much of alloy A and B should he melt?

25. A martini is made with 5 units of gin and 1 unit of vermouth. You want to know what fraction of a martini is alcohol. You know that gin is $\frac{2}{5}$ alcohol and vermouth is $\frac{1}{6}$ alcohol.

---

[*] From Deborah Hughes Hallet, *The Math Workshop*, Norton, New York, prob. 30, p. 271.
[†] From Hal Saunders, *When Are We Ever Gonna Have to Use This?*, HMS Publications, Santa Barbara, Calif, 1981, prob. 23, p. 4.

26. A porch is 3 ft 8 in above the sidewalk. You are building a stairway leading from the sidewalk to the porch. You know that the stair treads are $1\frac{1}{8}$ in thick and that the height of all risers should be equal and be between 5 and 7 in. You want to know how many risers there should be and the height of each.

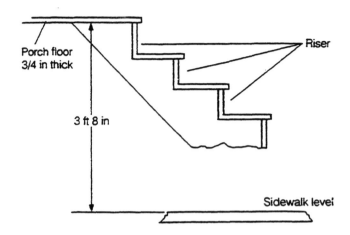

Porch floor
3/4 in thick

Riser

3 ft 8 in

Sidewalk level

27. One-twelfth of the money paid into the state lottery in the form of ticket sales actually returns to the citizens in the form of winnings. This amount is $\frac{3}{4}$ of what's left over after the expenses are taken out for running the lottery. What fraction of the lottery ticket sales goes for these expenses?

28. A new alloy is to be formed out of three other metal alloys. The new alloy will be made up of 4 parts of alloy X, 3 parts of alloy Y, and 1 part of alloy Z. Each of the three ingredients has a fraction of lead in it: $\frac{1}{12}$ of alloy X is lead, $\frac{1}{6}$ of alloy Y is lead, and $\frac{1}{4}$ of alloy Z is lead. You want to know what fraction of the new alloy is lead.

29. An enlargement with a longest edge of 7 in is to be made from a slide that is 24 × 35 mm.
    (a) How wide will the enlargement be?
    (b) An enlargement is to be made from the same slide in such a way that with a minimum of trimming it will just fill an 8- by 10-in frame. How large should the enlargement be before trimming?

For each question, several possible answers are given. Circle the letter just to the left of the item that best answers the problem.

1. The number 6,850,342,170 is evenly divisible by several numbers. Which of the following is not only a set of divisors of this number but also the most complete (has the most elements)?
   (a) {2,3,4,5,6,9,10,12,18}
   (b) {2,4,5,9,10,18,20}
   (c) {2,3,5,6,9,10,15,18,45}
   (d) {2,3,4,5,6,9,10,12,15}
   (e) {2,3,5,6,10,12,15,18}

2. The GCD of $2^2 3^3 5^3 7^1$ and $2^2 3^4 5^1 7^2 11^1$ is
   (a) $2^2 3^3 5^3 7^1$
   (b) $2^2 3^4 5^3 7^2 11^1$
   (c) $2^4 3^7 5^4 7^3 11^1$
   (d) $2^1 3^1 5^1 7^1 11^1$
   (e) $2^2 3^4 5^3 7^2$

3. Two engaged gears are shown in the picture. When the motor is turned on, gear 1 makes 70 rpm. How many revolutions per minute does gear 2 make?

   (a) 700
   (b) 7
   (c) 10
   (d) 70
   (e) 100

4. Before ordering campaign literature for a mailing, you must decide how many households there are among all registered voters. A rule of thumb is that there are $\frac{2}{3}$ as many households as registered voters. How many copies of a mailer should be ordered for a district in which there are 142,500 registered voters?
   (a) 47,500
   (b) 95,000
   (c) 71,250
   (d) 213,750
   (e) 190,000

5. Which of the following is a test for divisibility by 24?
   (a) Use the tests for divisibility by 4 and 6. If these tell you that the number is divisible by both 4 and 6, then the number is divisible by 24.
   (b) See if the number formed by the first three digits is divisible by 24. If it is, then the entire number is divisible by 24.
   (c) Add up all the digits of the number and see if it is divisible by 24. If it is, then the original number is divisible by 24.
   (d) Use the tests for divisibility by 3 and 8. If these tell you that the number is divisible by both 3 and 8, then the number is divisible by 24.
   (e) Use the tests for divisibility by 12 and 2. If these tell you that the number is divisible by both 2 and 12, then the number is divisible by 24.

6. Among people aged 18 to 25, the ratio of smokers to nonsmokers is 3 to 7. The fraction of nonsmokers in the same age group is
   (a) $\frac{3}{7}$ (b) $\frac{4}{7}$ (c) $\frac{3}{10}$ (d) $\frac{4}{10}$ (e) $\frac{7}{10}$

7. Which of the following fractions is the largest?
   (a) $\frac{3}{4}$ (b) $\frac{4}{5}$ (c) $\frac{5}{6}$ (d) $\frac{7}{10}$ (e) $\frac{23}{30}$

8. In a recent election, $\frac{2}{5}$ of those citizens of the city living north of the river favored recharge of the water table using water coming from a new federal irrigation canal, while $\frac{1}{3}$ of those living south of the river favored the recharge. What fraction of the citizens in the entire city favored the recharge?
   (a) $\frac{11}{15}$ (b) $\frac{11}{30}$ (c) $\frac{3}{8}$ (d) $\frac{5}{8}$ (e) not enough information to decide

9.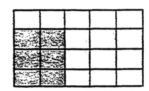

   The diagram best illustrates which of the following fraction problems?
   (a) $\frac{3}{4} \times \frac{2}{5}$ (b) $\frac{3}{5} \times \frac{2}{4}$ (c) $\frac{3}{4} + \frac{2}{5}$ (d) $\frac{3}{5} + \frac{1}{4}$ (e) $\frac{3}{5} \times \frac{1}{4}$

10. A cabinet $10\frac{1}{2}$ ft long must have five doors of equal size. There must be stiles between the doors and at both ends. Each stile must be $2\frac{1}{2}$ in wide.

    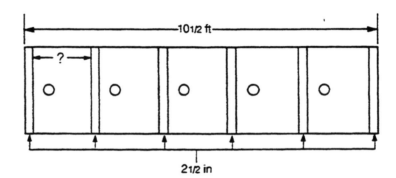

    What must the width of each door be?
    (a) 15 in (b) 111 in (c) $22\frac{1}{5}$ in (d) $\frac{37}{20}$ in (e) $9\frac{1}{4}$ in

ESSAY QUESTIONS   *For each remaining problem, document your solution carefully in the form of an essay.*

11. Three-fifths of the faculty members at the university bike to work. One-fourth of the rest walk. What fraction of the faculty come to work by some means other than biking or walking, such as car, bus, glider, or camel?

12. (a) A 264-tn (ton, tons) load of copper ore has arrived at the San Carlos smelter from the copper mine in Garlic. It is known that ore from Garlic has $\frac{3}{5}$ as much copper (by weight) as waste. How much copper is in the load?
    (b) A 215-tn load of ore has arrived at San Carlos from Goldenbell. It is known that $\frac{3}{10}$ of Goldenbell ore is copper (by weight). How much copper is in the load?
    (c) What is the ratio of copper to waste in the two loads combined?

13. A machine has three colored lights each of which flashes on for an instant at regular intervals. The yellow one flashes on 15 times/min, the blue one flashes on 9 times/min, and the red one flashes on 12 times/min. You watch the machine and see all three lights flash on simultaneously. How much longer must you wait before the three lights flash on again simultaneously?

14. In Washington County, $\frac{2}{3}$ of all registered voters are Democrats; the rest are Republicans. Four-fifths of all the Republicans voted in the last election, but $\frac{3}{10}$ of the Democrats did not vote. What fraction of the registered voters did vote in the last election?

INTRODUCTION TO MEASUREMENT: LENGTH, POSITION, AND SHAPES

13

C H A P T E R

Measurement is important in many activities. To teachers, homeowners, farmers, carpenters, plumbers, engineers, and architects, among others, a mastery of the mathematics and the techniques of measurement is essential. This is the first of several chapters devoted to measurement, and length is the first topic.

How do you tell when two lengths are the same? If they are not the same, which one is longer? We will discuss simple methods for answering these questions and, from there, proceed to more sophisticated methods, close to the ones with which we are familiar. Along the way we will describe the two modern systems of standardized units for measuring length, the traditional (so-called English) and metric systems.

The need to measure length arises in a variety of situations. One may be interested in finding a perimeter of a plane shape, or in measuring a length associated with a shape in space, or in determining a length that cannot be measured directly. To respond to these situations, we will introduce some language for talking about shapes in the plane, create flat patterns for three-dimensional shapes, and discuss scale drawings.

THE MOLDING PROBLEM

The Joneses are remodeling their living room and are installing new molding along the baseboard of one of the walls. They have a piece of the molding material and want to know if it will be enough for the whole wall and, if it is enough, whether they will have to cut the molding.

A Solution to the Molding Problem

One way to solve this problem is to use a yardstick to measure the length of the wall and the length of the molding and then compare the two. A simpler (perhaps more sensible) method is to lay the molding along the baseboard of the wall with one end of the molding at one end of the wall. If the molding extends exactly to the other end of the baseboard, then the wall's baseboard and the molding *have the same length*, and no cut will be necessary. If the molding extends beyond the other end, then the baseboard is *shorter in length* than the piece of molding, and a cut in the molding will be needed. If the molding doesn't extend to the corner, then the baseboard is *longer in length* than the piece of molding, and the piece of molding will not be enough.

THE PATIO FORM PROBLEM

The O'Briens are building the forms for a concrete slab that will make a kidney-shaped patio that they have marked out in their backyard.

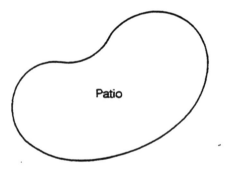

Patio

Try this before reading on.

To make the forms for the concrete, they will bend a piece of metal stripping and hold it in place with wooden stakes. A local hardware store has a roll of metal stripping from which they will purchase a piece for the job. The O'Briens want to know how much to have cut from the roll. In the meantime Mr. O'Brien seems to have misplaced the one tape measure the family ever owned. Help them solve this problem.

A Solution to the Patio Form Problem

If we had a metal tape measure long enough, we could lay it on edge along the path where the form is to be. But we don't. An alternative is to use a large spool of string. Fix the beginning of the string at some point along the path where the form is to go; draw string from the spool and lay it out along this path until you traverse it entirely, reaching the beginning of your path again; cut the string from the spool right at that point. The metal form and the piece of cut string should have the same length. Take the piece of string to the hardware store and ask for a piece of metal stripping the same length as the string.

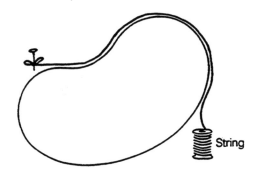

String

The Mathematical Idea: Determining Length without Measuring Tools or Numbers

The molding and patio form problems are problems of length, and we solved them without recourse to tools, such as rulers or tape measures, or to numbers, such as number of inches, feet, or centimeters.

Many other problems having to do with deciding whether one length is shorter (or longer) than another can be solved similarly—without the use of measuring tools. If you want to know whether a couch will fit along a certain part of a wall, you can move the couch to that part of the wall and see. If you want to know if a certain piece of rope can be used as a clothesline to be hung between two hooks, you can take the rope, attach one end of it to one hook, and see if it stretches to the other. If it doesn't, it's not long enough. If it does, it is long enough. These two problems and the molding problem are problems of Which length is longer? and are solved by taking one length and placing it next to the other.

The patio form problem was similar: Cut from one length a length equal to another length. For that problem, however, it was not convenient to place either length next to the other. An intermediary length was used: A piece of string equal in length to the edge of the curved form was created, and the string was then placed next to the length of metal stripping.

There are many situations in which some sort of intermediary length—a simple measuring device—is convenient, and often essential, for solving problems of length. You want to surround your pasture with fencing and go to the hardware store to buy some. You want to put molding along the baseboards of all of your bedrooms and go to the lumberyard to buy the right amount. You plan to make drapes for your living room windows and go to the fabric store to buy the right length of drape material. You have an old garage and want to know whether the car you are considering buying—now in a downtown showroom—will fit.

EXERCISE

1. Show how you would solve each of the problems in the preceding paragraph without using modern tools of measurement or modern units of measurement.

Evolution of Techniques for Measuring Length

When modern tools are not available, string may be convenient for determining length. When string is not available, you can *pace* along the path where the fence for your pasture is to go and *count* the number of paces it takes you to cover the whole path, then pace along the fencing the hardware store has for the same number of paces.

You can walk around the baseboards in your bedroom toe-heel-toe-heel and *count* the number of *feet* you use to walk along all the baseboards, then go to the lumberyard and walk along the molding in the same fashion, counting out the same number of feet. For smaller lengths you can use *hand spans* or *thumb widths*. The number of such lengths can be written down and easily carried from place to place. For many lengths, string does not have this convenience.

We still use such methods for comparing and replicating lengths. They make up the first steps in the evolution of length-measuring techniques.

1. Put a number of equal, small lengths end to end to cover another (longer) length, and *count* the *number* of small lengths that you get. (If it doesn't come out "even," estimate the fractional part of the small length left over.)

2. For the small lengths in 1 use "1s" that we "carry" with us (foot, thumb width [inch], hand, tip of nose to tip of outstretched finger [yard]).

To primitive people the foregoing methods may have been the only ones. Some next steps would have been the following.

3. Groups of people agree to use common *units* (foot, thumb, hand) for purposes of public commerce. The exact length of the unit used may vary depending on the person whose foot or thumb or hand is used.

4. One person's foot may not have the same length as another's. In a situation of controversy, whose foot shall we use to determine the length of that field? A solution to this and other similar problems is to *standardize* the units.

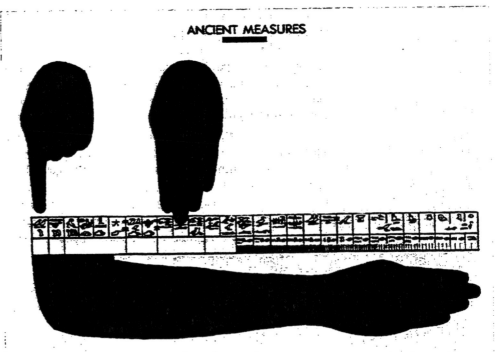

ANCIENT MEASURES

The illustration shows a cubit stick 3500 yr old. The cubit was the Egyptian standard unit of length and was equal to the distance from a man's elbow to the tip of his longest finger. The cubit was divided into smaller units, called digits, each the width of a finger. A larger unit, the palm (or hand), was equal to 4 digits. Seven palms, or 28 digits, was equal to 1 cubit.

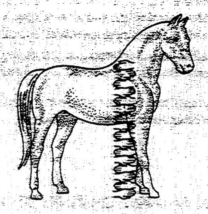

A horse that is 16 hands tall

The hand (palm) was used as a basic unit of measure by nearly all ancient civilizations and is still used in this country to measure the heights of horses. The height of a horse is the number of hand breadths from the ground to the horse's shoulders.

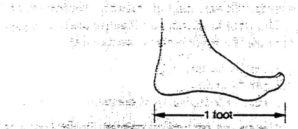

1 foot

In Roman times the foot was a basic unit of length and was divided into 12 equal parts, each one called an *uncia* (from *unus*, "one"). The English adopted the Roman system and *uncia* became "inch." The yard was established by royal decree in the twelfth century by King Henry I as the distance from his nose to his thumb.

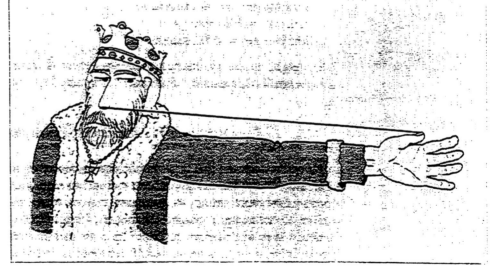

5. An easy way is arrived at to "convert" from one standardized unit to another, to enable the length of something measured using one unit (such as a foot) to be compared to the length of something measured in another unit (such as a thumb).

6. Measuring devices (foot ruler, yardstick, etc.) that convey the standard units and that also help to count the number of units are created.

EXERCISE 2. Measure the cover of this book using your thumb. Compare the number of thumbs you get with the numbers from other classmates.

13.2 STANDARD UNITS OF LENGTH

The Traditional System and the Metric System

Two systems of the kind just described, the traditional system and the metric system, are commonly in use in the United States. The *traditional system* finds its origin in the Roman system, which itself emerged from the use of units of length associated with the human body (in ways mentioned earlier). Until the creation of the metric system, this was the only broadly used system of standardized units.

The traditional system's familiar units of length are the inch, the foot, the yard, and the mile. Here are their conversion factors:

1 foot = 12 inches
1 yard = 3 feet
1 mile = 5280 feet = 1760 yards

The *metric system* was created by the French government in the 1790s after the French Revolution. This system has conversion factors that mesh nicely with the decimal place value system for representing numbers.

The basic unit of length in the metric system is the meter, longer than the traditional yard by a few inches. The conversion factors for other units relative to the meter are powers of 10. In addition to the meter, the most common units of length are the millimeter, the centimeter, and the kilometer. Here are their conversion factors:

1 millimeter = .001 meter
1 centimeter = 10 millimeters = .01 meter
1 meter = 100 centimeters
1 kilometer = 1000 meters

Throughout the whole metric system—there is more to it than length—the prefix *kilo-* means "thousand," *centi-* means "hundredth," and *milli-* means "thousandth.")

Converting from Traditional to Metric and Vice Versa

In this text, as in real life, it is not usually necessary to convert measurements made in units of the metric system into measurements from the traditional system and vice versa. For most situations all measurements are in a single system, and there is no need to translate from one to another. However, those of us not familiar with the metric system will need to relate its units to human scale. We want to know more than facts such as 1 meter = 100 centimeters. We want to have the same familiarity with the metric system as we do with the traditional system that enables us to say, "Oh, he's pretty tall, about 6'1"; "She lives about 10 miles from here"; or, "I think I'll need about a yard and a half of that material." Of course, the best way to get comfortable with the system is to use it—and we will. In the meantime, here are some comparisons between the two systems, some "rough," some more precise. Abbreviations for the units are also given. For the most part, as you will have noticed, I use abbreviations in this text.

UNIT (ABBREVIATION)	ROUGH COMPARISON	PRECISE COMPARISON
1 millimeter (mm)	Thickness of a dime; a bit longer than $\frac{1}{32}$ inch	.039 inch
1 centimeter (cm)	Width of fingernail on little finger; a little less than half an inch	.39 inch
1 meter (m)	Half the height of an average door; a little longer than a yard	39.37 inch
1 kilometer (km)	A little more than half a mile; .6 of a mile	.62 mile
1 inch (in)	2.5 centimeters	2.54 centimeters
1 foot (ft)	30 centimeters	30.48 centimeters
1 yard (yd)	90 centimeters; almost a meter	.9144 meter
1 mile (mi)	1.6 kilometers, a little over $1\frac{1}{2}$ kilometers	1.60 kilometers

EXERCISE

3. In the metric system, estimate the (a) width and length of the cover of this book, (b) height from the ground to a chair seat, (c) distance from New York City to San Francisco, (d) thickness of a nickel, (e) diameter of a quarter.

13.3   PERIMETER

THE FENCING PROBLEM   Mr. Ortega is building a corral for his cattle, shown in a bird's-eye view.

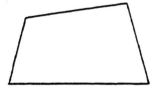

Try this before reading on.

He plans to buy the fencing that he needs from a hardware store. He wants to know how much fencing he will need to buy. Help him solve this problem.

To solve the problem, he thinks: "How much fencing will I need in all? When I install the fencing, I'll start at one corner, run the fencing to an adjacent corner, bend it, run it to another corner, bend it again, and so on, until I get back to where I started. So the amount of fencing I'll need is the same as if I 'unfolded' the corral to get one length.

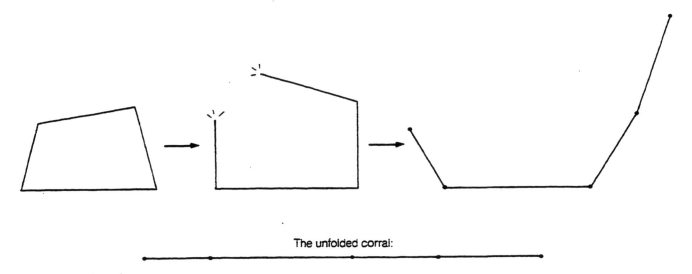

The unfolded corral:

Pacing off that one length would tell me how much fencing I would need; but if I were to pace off each side of my corral separately, the sum of the paces for the separate sides should add up to the number of paces for that one length."

So Mr. Ortega paced off each of the sides of the corral to be built and obtained the numbers indicated.

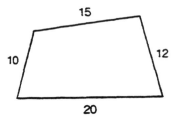

"Each of my paces is about 1 meter, so the figures tell me how much fencing I will need for each side in meters. How much will I need in all? Add all those figures up: 10 meters + 20 meters + 12 meters + 15 meters = 57 meters. Add in a few meters for error to get 60 meters."

The Mathematical Idea: Perimeter

In the fencing problem, Mr. Ortega was interested in finding out the "length around" his proposed corral, that is, the total length the sides would make if they were placed end to end. This length is called the *perimeter* of the corral. In general, the perimeter of a shape is the length of fencing needed to fit around it snugly. While figuring out his problem, Mr. Ortega made a discovery.

His principle was simple.

Here are some bird's-eye views of rooms, corrals, gardens, pastures, and backyards that need fencing or molding fitted snugly around them. To get an exact fit, you have to determine the perimeter of each. The length of each straight side has been measured and is shown in the picture, and the perimeter is calculated using the method just described.

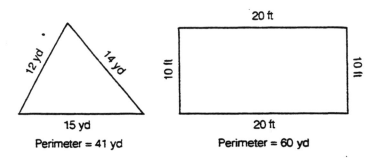

Perimeter = 41 yd   Perimeter = 60 yd

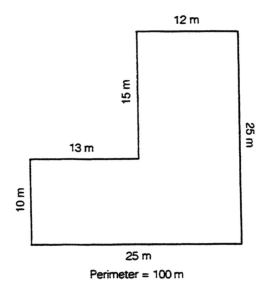

Perimeter = 100 m

In the patio problem, we were interested in the length of metal stripping needed to fit around the shape snugly; thus, we were interested in the perimeter of the patio. However, the method we used for finding the perimeter for the corral and other shapes will not work for finding the perimeter of the patio: The edge of the patio is curvy, whereas the other shapes have straight sides. A closed, flat shape with straight sides is called a *polygon*. A string is one way to measure the perimeter of a shape that is not a polygon. We will discuss other ways in chapter 16.

Look at some examples of flat shapes that are polygons, and some that aren't.

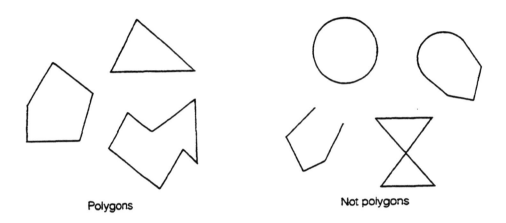

Polygons   Not polygons

EXERCISE   4. Find the perimeters of the polygons. The lengths of the straight sides have been written in.

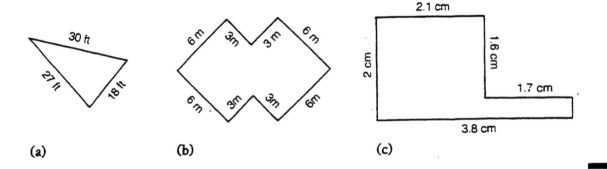

(a)   (b)   (c)

THE TABLE MOLDING
PROBLEM

The Joneses are covering a table with Formica. After the Formica has been glued on the table top they will finish the sides of the table with protective metal molding. The molding must be ordered in advance, and they need to find out how much of it they need. Here is a bird's-eye view of the table top.

The Joneses figure that they must measure the lengths of the sides of the table, then add them up to find the perimeter. Mr. Jones first measures one side and then another.

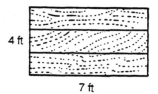

As he is about to measure a third side, Mrs. Jones interrupts him: "You don't need to measure the other two sides. The shape of the table top is a rectangle. Opposite sides are equal.

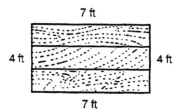

Here are the four lengths: 4 feet, 7 feet, 4 feet, and 7 feet. Add them up: $4 + 7 + 4 + 7 = 22$ feet."

The Mathematical Idea: Shapes, Formulas, and Terminology

The Joneses discovered that to figure out the perimeter of a rectangle, all you have to do is measure *two* adjacent sides. The lengths of the two unmeasured sides can be determined from the lengths of the measured sides. For a rectangle only *half* the sides have to be measured.

There is a condensed prescription for calculating the perimeter of a rectangle.

THE PERIMETER OF A RECTANGLE

If the lengths of two adjacent sides of a rectangle are H and B, then the *perimeter* of the rectangle is $H + H + B + B = 2(H + B)$.

The two lengths H and B are sometimes called the *height* and *base*, respectively, of the rectangle. The shorthand expression

$$\text{Perimeter of a rectangle} = 2(H + B)$$

is our first *formula*, the power of which is that it can be used for *any* rectangle.

The rectangle is one of many flat shapes that are frequently used in our culture and must be measured. Let's review some terminology for describing these shapes. First of all, a line segment is a piece of a line with a beginning and an end. A line extends indefinitely in both directions.

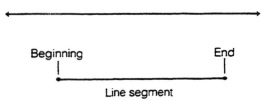

Line segment

Loosely, if you assemble a bunch of line segments together with the end point of one to the beginning point of another to make a closed shape, you obtain a *polygon.*

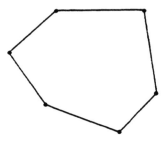

A point at which exactly two sides of a polygon meet is called a *vertex* (plural: *vertices*). Two sides of a polygon meeting in a vertex are called *adjacent* sides.

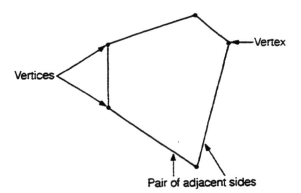

A *ray* is a piece of a line with a beginning point but no ending.

Beginning point

A configuration consisting of two rays joined at their beginning points is called an *angle.* The two rays are called the *sides* of the angle. The point at which the two rays meet is call the *vertex* of the angle.

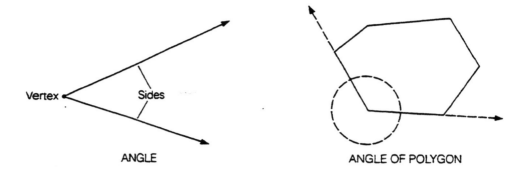

Vertex • Sides	
ANGLE	ANGLE OF POLYGON

You can think of two line segments that meet at a point as an angle by extending the ends of the segments that don't meet and making them into rays. In this sense, a polygon has many angles.

A rectangle has four sides, four vertices, and four angles. Many polygons have this property, but the distinguishing feature for the rectangle is that its four angles are "equal" in a certain sense.

CONGRUENT ANGLES

Two angles are *congruent* if the two sides and the vertex of a copy of one fit exactly on the two sides and the vertex of the other. (The actual drawn lengths of the sides of the angles are not important in determining whether the angles are congruent.)

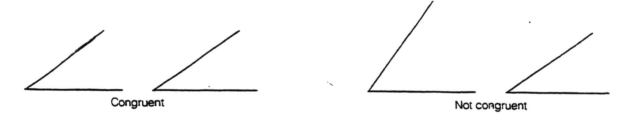

Congruent   Not congruent

The four congruent angles of a rectangle have a special property: They completely fill in the space around a point without overlapping, as shown.

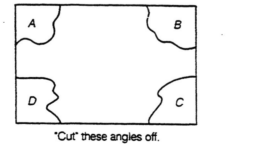

"Cut" these angles off.   Rearrange this way.

Take four congruent copies of an angle and fit them together at their vertices. If the angles can be arranged so that the space around their common vertex is filled without overlapping, then the original single angle is called a *right angle.*

So the four angles of a rectangle are right angles.

In a rectangle, a pair of sides that aren't adjacent are called *opposite* sides. A pair of opposite sides extended in both directions never meet. Two lines in a plane that never meet are called *parallel;* thus, opposite sides of a rectangle are parallel.

Pair of parallel lines:

_____

_____

EXERCISES

5. When the two lengths H and B of a rectangle are equal, then the rectangle is also a *square.* All four sides of a square are equal. There is a particularly nice formula for the perimeter of a square. What is it?

6. Find the perimeters of the polygons.

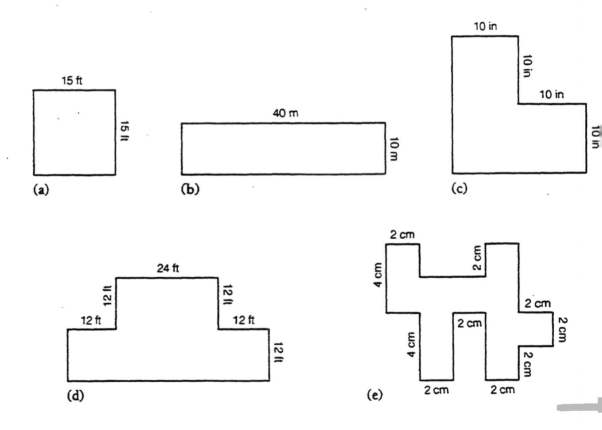

THE STREET PAVING PROBLEM Obregon is repaving all the numbered streets between Columbus St. and Washington St. To figure out the cost of this, engineers must figure out the total amount of paving. A map of the town is provided. All the streets in the city are the same width. Help the engineers solve this problem.

Try this yourself.

A Solution to the Street Paving Problem Realizing that the blocks in the town form rectangles, the city engineers conclude that the length of paving on one numbered street is the same as the length of paving of another—because these are lengths of opposite sides of a rectangle. All they have to do, then, is figure out the length of one cross street and multiply it by the number of cross streets to obtain the total length of paving for the project.

The Mathematical Idea: Using Rectangles to Measure Indirectly

The town engineers didn't have to measure the length of a numbered street several blocks away. All they had to do was measure the length of one nearby numbered street and use the fact that the other length was the opposite side of a rectangle and thus equal in length to the one nearby.

EXERCISE 7. You are replacing the cornice at the top of a several-story building. You need to know the length of the top of the building to estimate the cost of replacement. When you look at the picture of the building, can you think of an easy way to solve this problem?

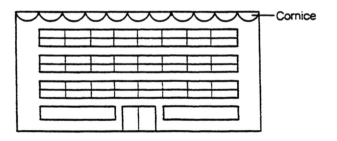

SCALE DRAWINGS

THE WATER PIPE PROBLEM The Jones family is planning to add a new bathroom to their house. One of the items that will affect the cost of this project is the water line. To estimate the cost of the water line and its installation, they figure they must know its projected length.

Mr. Jones cannot measure the length easily because there is no clear path from the present water source to its destination in the new bathroom. The water line must pass under several rooms. Mr. Jones decides to make a scale drawing of that part of the house and then measure the length of the line on the scale drawing. He decides on a scale: Every centimeter of length in the scale drawing will represent 1 m in the house. The rooms are all rectangular, so the scale drawing is not difficult. Here it is.

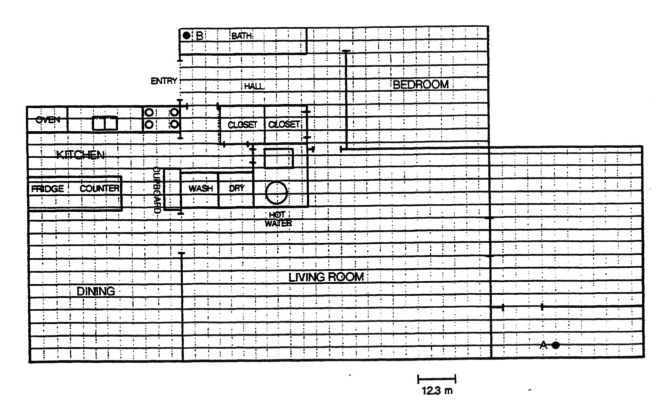

123 m

The bathroom will need water at point A; the water pipes nearest to this are at point B. On the scale drawing Mr. Jones measures the distance from A to B and finds it to be 123 cm. This represents 123 m in real life. This is Mr. Jones's estimate of the length of the new water line.

The Mathematical Idea: Using a Scale Drawing to Measure Length

When you reduce the size of a rectangular photograph, the ratio of one side in the original to the corresponding side in the reduction is equal to the ratio of the other side in the original to the other corresponding side in the reduction.

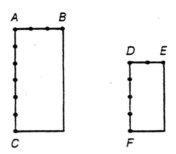

The ratio of the length of *AB* to the length of *DE* is 3 to 2, or $\frac{3}{2}$. The ratio of the length of *AC* to the length of *DF* is also 3 to 2.

You also expect any other length in the original photograph to be reduced using the same ratio. (One says that the lengths are in the *same proportion*.)

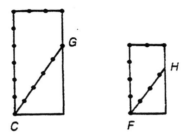

The ratio of the length of *CG* to the length of *FH* is 5 to $3\frac{1}{3}$, or $\frac{3}{2}$.

In the solution to the water pipe problem the ratio of a length from the original to the corresponding length in the scale drawing is 100 to 1, or $\frac{100}{1}$. The ratio of a length in the scale drawing to the corresponding length in the original is 1 to 100, or $\frac{1}{100}$. The latter is called the *scale factor* for a scale drawing. Frequently, a scale is given in which the two lengths have different units, for example, 1 cm represents 2 m. In this case the scale factor is *not* 1 to 2, or $\frac{1}{2}$. Since a centimeter is .01 m, the scale factor is .01 to 2, or $\frac{1}{200}$.

As in the solution to the water pipe problem, scale drawings can be used to measure lengths indirectly. There will be more on scale drawings in chapter 15.

EXERCISE
8. Water from the Colorado River is scheduled to arrive in Tucson, Arizona, in late 1989, thanks to the Central Arizona Project (CAP). Some water will arrive by open canal at the northwestern corner of the city. A cluster of industries at the southeastern corner of the city is considering the use of some of the unprocessed water because of the potential low cost per gallon. The city would have to tunnel a water main from the one corner to the other to get this water to the industries. To estimate the cost of the water main, the city needs to know the length of the main. A map (a scale drawing) of the city showing the two corners A and B is provided (page 522). Help the city solve this problem.

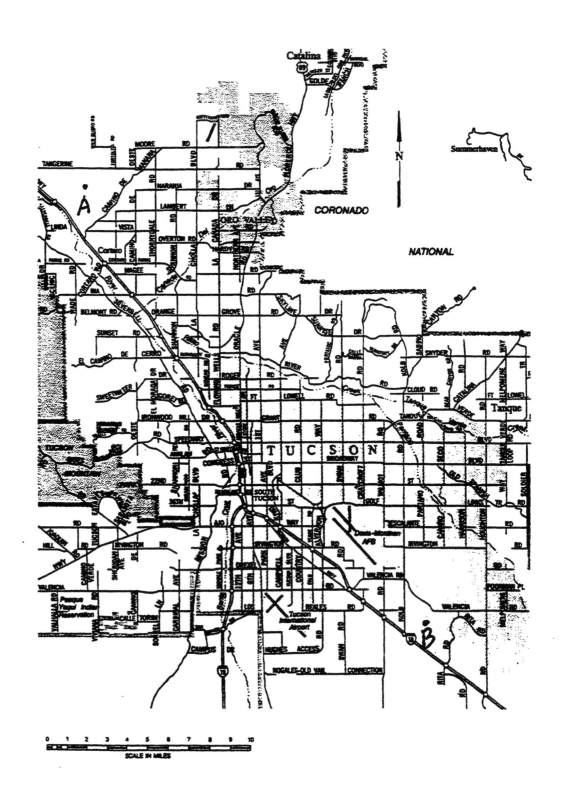

The Joneses have a house that was built around 1900. Many of the rooms had molding that went all around the baseboards, up all the corners of the rooms, and around the edges of the ceiling where the side walls and ceiling meet. They are planning to restore the molding in the room shown.

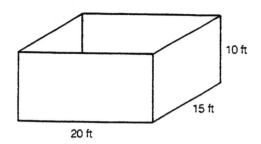

Try this first before reading on.

The room is a box. The floor is a rectangle 15 by 20 ft, and the ceiling is 10 ft from floor to ceiling. The Joneses need to know how much molding they will need so they can estimate the cost of this restoration. Molding is sold by the foot. Help them find the answer.

A Solution to the Room
Molding Problem

Mrs. Jones draws another picture of the room.

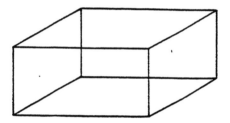

"This is a skeleton of the room," she says. "All those lines drawn correspond to pieces of molding. To solve our problem we must find the total length of all those lines.

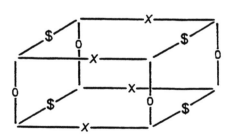

"The 4 pieces marked with an *X* are each 20 feet long. The 4 pieces marked with O are each 10 feet long. The 4 pieces marked with $ are each 15 feet long.

"There are 12 pieces in all. That makes 4 × 10 feet + 4 × 15 feet + 4 × 20 feet or 180 feet of molding in all."

EXERCISE
9. The Jones' house once had ornate trim all along the outside roof line. This has long since disappeared, but the Joneses are now planning to restore the trim on the front of the house to its original elegance. Such trim is sold by the foot; thus, the Joneses will need to determine the total length of trim on the front of the house in order to estimate the cost of their project. Below is a picture of the front of their house with measurements of the roof line marked in. Find the total amount of trim they will need.

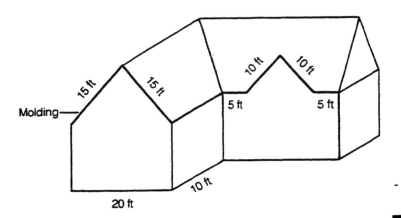

THE SPEAKER WIRING PROBLEM

John was lying in bed one morning listening to his stereo and imagining how nice it would be if he could place one of the speakers up near the ceiling in the corner opposite his turntable and amplifier. The latter were on a table in the corner just to his right where he could turn the stereo on easily without getting out of bed. He was wondering how much wire he would need to connect the speaker to his amplifier. He knew that his room was shaped like a cube: A square floor 9 by 9 ft and a ceiling 9 ft high. He figured that the speaker wire connection on the amplifier was 3 ft up from the floor in the corner and that the wire would attach to a point in back of the speaker exactly 3 ft down from the ceiling in the opposite corner. Help John figure out how long the wire should be if it takes the shortest route along the walls and floor of his room.

Try this yourself, first.

A Solution to the Speaker Wiring Problem

John decides to draw a picture of his room, marking on it the two ends of the wire.

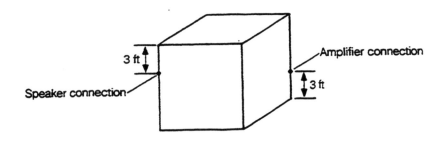

He thinks: "One way to do it would be to run the wire straight down the corner from the amplifier to the floor, across the floor diagonally, and up the opposite corner to the speaker.

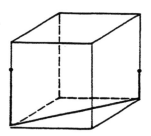

Is that the shortest way? I know that if the wire were to run on a flat surface, I could figure out the shortest way: I'd just draw a line between the two ends. Then I'd measure along the line from one end to the other to figure out the length. But my room is not flat! Is there a way I could make it flat? The ceiling, floor, and walls are flat themselves. It's the corners that mess things up. What if I were to 'cut' the room along the corners and flatten it out? I'd snip along the edges of the ceiling and bend it back, like this.

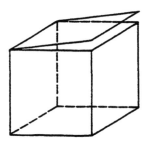

Then I'd snip along the corners from the ceiling to the floor, like this.

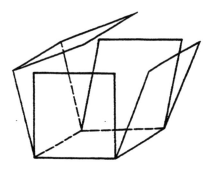

Then, I'd flatten it out. It would look like this.

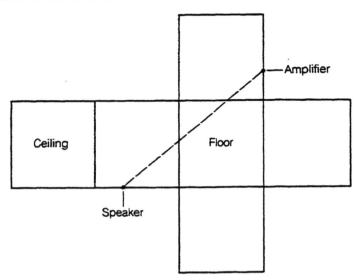

Then I could mark the two ends of the speaker connection and draw a straight line between the two points. Let me make a scale drawing of what I would get. From that I should be able to approximate pretty closely what the length of the wire should be. I'll get some graph paper and make the width of each little square on the graph paper represent a foot in the room. I won't have to include the ceiling.

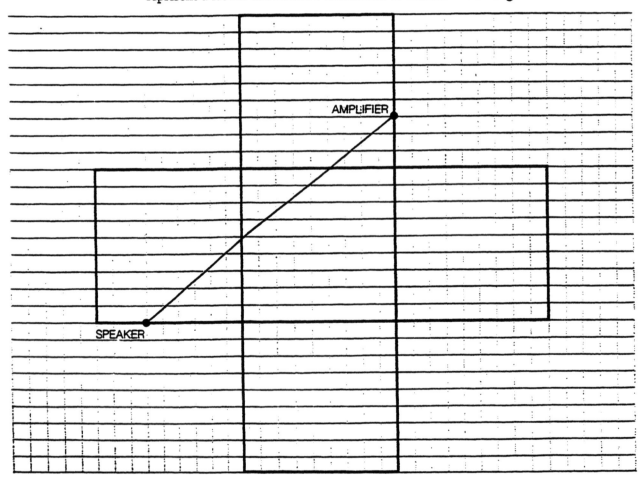

The side of each little square = 1 ft.

"On my scale drawing I've marked where the two ends of the wire will be and drawn the line between them. To measure the length of that line I'll take another piece of graph paper and use it to count the number of square-widths that will just fit along the line.

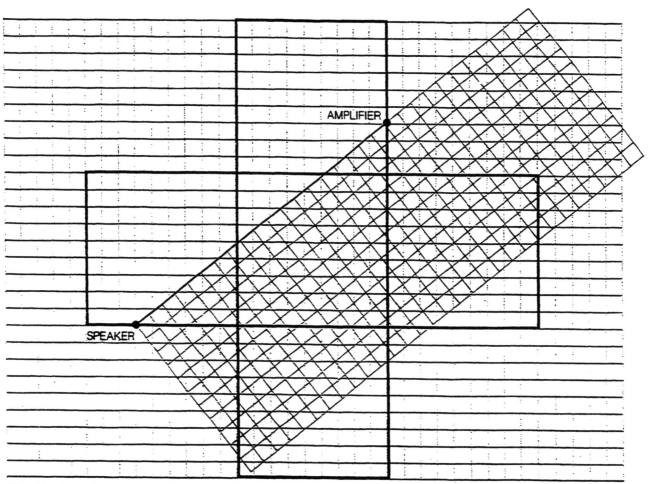

The side of each little square = 1 ft.

A little more than 19 squares. That represents a length of a little more than 19 feet in my room."

EXERCISE   10. Think some more about John's situation.
(a) The speaker can be located on the scale drawing differently than it is in our drawing. Find the way and draw the line between it and the amplifier. What is the length of the corresponding wire?
(b) Use the scale drawing to estimate the length of the wire John would need if he followed his original idea of running the wire down one corner from the speaker, across the room diagonally, and then up the other corner to the amplifier.

The Mathematical Idea: Making a Flattened Pattern
for a Three-Dimensional Shape

To measure the length of the speaker wire for his room John found it useful to "flatten the room out." He obtained a flat shape that if folded and taped together in the right places could be reassembled into the original room, or, in John's case, a scale model of the room. We call this flat shape a *(flat) pattern* for the three-dimensional shape.

Another example follows. In this case we have an open trough, shown on the left, and its pattern, shown on the right.

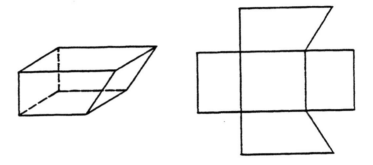

EXERCISES   11. Create a flat pattern for the shape.

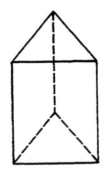

12. Trace a copy of the pattern below and assemble it. What do you get? (Fold on solid lines.)

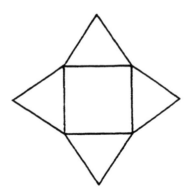

13. The Steins are installing a light in the cathedral ceiling of their living room. Here's a picture of the room and where they want to put the light.

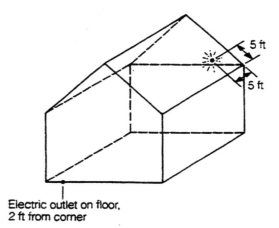

5 ft

5 ft

Electric outlet on floor,
2 ft from corner

The nearest electrical outlet is near the floor on the opposite side of the room. How should they run the wire from the outlet to the light in order to use the least amount of wire?

13.7 SUMMARY OF IMPORTANT IDEAS AND TECHNIQUES

- The evolution of length measurement
  Without modern tools
  Using an intermediate device
  Using convenient units
  Using standard units in the traditional system and metric system

- Perimeter of polygon; formula for perimeter of rectangle

- Measurement of length indirectly
  Using a rectangle
  Using a scale drawing
  Using a flat pattern of a three-dimensional model

- Basic terminology used to describe shapes
  Point, line, plane, parallel, angle, polygon
  Vertices and sides of angles and polygons
  Special terminology for angles, right angles
  Special terminology for polygons, especially triangles and quadrilaterals
  Symmetry of an object along line L

- Using length to describe position via a coordinate system

PROBLEM SET

1. Find the amount of fencing needed to fence in each pasture shown.

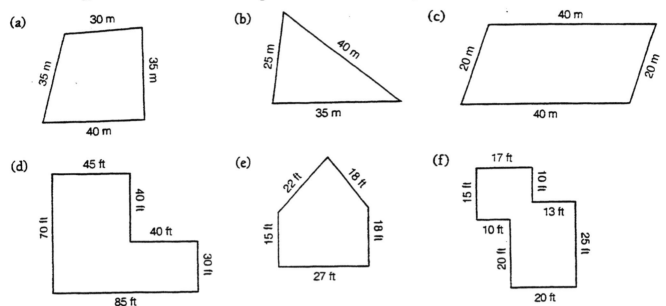

(a) 30 m, 35 m, 35 m, 40 m

(b) 25 m, 40 m, 35 m

(c) 40 m, 20 m, 20 m, 40 m

(d) 45 ft, 40 ft, 40 ft, 70 ft, 30 ft, 85 ft

(e) 22 ft, 18 ft, 15 ft, 18 ft, 27 ft

(f) 17 ft, 10 ft, 15 ft, 13 ft, 10 ft, 20 ft, 25 ft, 20 ft

2. You want to buy molding to place around the top of the wall in your living room, just next to the ceiling and above all doors and windows. You know that the room is a 10-ft-long by 15-ft-wide rectangle. How much molding do you need?

3. The owner of a small motel knows that all his rooms are identical. He wants to know the dimensions of room 18 at the end but has lent out the key to a carpenter who will not return until tomorrow. How can he find out the dimensions now?

4. Name five commonly used scale drawings. [Hint: look in the glove compartment of your car and at your owner's manuals.]

5. A housing contractor is building a tract of 20 homes each on same-size lots as in the picture. He wishes to buy fencing to fence in three sides of each lot; the side of each lot facing Grape, Apple, and Pear streets are to be left unfenced. How much fencing must he buy?

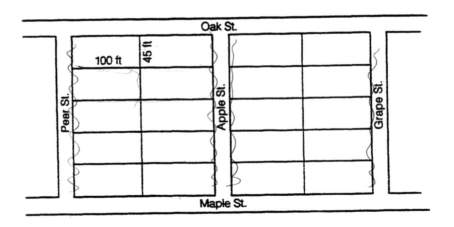

6. The contractor in problem 5 must also install curbing along both sides of all five streets shown. Each street is 15 ft wide, and each lot will have an 8-ft-wide break in the curbing to leave room for a driveway. What is the total length of curbing he must install?

7. Solve the speaker and wiring problem if your room is 12 ft by 15 ft with 8-ft ceilings, using John's method with a scale drawing and ruler.

8. Draw a flat pattern for each shape.

(a) 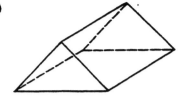 (b) 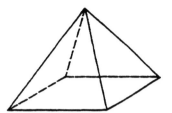 (c)

9. For each of the following prescriptions draw a polygon if you can. (If there is no polygon that fits the prescription, explain why not.)
   (a) a scalene right triangle   (b) an isosceles right triangle
   (c) an obtuse right triangle   (d) an equilateral right triangle
   (e) a regular rectangle   (f) a regular triangle
   (g) a regular trapezoid

10. Draw in all the lines of mirror symmetry for each shape.
    (a) 8   (b) B   (c) @
    (d) $ (e) H   (f) !
    (g) *   (h) +   (i) =

    (j)    (k)    (l)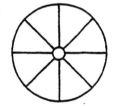

11. On a piece of graph paper, draw horizontal and vertical axes and plot the points the coordinates of which are as follows.
    (a) (2,−1)   (b) (3,8)   (c) (−2,1)   (d) (2,1)
    (e) (−2,−1)   (f) (−3,−8)   (g) (0,−2)   (h) (−2,0)

12. Find the coordinates of each of the plotted points.

13. You have a drawing $2\frac{1}{2}$ by $3\frac{1}{2}$ in that you want to enlarge to make a poster 4 ft tall. You want to know how wide the poster will be.

14. On an interior decorator's drawing, $\frac{1}{4}$ in represents 1 ft. On the drawing, a certain rug is 2 by 3 in. What are the dimensions of the real rug?

15. Use the map below to estimate the distance by air between the following pairs of cities.
    (a) Cincinnati and Chicago
    (b) Santa Fe and Kansas City
    (c) New York and Austin
    (d) Salt Lake City and Fargo
    (e) Seattle and Bangor
    (f) Helena and Washington, D.C.
    (g) Denver and Miami
    (h) New Orleans and Los Angeles

USING IDEAS   *For each remaining problem, write an essay to communicate clearly and completely the solution to the problem. Mention the steps you took in solving the problem, other problems or solutions that gave you ideas, and the strategies you used.*

16. In certain parts of the country drainage pipes must be laid around the periphery of a house to carry away rainwater that drips from the roof and to keep water away from the foundations and from getting into the basement. The house shown at the upper left is an example in which the pipe appears as a dotted line about 1.5 ft from the foundation. What is the length of piping that will be needed for each house indicated? (Only certain measurements have been provided. You must infer the rest from those that are given. A pair of sides that *look* parallel is parallel!)

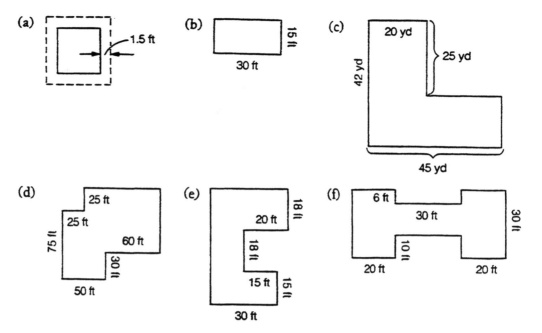

17. Below is the design for a rather unusual hand mirror. You plan to put a thin silver molding around its edge and want to know how much silver molding you will need. You decide to solve this in two ways:
    (a) Using string as in the text
    (b) Approximating the curved edge with a lot of short, straight lines (you draw them in), measuring the straight lines, and adding up their lengths.
    What do you get with each of these methods?

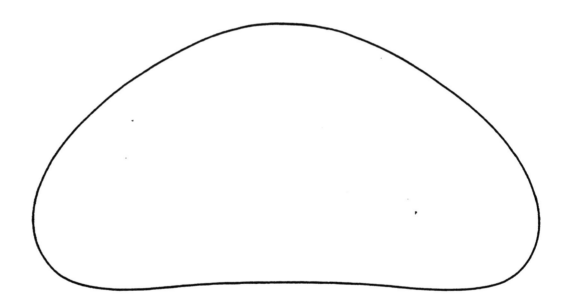

18. You work for the Perfect Packaging Company. Your supervisor tells you, "A large rush order has just come in, and we need to send out 140 cartons as soon as possible. I'd like you to fill the cartons and tape them up. Before doing that you will need to pick up enough tape from the store room." "How much tape will I need?" you ask. The reply: "The cartons are 65 centimeters long, 25 centimeters wide, and 10 centimeters thick; and we tape them twice around the long way and use two strips across the top." How much tape will you need? (See illustration on page 544.)

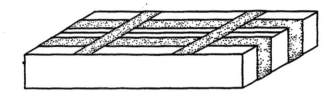

19. Below is the floor plan of your kitchen and dining nook. The whole room is a rectangle. You have laid linoleum tile on those parts of the floor that are not shaded in. (The shaded parts of the diagram correspond to items that are permanently fixed to the floor.) Now you plan to install protective rubber molding around the perimeter of the new linoleum. What length of rubber molding will you need?

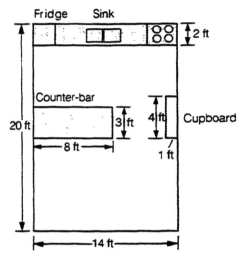

20. Here is some information regarding the planting of bush beans:

   ■ The distance between plants should be from 4 to 6 in.
   ■ 1 lb of seed will seed 100 row-feet.
   ■ 100 row-feet has an expected yield of 50 lb beans.

   (a) How many row-feet are necessary to bring an expected yield of 300 lb?

   Bush beans, like other vegetables, may benefit from being grown in a rectangular block rather than in one long row. In block planting, leaves shade the soil, keeping it moist and reducing the growth of weeds. Plants grown in this way are equally spaced in the directions of width and length of the block. To make weeding easier, it is best to make the block no more than 2 ft wide. The length of the block can then be adjusted to provide the desired yield.

   (b) If bush beans are planted in blocks 2 ft wide and at the minimum distance of 4 in, how long must the block be in order to yield 300 lb?

   (c) How many pounds of seed are required for this planting?*

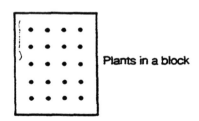

Plants in a block

---

* With thanks to D. Bushaw et al., *A Sourcebook of Applications of School Mathematics*, National Council of Teachers of Mathematics, Reston, Va., 1980, prob. 1.14, p. 24.

21. A photograph is to be reduced in size so that it can be mounted on an 8½- by 11-in sheet of paper. The photograph now measures 12 by 20 in. When mounted, the reduced photo should have a margin of at least 1¼ in all around. You'd like to have the reduced photo be as large as it can be, given these restrictions. What is the size of the reduced photo? What is the scale factor?

22. Adam and his sixth grade friends decide to lay out a scale model of the solar system in the school gymnasium. They decide that all nine planets should be included and that each orbit should be a circle with a radius equal to the planet's average distance from the Sun. Since the gym is 180 ft wide, this means that Pluto's circular orbit will also have a diameter of 180 ft. Using a calculator and the information provided, figure out what the diameters of the other planets' orbits should be.

PLANET	AVERAGE DISTANCE FROM SUN (IN MILLIONS OF MILES)
Mercury	36
Venus	67
Earth	93
Mars	142
Jupiter	484
Saturn	884
Uranus	1789
Neptune	2809
Pluto	3685

23. You are about to purchase an old upright piano. You want to put it in your living room but are worried about whether you can get it there through the rest of your house. Scale models of the floor plan of your house and of the piano are shown. Can you do it? If you can, how? If you can't, why?

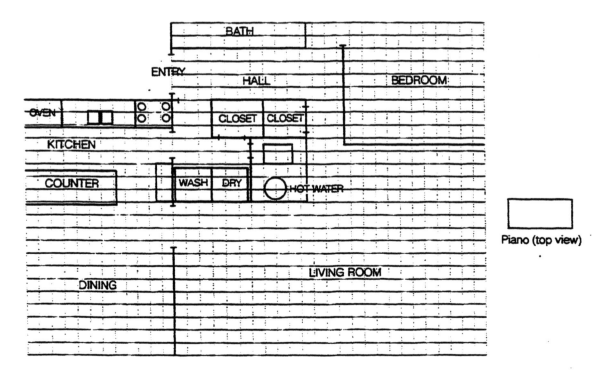

Piano (top view)

24. You have a rectangular garden surrounded by fencing. You plan to enlarge it by extending the rectangle 1 m in all directions as in the picture. You plan to take the fencing from the present garden and use it as fencing for the new garden. You will need some additional fencing, however. How much?

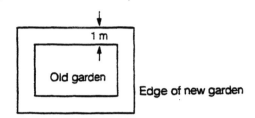

25. You have just purchased the ranch shown in the map. You have decided to replace all the existing fencing (marked on the map by a heavy dashed line). You want to know how much it will cost and how long it will take you to complete the job. Fencing costs $3.75/linear ft (including posts). It takes about 30 min to install each 10 linear ft.

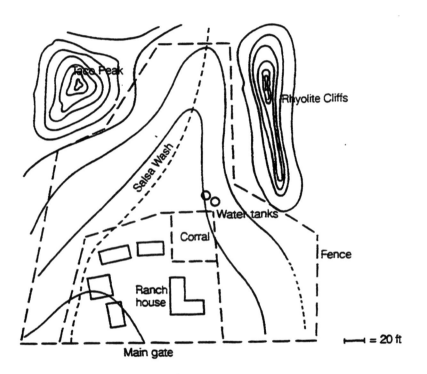

26. In this problem you will construct a scale model of a room using graph paper. (If you can, use graph paper with squares 2 cm on a side; otherwise, use graph paper having squares 1, .5, or .25 cm on a side.) The scale model will look like the one shown in the picture.

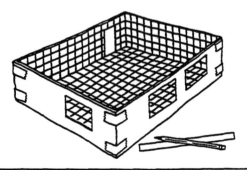

First, tape four sheets of paper together to make one piece, at least 17 by 22 cm.

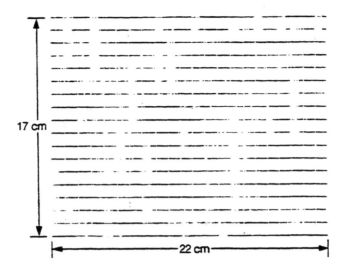

17 cm

22 cm

Next, draw a flattened pattern for the room on these sheets using certain requirements.
(a) Use a scale of 2 cm represents 1 yd (3 ft).
(b) The floor is a rectangle 50 by 32 ft.
(c) The ceiling is 8 ft off the floor.
(d) There are three windows, each 3 by 6 ft.
(e) There is one door, 4 by 7 ft.
Proceed as shown in the drawings.

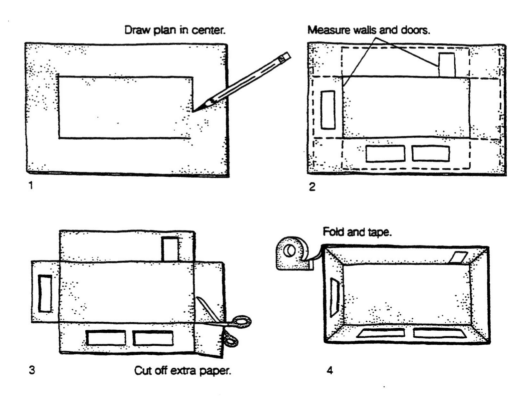

Draw plan in center.

Measure walls and doors.

1

2

3   Cut off extra paper.

Fold and tape.

4

You plan to install wooden molding trim around the door, all the windows, the baseboards, and on the ceiling at the tops of all the walls. Molding is sold by the (linear) foot. You want to know how much molding you will need. (Save this model for use in later problems.)*

27. Below are three views of the same cube. List the pairs of letters that appear on opposite faces of the cubes.

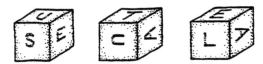

28. Below is a picture of a room. You want to install a light fixture right in the middle of the ceiling. You plan to run a wire from the fixture to the nearest electrical outlet, which is at the baseboard as shown. Use a dressmaker's pattern for the room to find the shortest route for the wire to take and find the length of the route.

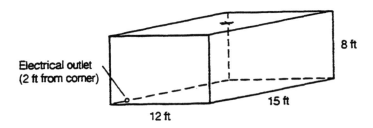

29. You, Officer Garcia, and your assistant, Officer O'Reilly, are needed as soon as possible to help capture criminals at the Wheeler Warehouse, corner of 11th and Wilson. You and O'Reilly are in your patrol car at 5th and Jefferson. You have two choices. You can drive there in your patrol car at an average speed of 60 mph, or you can go there by helicopter, which can travel at an average speed of 200 mph, with 5 additional min for takeoff and 5 min for landing. Of course, to use the helicopter, you must get to the police station and into the helicopter. You can radio ahead to have the helicopter waiting for you when you arrive. Once you arrive at the station, based on past experience it'll take you 6 min to park your car, get out, and get to the helicopter. Below is a map of the city showing the location of the warehouse and the police station with heliport. (Each city block is a mile square.) What should your choice be, helicopter or patrol car?

_____

* With thanks to Sherry Fraser, *Spaces: Solving Problems of Access to Careers in Engineering and Science*, Lawrence Hall of Science, Berkeley, Calif., 1982, pp. 9–11.

12th St.											
11th St.											
10th St.											
9th St.											
8th St.											
7th St.											
6th St.											
5th St.											
4th St.											
3rd St.	■ ←—Police										
2nd St.											
1st St.	Main	Washington	Jefferson	Adams	Franklin	Monroe	Jackson	Grant	Columbus	Wilson	Roosevelt

30. Which are flattened patterns for cubes?

(a)   (b)  (c)   (d)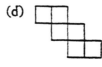

(e)   (f)   (g)  (h)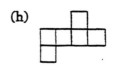

(i)   (j) 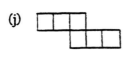 (k)   (l)

INTRODUCTION TO AREA

17

C H A P T E R

Let's look at a new set of problems: What is the crop yield of that plot of land? How many tiles will I need to tile that floor? How much paint will I need to paint that wall? How much will I have to pay for a rug that fits my floor? We have already discussed the measurement of length and the measurement of angles. These new problems lead us to create a new concept, the area of a planar shape. Part of working with this concept is developing techniques for measuring area.

We start with rectangles, the areas of which, of all shapes, are easiest to find. From there we move to simple shapes with areas more difficult to determine: triangles, parallelograms, trapezoids. To help us find the areas of these shapes, we discuss some basic principles concerning the measurement of area. We also use these principles to devise strategies for measuring the areas of more complicated shapes.

Using these principles and strategies, we will develop a formula for the area of a circle, a shape of particular interest to us. From this we can find the area of a sector, a piece of a circle bounded by an arc and two radii.

We will also consider the efficiency of shapes. We shall attempt to answer two types of questions.

■ You have a certain amount of fencing for a rectangular pasture. What should the dimensions of the rectangle be in order that the animals have the most grazing area?

■ You want your rectangular patio to have a certain area. What should its dimensions be in order to minimize the cost of the wall you plan to build to enclose it?

17.1   WHAT IS AREA?

The Smith family has a plot of land on which they grow potatoes. In the accompanying scale drawing of this plot, each of the little squares is a meter on a side.

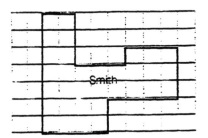

Try this yourself before reading on.

The local agricultural extension agent has told the Smiths that they can expect a yield of $7 worth of potatoes from each square. Help the family figure out what the value of their whole potato crop would be.

A Solution to the Garden Plot Problem

The members of the Smith family realize that if they are to solve the problem they must first figure out the number of small squares in their plot. They count them and get 33 squares. At $7 per square, that's 7 × 33 = $231.

THE FLOOR TILING PROBLEM

The Jaworskis are planning to tile their kitchen floor. They know that each square tile, a foot on a side, will cost them $3. They want to know what all the tiles for the kitchen will cost them. They have made a scale drawing of their kitchen, shown, in which each square represents a tile. Help them solve this problem.

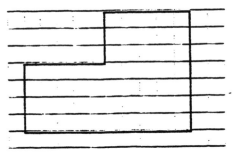

Please try to solve this first.

A Solution to the Floor Tiling Problem

The Jaworskis, like the Smiths, realize that to figure out the cost of the tiles for their kitchen, they must count the number of squares in the scale drawing. They do this and get 55 squares. At $3 per tile, that makes 3 × 55 = $165.

The Mathematical Idea: Area

In the garden plot problem, the Smiths wanted to know how many squares, a meter on a side, covered their plot. In the floor tiling problem, the Jaworskis wanted to know how many squares, a foot on a side, covered their kitchen floor.

Common units of area are squares with sides of common units of length: inch, foot, yard, mile, centimeter, meter, and kilometer. The units of area are usually called the *square inch, square foot, square yard, square mile, square centimeter, square meter, and square kilometer,* respectively.

THE SECOND GARDEN PLOT PROBLEM

The Ronstadts have planted their garden plot, sketched below, in cotton. To figure out what their yield will be, they need to know what the area of their plot is in square yards.

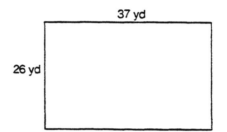

Please try this before reading the solution.

A Solution to the Second Garden Plot Problem

The Ronstadts realize that they must figure out how many squares, a yard on a side, exactly cover their garden plot. They decide to draw a scale drawing of their plot on graph paper, with each square representing a square yard.

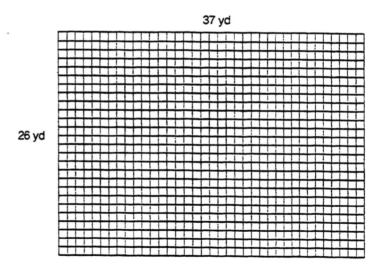

This turns their rectangular plot, 26 by 37 yd, into a 26 by 37 array, in which each item is a square yard. *Thinking of similar problems* involving arrays, they know that they don't have to count all the items: The number of items is the product of the number of rows (26) times the number of items in each row (37). Thus, they find that their plot has $26 \times 37 = 962$ yd^2 in it (yd^2 is a shorthand way of writing *square yards*; the superscript ^{2} with any unit of measure means "square" or "squared").

The Mathematical Idea: A Formula for the Area of a Rectangle

The solution to the second garden plot problem suggests a shortcut for determining the area of a region that happens to be a rectangle with sides a whole number of unit lengths. If these lengths are L and W units, then we can cover the rectangle with an L by W array of square units. The rectangle then has area LW square units. It would be tedious to have to count the square yards in the Ronstadt plot to determine its area. This formula represents a considerable saving in effort.

What about rectangles with sides that are not whole number lengths? We'll begin our investigation with a problem similar to one we did in chapter 9.

THE GOLD-PLATING PROBLEM

Try this first.

A dear friend has given you an antique rectangular medallion. The front needs to be gold plated. The cost of gold plating is \$12/in^2 of surface. The medallion measures $1\frac{1}{4}$ by $2\frac{2}{3}$ in. You want to know how much the gold plating will cost you.

A Solution to the Gold Plating Problem

You figure out that you must find the area of the rectangular medallion. Toward this end you draw a picture.

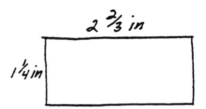

You *think of similar problems* involving area and decide to try turning the rectangle into an array of pieces all the same size. Then you will determine the number of pieces and figure out the area of just one of them. You decide to express the lengths of the sides as improper fractions, which enables you to divide up the rectangle naturally:

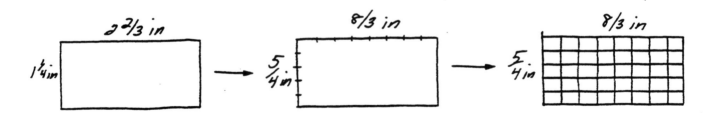

Your rectangle is now a 5 by 8 array of smaller, equal rectangles, each of which is $\frac{1}{4}$ by $\frac{1}{3}$ in. The area of the latter times 40 ($= 5 \times 8$) will give you the area of your medallion.

To figure out the area of the $\frac{1}{4}$ by $\frac{1}{3}$ in, you take a square inch, mark fourths on one side and thirds on the other. This, in turn, divides the square inch naturally into smaller rectangles each one of size $\frac{1}{4}$ by $\frac{1}{3}$ in.

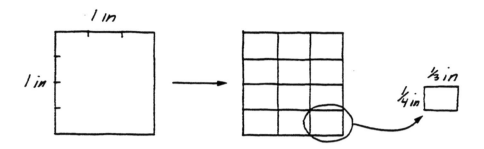

This makes the square inch into a 4 by 3 array of rectangles of size $\frac{1}{4}$ by $\frac{1}{3}$ in. A square inch has thus been cut up into $4 \times 3 = 12$ equal pieces. Each of the pieces must be $\frac{1}{12}$ in^2.

To complete the problem, we remember that the original medallion was divided into an 5 by 8 array of small rectangles. We have just shown that each small rectangle has area $\frac{1}{12}$ in^2. Thus,

$$\text{Area of medallion} = \frac{40}{12} = \frac{5 \times 8}{4 \times 3} = \frac{5}{4} \times \frac{8}{3} = 1\frac{1}{4} \times 2\frac{2}{3}$$

$$= 3\frac{4}{12} = 3\frac{1}{3} \text{ in}^2.$$

The Mathematical Idea: Fractions and Area

An important concept in the solution to the gold-plating problem is fractional area. The square inch is divided into 12 pieces of the same size and shape. It is assumed that each of these pieces has area equal to $\frac{1}{12}$ in^2. Thus, the rectangle of size $\frac{5}{4}$ by $\frac{8}{3}$ in has area $\frac{40}{12}$ in^2.

This suggests that the formula for the area of a rectangle with whole number sides works when the two sides are any fractional lengths. We can summarize this.

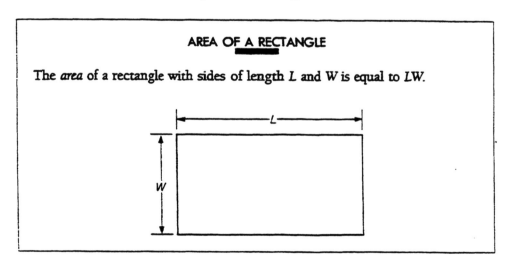

AREA OF A RECTANGLE

The *area* of a rectangle with sides of length L and W is equal to LW.

1. Find the areas of the rectangles.

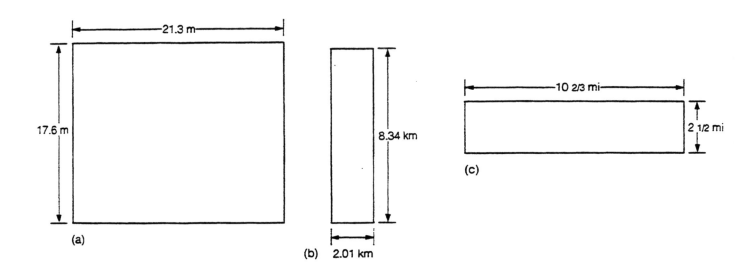

(a)

(b) 2.01 km

(c)

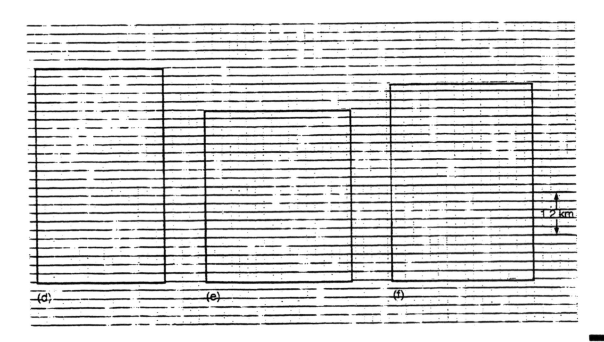

(d)   (e)   (f)

17.2   FORMULAS FOR AREA

THE THIRD GARDEN PLOT PROBLEM   The Joneses have a (right) triangular plot on which they grow alfalfa. A scale drawing of the plot, drawn on graph paper, is shown. Each square on the graph paper represents a square yard.

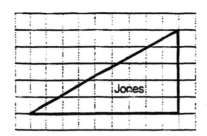

Please try this before
reading on.

Like the Smiths and the Jaworskis, the Joneses are interested in the value of the yield from their plot. Help them solve this problem.

A Solution to the Third Garden Plot Problem

The Joneses realize that if they are to solve the problem they must figure out the area of their plot. Unfortunately, their plot does not have the shape of a rectangle with an easily determined area. Furthermore, it is not easy to count the square yards one by one, because the plot as shown on the graph paper has many little pieces of square yards that are not themselves rectangles.

Tom Jones has an idea: "Our plot is not a rectangle. Is there any way we can solve our problem by *solving a simpler problem* with rectangles? Look, our plot is sitting inside a larger rectangular plot.

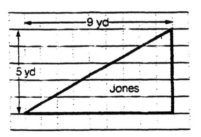

The area of that rectangle is 45 square yards. I notice that the rectangle is made up of two triangles, one of which is our plot and the other of which is congruent to our plot.

"The area of the other triangle is the same as the area of our plot. And the two equal areas should add up to the area of that rectangle. That means that the area of our triangular plot is half the area of the rectangle or $22\frac{1}{2}$ square yards."

The Mathematical Idea: Principles for Area and a Formula for the Area of a Triangle

In solving the third garden plot problem, Tom Jones used two facts (or principles) about area that we will find useful in solving other area problems. Both principles were also used to extend the formula for the area of a rectangle with whole-number sides to encompass rectangles with fractional sides.

1. Two regions that are congruent also have the same area.

2. If a region is broken up into two or more small pieces, then the area of the whole region is equal to the sum of the areas of the pieces.

Using these principles, Tom Jones showed that

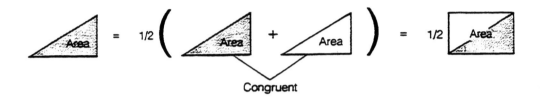

Consider two more examples in which these principles can be used to find areas.

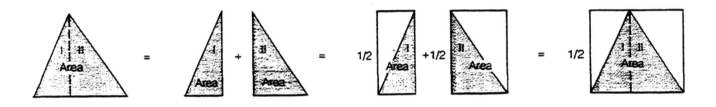

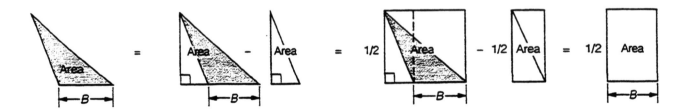

These three examples suggest a formula for finding the area of a triangle. First, a bit of terminology. Take a triangle, choose one of its sides, and place it along a horizontal line.

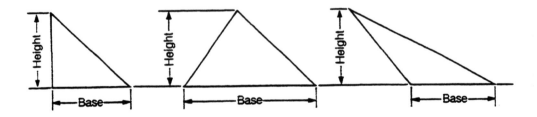

Call this side the *base* of the triangle. Draw a vertical line from the opposite vertex perpendicular to the horizontal line. The length of this line is called the *height* of the triangle relative to this base. Notice that the base and the height of the triangle depend on the choice of the side that is to function as the base.

FORMULA FOR THE AREA OF A TRIANGLE

Choose a side of the triangle to be its base. Call the length of this side B. Measure the height of the triangle relative to this base. Call this length H. Then the area of the triangle is equal to $\frac{1}{2}BH$.

EXERCISES 2. Find the areas of the triangles.

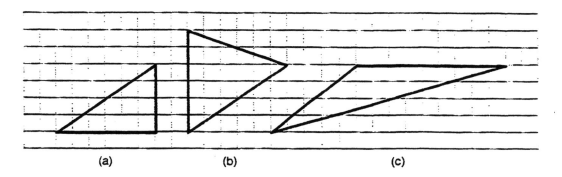

(a) (b) (c)

3. Use the principles and the formulas to find the areas of the shapes.

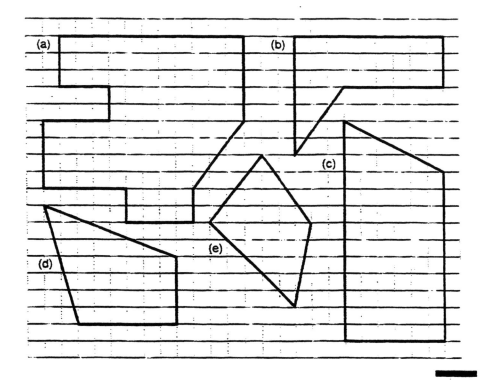

The Area of a Parallelogram

A *parallelogram* is a four-sided polygon such that pairs of opposite sides are parallel.

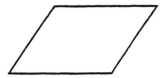

A rectangle is a special case of a parallelogram. There is a way to find the area of the illustrated parallelogram using the area of a rectangle (*a simpler problem*) and the principles for area presented earlier.

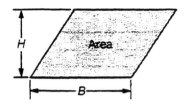 = 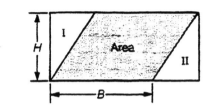 − =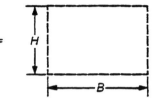

First find the length of one side of the parallelogram, calling this side the *base* of the parallelogram and orienting it horizontally. Then find the length of a vertical from the opposite side perpendicular to this horizontal, calling this length the *height* above the base. This information gives you a formula.

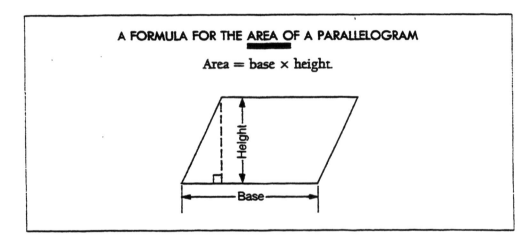

A FORMULA FOR THE AREA OF A PARALLELOGRAM

Area = base × height.

EXERCISE 4. Find the areas of the parallelograms.

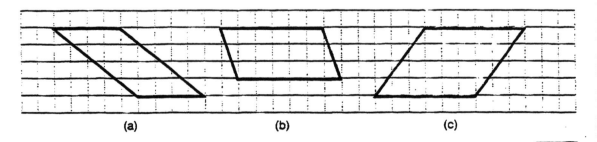

(a)　　　　(b)　　　　(c)

The Area of a Trapezoid

A *trapezoid* is a four-sided polygon having one pair of sides that is parallel and another pair that isn't.

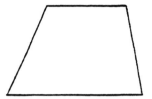

There is a way to find the area of a trapezoid using the area of a triangle and the principles for area.

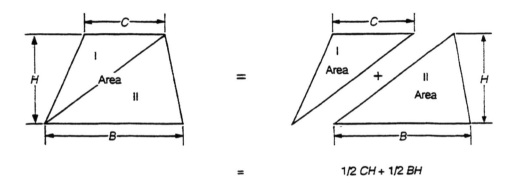

$$= \quad 1/2\ CH + 1/2\ BH$$

This gives us a formula for the area of a trapezoid.

FORMULA FOR THE AREA OF A TRAPEZOID

If the lengths of the two parallel sides of the trapezoid are B and C and the (vertical) distance between these two parallel sides is H, the *height* of the trapezoid, then

$$\text{Area of trapezoid} = \frac{1}{2}\,H(B + C).$$

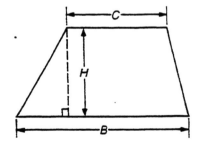

---

5. Find the areas of the following trapezoids.

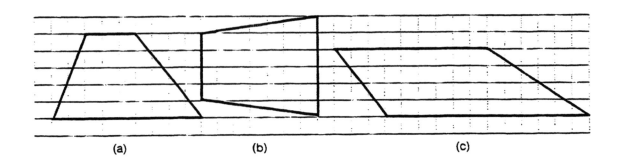

(a)   (b)   (c)

6. Use the principles and the formulas to help you find the areas of the shapes.

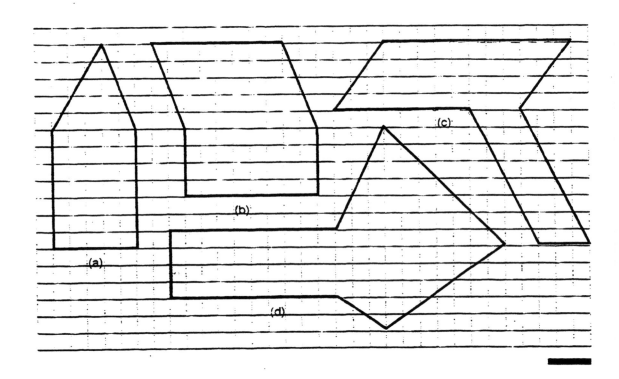

Look at the scale drawing of the Andrews' garden plot. Each square in the drawing represents a square yard. They want to find the area of their plot in square yards. Help them do this.

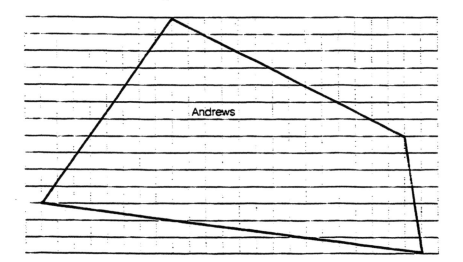

Try this yourself, first.

A Solution to the Fourth Garden Plot Problem

The Andrews family members quickly realize that their plot has a shape for which there is no area formula, no formula that they know of, in any case. Sally Andrews thinks of the principles for area and of how she can *break the problem up into simpler problems*. She divides the area up into two pieces.

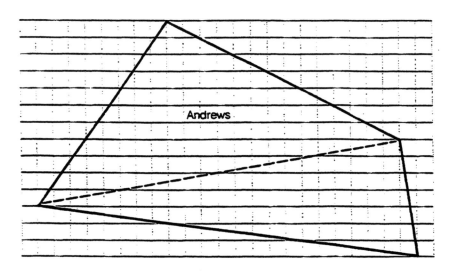

She thinks: "Each of those pieces is a triangle. I know how to find their areas. The area of the plot will be the sum of the areas of the two triangles. I will need to use another piece of graph paper to measure a base for each triangle and to measure the height on each base. Since the lines I will be measuring don't lie along horizontal or vertical lines of the graph, these measurements will be estimates.

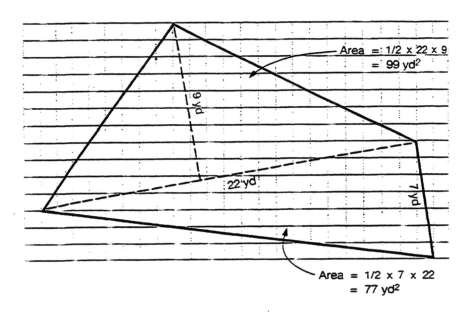

Area = 1/2 x 22 x 9
= 99 yd^2

9 yd

22 yd

7 yd

Area = 1/2 x 7 x 22
= 77 yd^2

The areas of the two triangles are about 99 square yards and 77 square yards. So the area of our plot is about 176 square yards."

Arthur Andrews has been looking on and suggests an alternative solution: "I have an idea for a solution that doesn't involve as much estimation. My idea is to put the scale drawing of our plot inside a rectangle with sides of lengths easy to figure out.

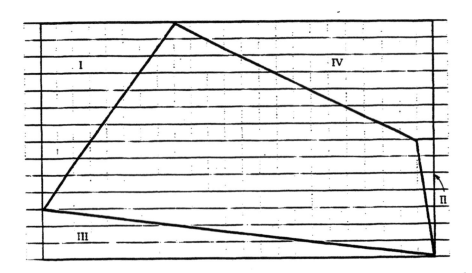

Since the sides of the rectangle are 14 yards and 23 yards, its area is 322 square yards. The area of the rectangle is also equal to the area of our plot plus the area of the three triangles and a trapezoid—labeled I, II, III, and IV, respectively. It's easy to figure out the areas of the triangles and trapezoid.

$$\text{Area of triangle I} = \frac{1}{2} \times 8 \times 11 = 44 \text{ yd}^2$$

$$\text{Area of triangle II} = \frac{1}{2} \times 1 \times 7 = 3\frac{1}{2} \text{ yd}^2$$

$$\text{Area of triangle III} = \frac{1}{2} \times 23 \times 3 = 34\frac{1}{2} \text{ yd}^2$$

$$\text{Area of trapezoid IV} = \frac{1}{2}(1 + 15)7 = 56 \text{ yd}^2$$

"Thus, we have the sums

$$\text{Area of rectangle} = 322 \text{ yd}^2$$
$$\text{Sum of areas of I, II, III, and IV} = 44 + 56 + 34.5 + 3.5 = 138 \text{ yd}^2$$

and can conclude

$$322 \text{ yd}^2 = 138 \text{ yd}^2 + \text{area of our plot,}$$

or

$$\text{Area of our plot} = 322 \text{ yd}^2 - 138 \text{ yd}^2 = 184 \text{ yd}^2.$$

That's a little different from what you got. But then I didn't have to do any estimating by eye."

The Mathematical Idea: Strategies for Finding Areas

We have used several strategies to find formulas for areas and to solve other area problems.

STRATEGY 1 *Break the problem up into simple problems.* Take a complicated area and break it up into "simple" pieces, pieces with areas you already know how to find.

STRATEGY 2 Add pieces to the region you are interested in to create a larger region. Do this so that the areas of the pieces you add as well as the area of the large region are easy to find. This strategy is a second way to *turn the original problem into a bunch of simpler problems.*

STRATEGY 3 Break the region you are interested in into pieces and rearrange the pieces into another region that has an area you know how to find. This strategy is a third way to *turn the original problem into a bunch of simpler, previously solved problems.*

STRATEGY 4 Use combinations of strategies 1 through 3. Use the principles for area, too.

7. Find the areas of the shapes using the strategies.

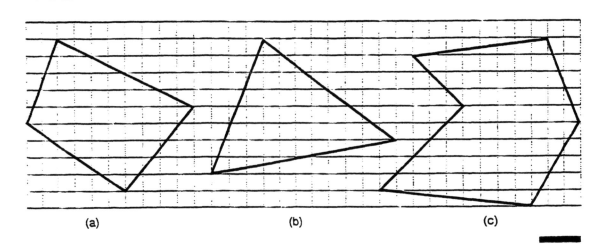

(a)   (b)   (c)

THE RUG PROBLEM

Try this yourself.

The Gonzales family is planning to have wall-to-wall carpeting laid in their living room. The members of the family have measured the living room floor and calculated its area to be 433.5 ft². They are now out looking in rug stores for ideas and prices and find that rugs are sold by the square yard. They realize that they need to know what the area of the floor is in square yards. Help them solve this.

A Solution to the Rug Problem

The members of the family figure that one way to solve the problem is to remeasure the living room in yards and from that calculate the area in square yards. If they can remember the measurements of the living room in feet, they can convert feet to yards and go from there.

Bernice Gonzales thinks out loud: "We know how many square feet the living room floor has: 433.5. What about a square yard? A yard is 3 feet in length. Here's a picture of a square yard.

1 yd

1 yd

I can divide the square yard into square feet easily.

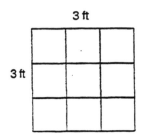

3 ft

3 ft

There are $3 \times 3 = 9$ square feet in a square yard. We've got 433.5 square feet. The number N of square yards in our living room floor times 9 should equal 433.5:

$$9N = 433.5.$$

The number we are looking for is $N = 433.5/9$, or about 48.17 square yards."

The Mathematical Idea: Area Conversions

Problems such as the rug problem arise when an area is calculated using one unit of area and you need to know what the area is in some other unit. These are problems of *conversion of units.*

One way to solve the Gonzales problem was suggested: Remeasure the room with the other units of length (yards) or convert one unit of length to the other (if you happen to know it). Here is a sketch of the Gonzales living room floor.

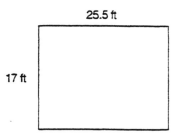

Since 1 yd = 3 ft, these measurements in yards are

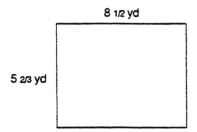

Thus, the area in square yards is $5\frac{2}{3} \times 8\frac{1}{2} \sim 48.17$ ft^2. This is what Bernice got.

The solution that Bernice used involved converting the units of area directly. She found that 1 yd^2 = 9 ft^2.

We can give more examples of conversions from one unit of area to another.

$$1 \text{ ft}^2 = 144 \text{ in}^2 \ (1 \text{ ft} = 12 \text{ in}; \ 12^2 = 144)$$

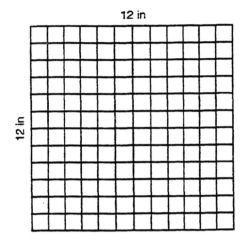

$$1 \text{ mi}^2 = 27{,}878{,}400 \text{ ft}^2 \ (1 \text{ mi} = 5280 \text{ ft}; \ 5280^2 = 27{,}878{,}400)$$

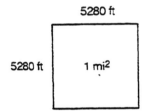

$$1 \text{ m}^2 = 10{,}000 \text{ cm}^2 \ (1 \text{ m} = 100 \text{ cm}; \ 100^2 = 10{,}000)$$

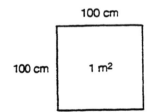

$$1 \text{ km}^2 = 1{,}000{,}000 \text{ m}^2 \ (1 \text{ km} = 1000 \text{ m}; \ 1000^2 = 1{,}000{,}000)$$

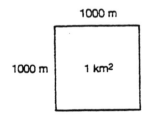

These conversions are not meant to be memorized! They are meant to give you a sample of typical conversions and how they are calculated.

8. An acre is a unit of area having the property that there are 640 acres in a square mile. How many square feet are there in an acre?

9. An average urban residential lot in the United States is $\frac{1}{4}$a. How much is this in square feet?

10. The area of 433.5 ft^2 is equal to how many square inches?

11. The area of 15,742,432 m^2 is equal to how many square kilometers?

12. The area of 5,350 in^2 is equal to how many square yards?

17.3 THE AREA OF A CIRCLE

THE CIRCULAR GARDEN PLOT PROBLEM

The Cohens own and operate a farm near Phoenix, Arizona. Because there is so little rainfall there, they must irrigate all cultivated land. They use a system that involves a long pipe to which nozzles that spray water are intermittently attached. One end of the pipe is fixed to a water source, while the rest of the pipe is on wheels and rotates about the fixed end.

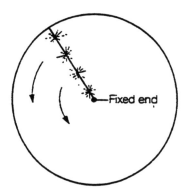

The Cohen farm consists of several of these circular fields. The family is interested in comparing the yield of their fields with the yields of other farms in Arizona and in other parts of the country. Yield is typically measured in so many pounds per square yard. The family knows their yield from last summer, and they know how many circular fields they had under cultivation. What they need to know is the area of each circular field.

A Solution to the Circular Garden Plot Problem

Tom Cohen thinks: "Is there some way we could *break up the circle into simple pieces?* I cut up a circle every time I cut up a pie. Let me draw a picture of that.

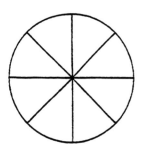

That breaks the circle up into a lot of wedges that are almost triangles. Then the area of the circle is equal to the sum of the areas of all the triangularlike wedges. Let me cut out those wedges to see if I can rearrange them into some nice, simple shape.

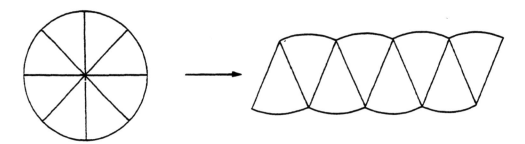

"That's sort of a parallelogram. If I had cut the circle up into many more, smaller, wedges, then the shape would be even more like a parallelogram. A parallelogram is a shape with an area I know how to find:

Area of parallelogram = length of base × height.

The "base" of this "parallelogram" is half the circumference of the original circle. The "height" of this "parallelogram" is a radius of the original circle. That leads me to

Area of the circle = area of "parallelogram" ≅ half the circumference × radius of circle.

"Since

Circumference of circle of radius $R = 2\pi R$,

Half the circumference of circle of radius $R = \pi R$.

That means that

Area of circle of radius $R \cong \pi RR$,

or

Area of circle of radius $R \cong \pi R^2$.

That should be pretty useful!"

The Mathematical Idea: A Formula for the Area of a Circle

The solution to the circular garden plot problem suggests that there is a formula for finding the area of a circle once you know its radius R.

FORMULA FOR THE AREA OF A CIRCLE

Area of circle of radius $R = \pi R^2$.

As the wedges in Tom Cohen's argument become smaller and smaller, the "parallelogram" becomes more and more like a "real" parallelogram, and it becomes increasingly plausible that the formula is a true formula for the area of a circle. With more advanced techniques, such as those of calculus, a more rigorous argument justifying this formula could be provided; but that is beyond the scope of this book. We will accept this as the formula for the area of a circle.

Now let's make the formula work for us. Recall that we used angle measure and the formula for the circumference of a circle to find the length of an arc of a circle. We can also use angle measure and the formula for the area of a circle to find the area of a pie-shaped piece of a circle, a shape formed by two radii and an arc.

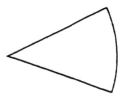

Such a piece is called a *sector* of a circle. If you measure the angle formed by the two radii and find that it measures 1°, then you would agree that the area of the sector is $\frac{1}{360}$ the area of the whole circle. If the angle, called the *angle of the sector*, measured 10°, then the area of the sector would be $\frac{10}{360}$ of the area of the whole circle.

FORMULA FOR THE AREA OF A SECTOR OF A CIRCLE

For a sector of angle D degrees in a circle of radius R,

$$\text{Area of sector} = \frac{D}{360}\pi R^2.$$

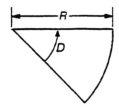

For example, suppose you have a sector with an angle of 15° in a circle of radius 10 ft, then from the formula

$$\text{Area of the sector} = \left(\frac{15}{360}\right)\pi \, 10^2 \cong .0417 \times 3.14 \times 100 = .0417 \times 314 = 13.09 \text{ ft}^2.$$

EXERCISES 13. Find the areas of the circles and sectors of circles.

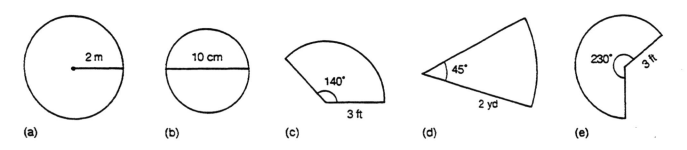

(a)   (b)   (c)   (d)   (e)

14. Roofing material is sold by the square foot. Roofing material is needed for each flat roof indicated. Find the area of each roof.

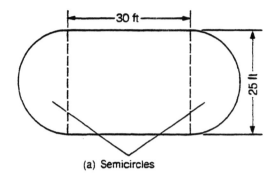

(a) Semicircles

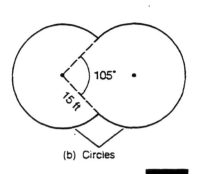

(b) Circles

17.4   EFFICIENT SHAPES

THE GARDEN FENCING
PROBLEM

Try this yourself.

You are planning to dig a garden. Because of the rabbits and squirrels that live nearby, you must surround the garden with a fence. You have purchased 160 ft of fencing, which is all you can afford. The garden is to be in the shape of a rectangle. You are wondering what the length and the width of the rectangle should be. You want the area of the garden to be as large as possible, of course, but as long as you make a rectangle using up all the fencing, will the dimensions of the rectangle make a difference? And if this does make a difference, what should the dimensions of the rectangle be in order to have the largest possible area?

A Solution to the Garden Fencing Problem

You decide to begin by *making some guesses*. You think: "Suppose my garden has a width of 10 feet. I've got 160 feet of fencing. One side will use up 10 feet; the opposite side will use up 10 feet. That leaves me 160 feet − 20 feet = 140 feet for the other two sides. I could use up only a part of the 140 feet. For example, I could make each of the other two sides 20 feet, which would then use up 40 of the 140 feet.

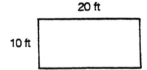

But certainly I would have a larger area if I use up *all* of the 140 feet. If I were to use all the 140 feet on the other two sides, then each side would have to be 70 feet.

70 ft

10 ft

The area of this garden is 10 feet × 70 feet = 700 square feet. Is that the largest area I can get? Let me try another width: 15 feet. That and the opposite side would use up 30 feet of the fencing, leaving 130 feet for the other two sides. If I use up all this remaining fencing (which I must), then the *other* two sides must have length 65 feet each.

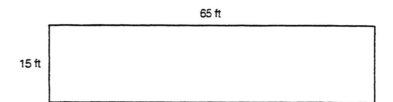

"The area of *this* garden is 15 feet × 65 feet = 975 square feet. That's a greater area than the other garden. That means that the dimensions of the rectangle do have an effect on the area—even when all the fencing is used up! Let me *make a chart* showing what I know already.

WIDTH	LENGTH	PERIMETER (MUST = 160 FT)	AREA
10 ft	70 ft	160 ft	700 ft²
15 ft	65 ft	160 ft	975 ft²

Let me try some more choices.

WIDTH	LENGTH	PERIMETER (MUST = 160 FT)	AREA
10 ft	70 ft	160 ft	700 ft²
15 ft	65 ft	160 ft	975 ft²
20 ft	60 ft	160 ft	1200 ft²
25 ft	55 ft	160 ft	1375 ft²
30 ft	50 ft	160 ft	1500 ft²
35 ft	45 ft	160 ft	1575 ft²
40 ft	40 ft	160 ft	1660 ft²

"The next width to consider would be 45 feet. That would mean a length of 35 feet. A rectangle of width 45 feet and length 35 feet is really the "same" as a rectangle of width 35 feet and length 45 feet (it's just tilted on its side). That rectangle is already considered on the chart. When the width is equal to 40 feet, the width and the length are the same. For every rectangle with a width bigger than 40 feet (and thus with a length less than 40 feet) there is an "equal" rectangle with width less than 40 feet. It's enough to look at rectangles with widths 40 feet or less.

"If I'm going to add more to the chart, I should add guesses between the values I've already got. Before doing that, let me *look for patterns*. One thing I see is that as widths increase from 10 feet to 40 feet, the areas increase as well. Does the rectangle with width of 40 feet have the greatest area? Maybe between a rectangle of width 35 feet and one of 40 feet the area gets larger, then smaller. Let me try a few values.

WIDTH	LENGTH	PERIMETER (MUST = 160 FT)	AREA
35 ft	45 ft	160 ft	1575 ft^2
40 ft	40 ft	160 ft	1600 ft^2
37 ft	43 ft		1591 ft^2
39 ft	41 ft		1599 ft^2

"It looks as if the pattern persists: As widths increase to 40 feet, areas increase, too. So it appears that a rectangle of width 40 feet and length 40 feet is my best bet. That's a square!"

The Mathematical Idea: Efficient Shapes

According to the solution to the garden fencing problem, it seems that if you set out to make a rectangular garden with a fixed amount of fencing, then the best you can do is to split up the fencing into four equal pieces and make a square garden. The square is the *most efficient* rectangle for this situation. It will give you the most area for your fencing. We arrived at this conclusion by *making guesses and organizing them into a chart*. We might be even more convinced if we *made a graph* of area versus width. We add a few widths to the previous table to make the table of values we want to plot yield a more effective graph.

WIDTH (FEET)	AREA (SQUARE FEET)	WIDTH (FEET)	AREA (SQUARE FEET)
5	375	45	1575
10	700	50	1500
15	975	55	1375
20	1200	60	1200
25	1375	65	975
30	1500	70	700
35	1575	75	375
40	1600		

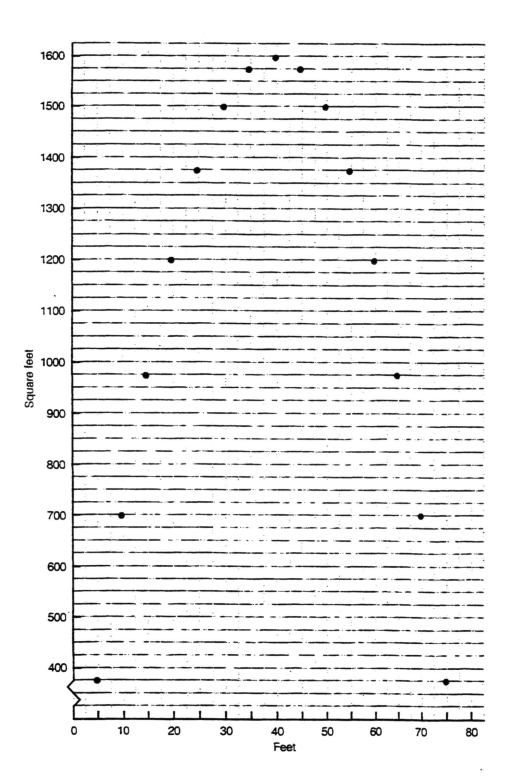

15. You are building an outdoor storage area for lumber and tools. You want the area to be in the shape of a rectangle having 900 ft². You want to know what dimensions of the rectangle would minimize the cost of the fencing that will surround it. Will the dimensions of the rectangle make any difference as long as the rectangle has an area of 900 ft²? (*Warning:* This is not the same as the garden fencing problem, in which the *perimeter* was fixed. In this problem, the *area* is fixed.)

17.8   SUMMARY OF IMPORTANT IDEAS AND TECHNIQUES

- The area of a rectangle with whole-number sides
- The area of a rectangle with fractional sides
- A formula for the area of any rectangle
- Development of formulas for areas of triangles, parallelograms, and trapezoids
- Useful principles and strategies for finding areas
- Formula for the area of a circle
- Formula for the area of a sector of a circle
- Efficient rectangular shapes: with fixed perimeter, the rectangle having the greatest area; with fixed area, the rectangle having the least perimeter
- Constructing graphs of quadratic functions
- Tiling patterns

PROBLEM SET

**PRACTICING
SKILLS**

1. Find the areas of the rectangles: (a) length $3\frac{1}{4}$, width $2\frac{1}{3}$ and (b) length 2, width $3\frac{2}{3}$.

2. Use an argument similar to that found in "Solution to the Gold Plating Problem" to show that a rectangle $3\frac{5}{8}$ by $2\frac{1}{3}$ has area $\frac{203}{24}$.

3. Find the areas of the right triangles: (a) length of base 2, height $3\frac{1}{2}$ (b) length of base $3\frac{1}{3}$, height $2\frac{1}{2}$.

4. Use an argument similar to that found in "Solution to the Third Garden Plot Problem" to show that a right triangle with a base $3\frac{1}{3}$ cm long and height $2\frac{1}{2}$ cm has an area $\frac{50}{6}$ cm.

5. Find the areas of the pastures. Each square in the grid has sides equal to 1 ft.

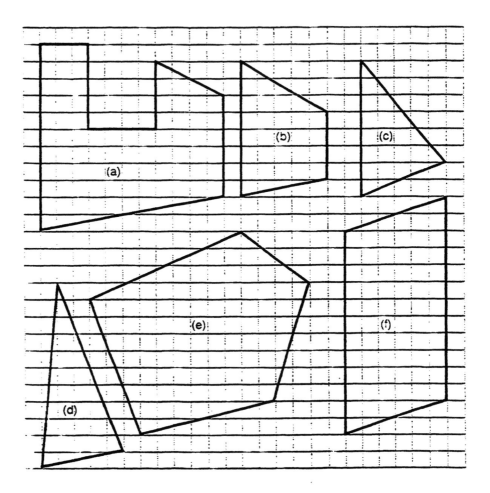

6. How many square yards are in a square mile?

7. If the area of a room is 108 yd², what is its area in square feet? In square inches?

8. If the area of a garden is 218 ft², what is its area in square yards?

9. Find the areas of the circles and sectors of circles.

(a) 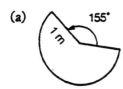   155°   1 m

(b) 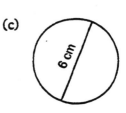   2 ft   120°

(c) 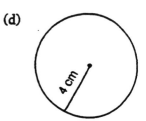   6 cm

(d) 4 cm

10. Find the area of the window.

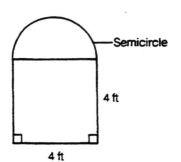

Semicircle

4 ft

4 ft

11. Find the dimensions of the rectangle of least perimeter with area 625 ft².

12. Find the rectangle of largest area with perimeter 12 ft.

13. Graph the functions.
    (a) $D(T) = T^2$
    (b) $D(T) = 5T^2$
    (c) $D(T) = 5(T - 1)^2$
    (d) $D(T) = (T + 1)^2$
    (e) $D(T) = 5(T + 1)^2 + 3$
    (f) $D(T) = 5(T - 1)^2 + 3$
    (g) $D(T) = 5(T + 1)^2 - 3$
    (h) $D(T) = 5(T - 1)^2 - 3$

14. Graph the functions.
    (a) $D(T) = -T^2$
    (b) $D(T) = -2T^2$
    (c) $D(T) = -2(T - 1)^2$
    (d) $D(T) = -2(T + 1)^2$
    (e) $D(T) = -2(T - 1)^2 + 2$
    (f) $D(T) = -2(T - 1)^2 - 2$
    (g) $D(T) = -2(T + 1)^2 + 2$
    (h) $D(T) = -2(T + 1)^2 - 2$

15. Write a program in BASIC to solve problem 11.

16. Write a program in BASIC to solve problem 12.

USING IDEAS *Write the solution to each remaining problem carefully and clearly in the form of an essay. In it mention the steps you took to solve the problem, the principles, tools, or formulas you used, other problems or solutions that gave you ideas, and the problem-solving strategies you found helpful.*

17. Here is the western end of a house that is to be stuccoed. To determine the cost of the stuccoing, you need to know the area. What is it?

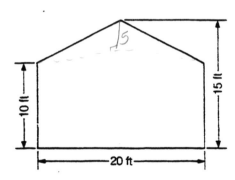

18. It ought to be possible to determine the area and perimeter of a region by figuring out the area and perimeter of a scale drawing of the region.
    (a) Find the area and perimeter of each square and compare them.

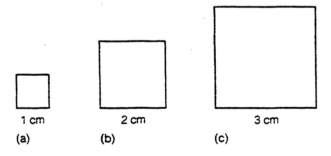

| 1 cm | 2 cm | 3 cm |
| (a) | (b) | (c) |

(b) Find the area and perimeter of each rectangle and compare them.

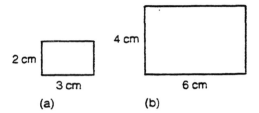

(a)   (b)

(c) Find the area and perimeter of each triangle and compare them.

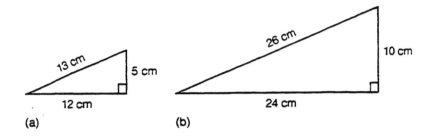

(a)   (b)

(d) Suppose the ratio of lengths of an original to a scale drawing is 5 to 3. Suppose the perimeter of the scale drawing is 21 ft. What is the perimeter of the original? Suppose the area of the scale drawing is 12 ft². What is the area of the original?

(e) Find a general rule for comparing the perimeter of a scale drawing with the perimeter of the original. Find a general rule for comparing the area of a scale drawing with the area of the original.

19. A store sells two types of gift wrapping paper. Type A has four rolls in each package, each roll is 75 by 150 cm, and the package costs $5.98. Type B has a single roll that is 88 by 500 cm and costs $6.38. Which choice gives you more paper for the money?

20. Your backyard has a pool and patio. You are thinking of tiling your patio with mosaic tiles. To figure out how much it would cost, you need to know its area. Find it.

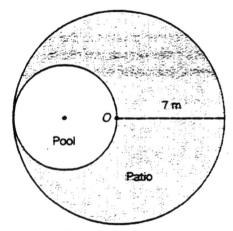

Point O is the center of
the larger circle.

21. In a park there is a circular garden of diameter 26 ft. Maintenance personnel will be building a circular sidewalk 3.5 ft wide to surround the garden. To figure out how much concrete they will need, they need to know the surface area of the sidewalk. What is it?

22. For tax purposes, buildings are assessed at a rate of $189/m².

   Rectangular: 8 m by 13.75 m
   L-shaped: 8.7 by 11 m plus 8 by 9.5 m

   The tax rate is $52 for every $1000 of assessment. What must the owners of each of these houses pay in real estate taxes?

23. Here is a picture of your house and the lot on which it is situated. You plan to sow grass everywhere on the lot except where the house is. You will need 1 lb of grass seed for every 100 ft² of ground to be covered. How many pounds of grass seed will you need?

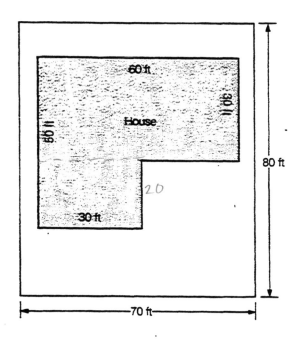

24. Which of these two pasture has the largest area, (a) or (b)? Which needs the most fencing?

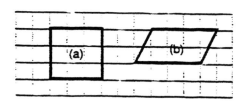

25. The floor plan of your kitchen and eating room shows that the whole room is a rectangle. You plan to lay new linoleum on the parts of the floor not shaded in. Using the measurements given, find the area in square feet of the part to be covered with linoleum.

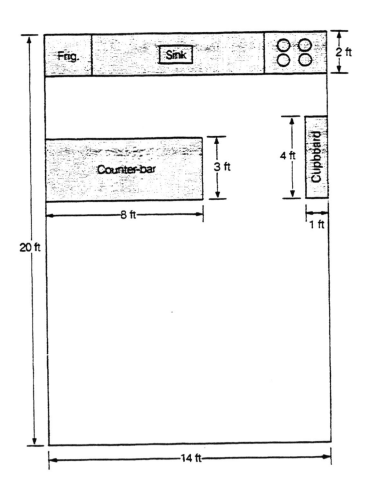

26. You plan to paint a bedroom with a square-shaped floor 12 ft on a side and a ceiling that slopes from a height of 9 ft 6 in on one side to 7 ft on the other. The room has a 30 in by 6 ft 8 in doorway, a 5 by 6 ft closet opening, and a 40 by 60 in window opening. About how much paint will be needed to paint the walls of this room with two coats, if 1 qt of paint covers about 110 ft²? Do the door, window, and closet openings significantly affect the calculation of how much paint to buy?

27. A chair with thin legs can be tough on floors when it is tilted back. To see why, suppose the legs of a chair are round with a bottom diameter of 1 in and suppose the chair is occupied by a person weighing 200 lb.
    (a) What is the pressure (in pounds per square inch) exerted on the floor when the person is sitting squarely and all four legs of the chair are on the floor?
    (b) What is the pressure on the floor when the person is tilted back and only $\frac{1}{10}$ of the two rear legs of the chair have contact with the floor?

28. You plan to build a pen for your goat. It will be a rectangular pen with area 25 m². One side of the pen will be an existing wall of your house. What length and width of the pen will require the smallest amount of fencing? How much fencing material will you need in this case?

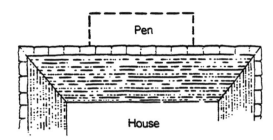

29. You and a neighbor are planning to plant gardens side by side as in the picture, with fencing all around and dividing the two plots. The two of you together can afford a total of 100 ft of fencing. What should the dimensions of the big plot be in order that area of the two gardens be as large as possible?

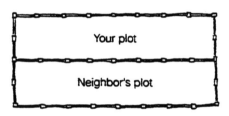

30. Trees lose moisture through their leaves. The amount of moisture lost is directly related to the total surface area of a tree's leaves. Estimate the area of the leaf below. Assume that each square in the grid is ¼ in on a side.

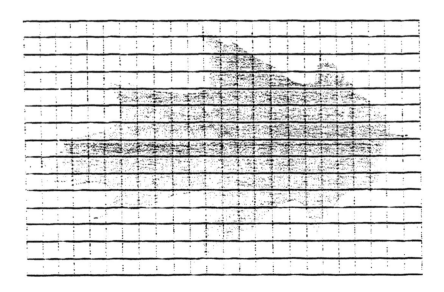

31. A scale drawing of the Palm Grove subdivision is shown.

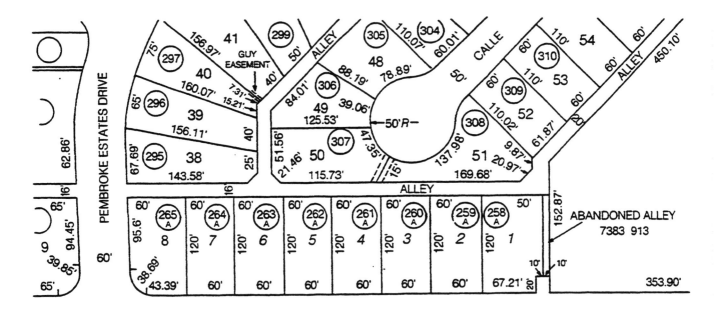

You are thinking of purchasing lot number 308. If you buy it, you will place mobile homes on the lot and rent them out. The county requires an area of 350 ft² for every mobile home. To determine what your income from the lot would be, you want to know how many mobile homes you can place on the lot. Thus, you need to find the area of the lot. Since the lot has an irregular shape, this requires some ingenuity. You decide to: (a) enlarge the scale drawing of the lot using a fancy photo copier, (b) trace the outline of the lot onto graph paper, (c) estimate the number of squares that would cover the enlargement, (d) figure out the area of each of these squares in real life, and (e) multiply the answer in (d) by the answer in (c).

We've done (a). Carry out the rest of the procedure to estimate the area of the lot and determine the number of mobile homes allowed on it.

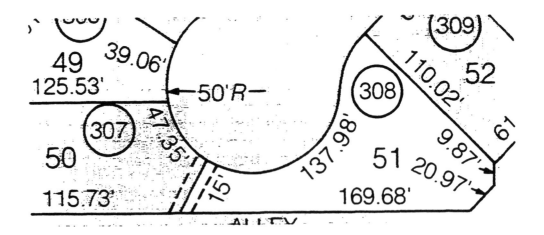

SOLUTIONS TO SELECTED PROBLEMS

CHAPTER 1

Exercise Answers

1. 3 more days 2. 16 inches 3. walk about 4/5 mile, exact answer 45/56 mile 4. 10 or 11 order large dishes, there may be more answers 5. 1 boy 3/8 bottle/wk; 1 girl 4/15 bottle/wk; boys use 12/120 more/wk 8. 47 lb peanuts, 23 lb cashews 9. must sell 6 color 10. 10:17 pm 11. 5:36 am 12. 2 13. 2 14. 3 15. no 16. $23 17. (a) [2][+][5][×][2][0][=]
(b) [([2][+][5][)][×][2][0][=] (c) [2][+][5][×][2][0][+][3][=] (d) [([2][+][5][)][×][2][0][+][3][=]
(e) [([2][+][5][)][×][([2][0][+][3][)][=] (f) [2][+][5][×][([2][0][+][3][)][=] 18. (a) [([4][+][5][+][6][)][÷][3][=]
(b) [2][0][÷][([4][+][6][)][=] (c) [([1][0][+][1][2][+][1][6][)][÷][([9][+][1][0][)][=]
19. (a) [1][7][×][([1][3][×][([2][3][+][5][9][)][−][5][7][)][+][2][9][=]
(b) [([1][2][×][1][4][+][2][4][×][3][3][)][÷][([3][7][×][4][2][+][5][7][)][=]
(c) [([7][×][([5][2][−][1][7][)][+][1][3][)][÷][([8][3][−][3][5][)][=] 21. $106.80, $147.60, $78.00, $56.40
23. (a) prints N^2 (b) prints "This program will square a number. What number do you want to square? N^2"
(c) square all the numbers from 1 to 10 (d) prints all the numbers from 1 to 10 with their square (e) no difference
(f) open-ended loop, l must be loaded in separately (g) increments p by 2 (h) prints headings for the columns

Practicing Skills Answers

1. Bill $4.50, Bryan $1.50 3. 2.5 hours, 3:30 am 5. $60.89 7. smaller, guess (a) 9. 16¢ 11. 6:40 a.m. 13. Chef Andres, Farmer Cohen, Teller Brown 15. yes

CHAPTER 3

Exercise Answers

3. more sheepskins than spears 4. 1 minute = 60 seconds; 1 hour = 60 minutes; 1 day = 24 hours; 1 week = 7 days; 1 year = 52 weeks 5. 1 cup = 8 ounces; 1 pint = 2 cups; 1 quart = 2 pints; 1 gallon = 4 quarts; 1 barrel = 42 gallons (This may vary.) 6. Farida has more than enough wheat. 7. (abacus/numeral figures) 99 |||||| 8. The larger number is on the left. 9. (a) $165 = 1 \times 100 + 6 \times 10 + 5$;

(b) $4073 = 4 \times 1000 + 0 \times 100 + 7 \times 10 + 3$; (c) $17{,}078 = 1 \times 10{,}000 + 7 \times 1{,}000 + 0 \times 100 + 7 \times 10 + 8$;
(d) $245{,}673 = 2 \times 100{,}000 + 4 \times 10{,}000 + 5 \times 1000 + 6 \times 100 + 7 \times 10 + 3$ 10. 2,542 12. 6304

13. 14. one ⊢, two ⊨, three ≡, four ≣, five ⌐, six ⌐, ..., nine ⌐, ten †, eleven †, ..., sixteen ⊧, etc.

15. + | ≢ 16. (a) ≢ ≢ | ≢ smaller than ≢ ≢ + | (b) ≢ | | ∓ larger than + ≢ ≢ ≢
(c) ≣ ≢ | + smaller than ≣ ≢ + | 17. (a) 10^6 (b) 10^9 (c) 10^{12}

18. (a) $12{,}378 = 1 \times 10^4 + 2 \times 10^3 + 3 \times 10^2 + 7 \times 10 + 8$ (b) $508{,}122 = 5 \times 10^5 + 0 \times 10^4 + 8 \times 10^3 + 1 \times 10^2 + 2 \times 10 + 2$
(c) $89{,}142{,}693 = 8 \times 10^7 + 9 \times 10^6 + 1 \times 10^5 + 4 \times 10^4 + 2 \times 10^3 + 6 \times 10^2 + 9 \times 10^1 + 3$ 19. 39,487 20. 203 21. 299
22. 10333_{six} 23. 1707_{eight} 24. 1111000111_{two} 25. (a) 4201 (b) 25 (c) 1281 (d) 40,803 (e) 82,853

26. (a)  (b) (c)

27. The scale below is $\frac{11}{4}$ inch = 125 million miles

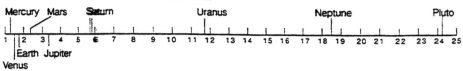

28. The following scale is $\frac{1}{4}$ inch = 500

29. (a) $A \leq B$ (b) $A \leq B$ (c) $A > B$ (d) $A < B$

Practicing Skills Answers

3. (a) 2058 (b) 3000 (c) 1111 (d) 9109 5. The bottom one is larger. 7. (a) 452 (b) 31 (c) 3,142

9. (a) 13,423 (b) 3021 11. (a) ╪│ (b) ╪╪╪╪ (c) ╪││ (d) ╪╪│ (e) ╪╪╪╪ (f) ╪╪│ 13. (a) 4214 > 3124 (b) 3210 < 31,320 15. (a) 3243 (b) 437 (c) 115 (d) 714 17. (a) 50,593 (b) 3148

Review Test: Chapters 1, 2, 3

1. E 2. C 3. B 4. B 5. E 6. D 7. A 8. E 9. E 10. B 11. 12 12. 13°C 13. no 14. 46¢

CHAPTER 4

Exercise Answers

1. two camels extra 2. 84 3. ╪╪ 4. (a) 843 (b) 1315 5. ╪│╪╪ 6. (a) 843 (b) 1315 7. ╪│╪╪ 8. (a) 843 (b) 1315 9. ╪│╪╪ 10. ╪│╪╪ 11. 1 + 1 = 2, 1 + 2 = 3, 1 + 3 = 4, 1 + 4 = 5, 1 + 5 = 10, 2 + 2 = 4, 2 + 3 = 5, 2 + 4 = 10, 2 + 5 = 11, 3 + 3 = 10, 3 + 4 = 11, 3 + 5 = 12, 4 + 4 = 12, 4 + 5 = 13, 5 + 5 = 14, 15 − 5 = 10, 15 − 4 = 11, 15 − 3 = 12, 15 − 2 = 14, 15 − 1 = 14, 14 − 5 = 5, 14 − 4 = 10, 14 − 3 = 11, 14 − 2 = 12, 14 − 1 = 13, 13 − 5 = 4, 13 − 4 = 5, 13 − 3 = 10, 13 − 2 = 11, 13 − 1 = 12, 12 − 5 = 3, 12 − 4 = 4, 12 − 3 = 5, 12 − 2 = 10, 12 − 1 = 11, 11 − 5 = 2, 11 − 4 = 3, 11 − 3 = 4, 11 − 2 = 5, 11 − 1 = 10, 10 − 1 = 5, 10 − 2 = 4, 10 − 3 = 3, 10 − 4 = 2, 10 − 5 = 1, 5 − 1 = 4, 5 − 2 = 3, 5 − 3 = 2, 5 − 4 = 1, 4 − 1 = 0, 4 − 2 = 2, 4 − 3 = 1, 3 − 1 = 2, 3 − 2 = 1, 2 − 1 = 1 12. 34 13. 47 14. ╪╪ 15. 167

16. 267 17. ╪╪╪ 18. (a) 348 (b) 2816 19. (a) 14_{six} (b) 1224_{six} 20. (a) 348 (b) 2816 22. (a) 4049 (b) 32,338 (c) 4588 23. (a) 38 (b) 367 (c) 581 24. (a) $(a - b) + c \neq a - (b + c)$ (b) $(a + c) - b = a + (b - c)$ (c) $(a - b) - c \neq a - (b - c)$ (d) $a - (b + c) \neq (a - b) + c$ (e) $a - (b - c) \neq (a - b) - c$ (f) $(a + c) - b = a + (c - b)$ 25. (a) 25 (b) 68 (c) 28 (d) 4 (e) 24 (f) 429 26. (a) 43 (b) 63 29. yes 30. yes 31. (a) 900 to 1100 (b) 4300 to 4500 (c) 60,100 to 60,300 (d) 400 to 600 (e) 4000 to 4200 (f) 16,000 to 18,000

1. yes 3. (a) 982 (b) 1605 7. (a) 194 (b) 6649 9. (a) 4584 (b) 2557 11. (a) 103 (b) 17

CHAPTER 5

Exercise Answers

1. 962 2. ÷ ÷ 3. 43$_{eig}$ 4.

x	1	2	3	4	5	6	7
1	1	2	3	4	5	6	7
2	2	4	6	10	12	14	16
3	3	6	11	14	17	22	25
4	4	10	14	20	24	30	34
5	5	12	17	24	31	36	43
6	6	14	22	30	36	44	52
7	7	16	25	34	43	52	61

5. 54 6. 962 7. ÷ ≡ ≡ ÷ 8. 120 9. 133$_{eight}$ 10. 270 11. 322$_{eight}$ 14. 560 18. 1440 19. 918 20. ÷ ≡ ≡ ÷

21. 25,228 22. ÷ | | | ≡ 23. (a) 1702$_{eight}$ (b) 32,552$_{eight}$ 24. 3876 25. 24 26. 60 27. (a) 3000; 4200

(b) 30,000; 80,000 (c) 300,000; 420,000 (d) 15,000,000; 24,000,000 28. (a) 5 (b) 4 (c) 7 (d) 6 (e) 10 30. 8

31.
```
  1 LET A = }
  2 LET B = } any numbers you choose.
  5 LET S = A
 10 FOR I = 1 to B
 15 PRINT S
 20 LET S = S + A
 30 NEXT I
100 END
```

Practicing Skills Answers

1. 962 7. 33,075 9. (a) 12 (b) 7 (c) 8 (d) 8 11. Grant 35 miles, Adam 42 miles 13. 30

CHAPTER 6

Exercise Answers

1. (a) ≡ (b) ÷ (c) ≡ 2. (a) 7$_{eight}$ (b) 4$_{eight}$ (c) 547$_{eight}$ (d) 123$_{eight}$ 3. 7 5. (a) 123 × 10 + 4

(b) 1436 × 100 + 28 6. (a) 47$_{eight}$ = 6$_{eight}$ × 6$_{eight}$ + 3 (b) 50$_{eight}$ = 5$_{eight}$ × 7$_{eight}$ + 5 (c) 1234$_{eight}$ = 123$_{eight}$ × 10$_{eight}$ + 4
(d) 143,627$_{eight}$ = 1436$_{eight}$ × 100$_{eight}$ + 27$_{eight}$ 8. 3 9. (a) 1542 ÷ 5 = 308 R2 (b) 2364 ÷ 5 = 472 R4 10. 542$_{eight}$ ÷ 6$_{eight}$ = 73$_{eight}$

11. 6072$_{eight}$ ÷ 5$_{eight}$ = 1162$_{eight}$ 12. 8 dolls 13. 253$_{eight}$ ÷ 32$_{eight}$ = 6 R17$_{eight}$ 14. ÷ ≡ ÷ ÷ ÷ ≡ = ≡ R ÷ |

15. (a) 60,983 ÷ 87 = 700 R83 (b) 57,041 ÷ 263 = 216 R233 16. (a) 653$_{eight}$ ÷ 7 = 75$_{eight}$ (b) 3054$_{eight}$ ÷ 41$_{eight}$ = 57$_{eight}$ R35$_{eight}$
17. 22 R9 19. 49 tables plus speaker's table 20. 52 miles east of city center at 11 am 21. (a) 4 (b) 4 (c) 5 (d) 3 (e) 1
22. Last Q value, 8, is quotient and last R value, 30, is remainder
23.
```
10 INPUT A,B
15 IF A<B GOTO 100
30 LET R=A
45 IF R<B THEN GOTO 100
50 LET R=R-B
```

Rest of program is unchanged.

1. repeated subtraction 3. repeated subtraction 5. 28 chairs 7. (a) $6862 \div 78 = 87$ R76 (b) $57,290 \div 59 = 971$ R1
(c) $1,873,402 \div 428 = 4377$ R46 9. $5 11. 11 13. (a) 4 (b) 1 (c) 3 (d) 6 (e) 3

Review Test: Chapters 4, 5, 6

1. C 2. D 3. C 4. A 5. E 6. A 7. A 8. C 9. B 10. E 11. 295 R36

12. (i)

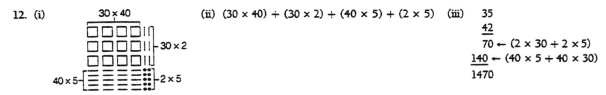

30 × 40

30 × 2

40 × 5

2 × 5

(ii) $(30 \times 40) \div (30 \times 2) + (40 \times 5) + (2 \times 5)$

(iii)
$$\begin{array}{r} 35 \\ 42 \\ \hline 70 \leftarrow (2 \times 30 + 2 \times 5) \\ 140 \leftarrow (40 \times 5 + 40 \times 30) \\ \hline 1470 \end{array}$$

CHAPTER 8

Exercise Answers

1. 3 and 4 sixths 2. (a) $\frac{1}{3} \neq \frac{1}{6}$ (b) $\frac{3}{4} = \frac{15}{20}$ (c) $\frac{10}{12} = \frac{15}{18}$ 3. (a) $\frac{2}{3} < \frac{5}{7}$ (b) $\frac{2}{3} > \frac{7}{11}$ (c) $\frac{7}{12} < \frac{5}{8}$ 4. $\frac{7}{15} > \frac{9}{20}, \frac{235}{500}, \frac{5}{500}$
5. 1 pt R5; 3 halfpints R3 or $27\frac{3}{7}$ oz 6. 6 R2 7. 7 to 11 8. strongest—Utah; weakest—New Mexico 9. (a) $\frac{1}{3}$; (b) $\frac{2}{5}$;
(c) $\frac{2}{11}$; (d) $\frac{4}{7}$; (e) $\frac{1}{5}$ 10. (a) 36; $\frac{28}{36}, \frac{15}{36}$ (b) 40; $\frac{6}{40}, \frac{35}{40}$ (c) 75; $\frac{12}{75}, \frac{40}{75}$ (d) 450; $\frac{160}{450}, \frac{219}{450}$ 13. $A - B - 1$
14. C any number, $D = C + m + 1$ 15. $\frac{13}{16}$ 16. any x where $\frac{5952}{24924} < x < \frac{7437}{24924}$ 17. $\frac{29}{32}, \frac{30}{32}$ and $\frac{31}{32}$

1. (a) $\frac{5}{6} = \frac{15}{18}$ (b) $\frac{15}{20} \neq \frac{24}{32}$ (c) $\frac{0}{3} = \frac{0}{1}$ (d) $\frac{3}{4} \neq \frac{3}{5}$ 3. (a) 19 (b) 6 (c) $5\frac{721}{1000}$ (d) $57\frac{21}{100}$ 5. (a) $\frac{11}{30}$ (b) $\frac{14}{15}$ (c) $\frac{40}{45}$ (d) $\frac{65}{108}$
(e) $\frac{3}{11}$ 7. $\frac{11}{60}$ left over 9. (a) 9 R2 (b) 12 (c) $6\frac{9}{11}$ 11. 11 to 20; 18 to 35 13. (b) $\frac{7}{12}; \frac{7}{3}$ (c) $\frac{3}{8}$ or $\frac{7}{8}$ 15. (a) $\frac{25}{60}; \frac{32}{60}$
(b) $\frac{100}{168}; \frac{49}{168}$ (c) $\frac{176}{363}; \frac{90}{363}$ (d) $\frac{260}{546}; \frac{378}{546}$ 17. (g) $\frac{3}{4}$ (h) $\frac{1}{2}$ (i) $\frac{1}{2}$ (j) $\frac{1}{3}$ (k) $\frac{1}{2}$ (l) $\frac{3}{3}$ (m) $\frac{40}{1}$ (n) $\frac{8}{1}$

C H A P T E R 9

Exercise Answers

1. $10\frac{2}{3}$ 2. 64 3. \$9 4. $6\frac{1}{4}$ 5. $\frac{3}{20}$ 6. $8\frac{17}{18}$ 7. $3\frac{15}{16}$ 8. 38 9. $13\frac{4}{17}$ 10. $\frac{25}{16}$ 11. $14\frac{10}{43}$ 12. $22\frac{1}{2}$ in 13. $\frac{10}{21}; 3\frac{59}{92}$ 14. (a) $\frac{17}{24}$
(b) $\frac{1}{6}$ (c) $\frac{203}{180}$ 15. (a) 60; 78 (b) 72; 90 (c) $5\frac{1}{3}; 6\frac{1}{8}$ (d) $3\frac{16}{21}; 4$ 16. (a) $\frac{169}{84}$ (b) $\frac{6}{7}$ (c) 1 17. (a) $\frac{5a}{4}$ (b) $\frac{c+d}{3}$ (c) xy
(d) a 18. $\frac{2(1+R)}{R}$ 19. $\frac{320x^2 + 10,000}{x}$ 20. $\frac{DT}{(T+D)}$ 25. $z = 2$

Practicing Skills Answers

1. 100 3. $\frac{3}{10}$ 5. 5 vests, $\frac{3}{8}$ yard left 7. 18 9. 72 chickens, 108 geese 11. (a) $\frac{1}{2}$ (b) $\frac{4}{7}$ (c) $\frac{245}{144}$ 13. (a) $2\frac{31}{70}$ (b) $\frac{11}{40}$
(c) $\frac{9}{14}$ (d) $\frac{15}{104}$ 15. $r_1 = \frac{Rr_2}{r_2 - R}$

Review Test: Chapters 7, 8, 9

1. C 2. A 3. E 4. B 5. D 6. E 7. C 8. E 9. A 10. C 11. 3/20 12. (a) 165 (b) 64.5
(c) 459 to 499 or about 9 to 10 13. 20 minutes 14. 11/15

CHAPTER 13

Exercise Answers

3. (b) $\frac{1}{2}$ meter   (c) 4160K   (d) 2 millimeters   (e) 3 centimeters   4. 75 ft; 36 m; 11.2 cm   5. $p = 4S$ 6. (a) 60 ft   (b) 100 m
(c) 80 inches ·   (d) 144 feet   (e) 48 centimeters   8. 21 miles   9. 70 ft   10. (b) 21.7 feet

14.
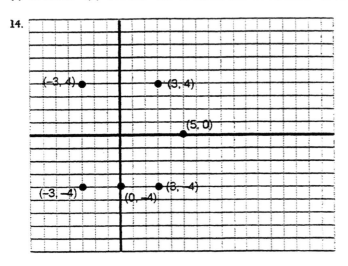

15. $A(-3,-3)$, $B(-7,0)$, $C(8,1)$, $D(0,3)$, $E(-6,3)$, $F(2,-5)$
16. isosceles right triangle; square; trapezoid; parallelogram; scalene triangle; trapezoid. All are convex.

17.
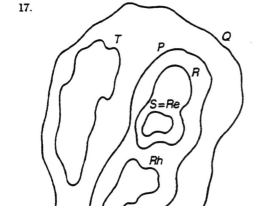

18.
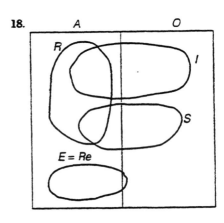

19. 5 lines; 1 line; 2 lines; none; 6 lines   20. (a), (b), and (d) have mirror symmetry

Practicing Skills Answers

1. (a) 140 m   (b) 100 m   (c) 120 m   (d) 310 ft   (e) 100 ft   (f) 130 ft   5. 2850 feet   7. 26 feet   9. c, d, and g are not possible

11.

Points plotted: (3, 8), (−2, 1), (−2, 0), (2, 1), (2, −1), (−2, −1), (0, −2), (−3, −8)

13. $34\frac{2}{7}$ in   15. (a) 250   (b) 650   (c) 1500   (d) 850   (e) 2450   (f) 1900   (g) 1700   (h) 1625

Exercise Answers

1. 374.88 m; 16.7634 km; $26\frac{2}{3}$ mi; 21.6 km; 20.16 km; 20.5344 km   2. 12; 18; 18   3. 99; 33; 37.9; 27; 69   4. 16; 18; 24

5. 30; 35; 42   6. 47.5; 72; 68; 106   7. 47; 42; 74   8. 43,560   9. 10,890   10. 62,424   11. 15.742432   12. about 4.128

13. 4π; 25π; $\dfrac{7\pi}{2}$; $\dfrac{\pi}{2}$; $\dfrac{23\pi}{4}$ 14. 1240.87; 1207.5497   15. 30 × 30

18.
```
 10 PRINT "WIDTH","LENGTH", "PERIMETER"
 20 FOR W=5 TO 30
 30 LET L=900/W
 40 LET P=2*L+2*W
 50 PRINT W,L,P
 60 NEXT W
100 END
```
21. squares, equilateral triangles, hexagons

Practicing Skills Answers

1. (a) $\dfrac{91}{12}$ (b) $\dfrac{22}{5}$ 3. (a) $\dfrac{7}{2}$ (b) $\dfrac{25}{6}$ 5. 82; 30; 21; 27.5; 101; 72   7. 972 ft^2; 139,968 in^2 9. $\dfrac{41\pi}{72}$ m^2; 12π ft^2; 9π cm^2; 16π cm^2

11. 25 × 25   15.
```
 10 PRINT "WIDTH", "LENGTH", "AREA"
 20 FOR W=5 TO 25
 30 LET L=625/W
 40 LET P=2*L+2*W
 50 PRINT W,L,P
 60 NEXT W
100 END
```

INDEX

SOLVING PROBLEMS USING

ELEMENTARY
MATHEMATICS

CONTENTS

LABORATORY MANUAL

TO ACCOMPANY

SOLVING PROBLEMS USING ELEMENTARY MATHEMATICS

PREFACE

This manual of laboratory activities was designed to be used with the text, *Solving Problems using Elementary Mathematics*. It could be used in *any* mathematics course (or course in the methods of teaching K-8 mathematics) for prospective or current elementary or middle school teachers.

Each activity is self-contained in the sense that, if you use it in conjunction with the text, you will need very little explanation beyond what is included in the instructions. Because you may encounter difficulties or get off track, a guide should be present—an instructor in the course or another qualified person—as a resource person and a facilitator of the problem-solving process. The guide should be attentive to your frustrations and help you to resolve them, not by giving you answers but by asking you questions that will lead you to discover the solutions to the problems yourselves.

You should work cooperatively, in a group with two or three other students, exploring the ideas and solving the problems in each activity.

Each activity involves the use of concrete materials (there are a couple of exceptions). Because many of these materials are commercially available for use with children in elementary and middle schools to help them learn mathematics, one purpose of these activities is to introduce you to items you might use when you teach mathematics. Another is to give you an experience of solving problems cooperatively with your fellow students using real objects. It is important that each activity be carried out using the appropriate, hands-on materials.

Each activity should take approximately 50 minutes to complete.

ORGANIZATION OF EACH ACTIVITY

The instructions for each lab activity are organized in the following way.

- Introduction.
- List of equipment needed for the activity.
- The point in the course where the activity should be used.
- The main activity.
- Extensions—additional, related activities.
- Reflections—questions about the educational value of the activity.
- Summary of important ideas and techniques.

CUTOUTS

Many of the hands-on materials needed for these activities can be assembled from pages in the back of this manual. Each activity indicates the pages where the cut-outs for that activity are located.

COMPUTERS

Four of the activities involve the use of microcomputers. One of these (LAB 1B) is an introduction to programming in BASIC. The other three (LABS 12, 14, and 22) involve the use of a computer spreadsheet. The particular commercially available spreadsheet for which these activities were designed is ALITE. An instructor who has adopted the text *Solving Problems Using Elementary Mathematics* may obtain this software (with user's manual) free by writing to the publisher, Dellen Publishing Company, 400 Pacific Avenue, San Francisco, CA 94133.

COMMERCIAL SOURCES OF MATERIALS
TO USE WITH THIS MANUAL

Source	Abbreviation
Activity Resources Company, Inc. P.O.Box 4875 Hayward, CA 94540	ARC
Creative Publications 5040 West 111th St. Oak Lawn, IL 60453	CP
Cuisenaire Company of America, Inc. 12 Church St., Box D New Rochelle, NY 10802	CCA
Dale Seymour Publications P.O.Box 10888 Palo Alto, CA 94303-0879	DS
Educational Teaching Aids 199 Carpenter Ave. Wheeling, IL 60090	ETA

TRADING CHIPS AND COUNTING BOARDS

Four hundred years ago or so persons in the Western world began to calculate with written numerals, much the way we do today. But people have been able to calculate for thousands of years. Children can also work with numbers before learning to write the abstract symbols representing them. The purposes of this lab are to see what you can do with numbers but without written or spoken numerals, to feel as child does while she learns a system for dealing with quantities, and to understand and appreciate our own system. To do all this we take you to the Kingdom of Zorandria.

EQUIPMENT NEEDED

- Chip Trading Set, commercially available from ARC, CCA and ETA. Alternatively, cut out sqaures (1/2" – 3/4") from yellow, green, red and blue paper.
- Counting Board. Use the pair of counting boards on pages 229 and 231 of this manual. (A commercial set of Trading Chips comes with one or more spindle boards which may be used in place of counting boards.)

WHEN TO USE THIS LAB

I suggest that you use this lab shortly before Chapter 3 or at the beginning of study of Chapter 3.

KINGDOM OF ZORANDRIA

In Zorandria, there are neither written nor spoken numerals. For transacting business the kingdom has developed a coinage system. The Royal Yellow Ⓨ is the basic coin. The other coins are worth more: Royal Green Ⓖ, the Royal Red Ⓡ, and the Royal Blue Ⓑ. The system is the following:

Ⓨ is the basic coin

Ⓖ is worth ⓎⓎⓎⓎ

Ⓡ is worth ⓖⓖ

Ⓑ is worth ⓇⓇⓇ

To indicate the price of a certain article, a Zorandrian merchant places a pile of Zorandrian coins on one side of a board in front of him. This is the price. A buyer shows his desire to buy the article by placing a pile of his own coins on the other side of the table. This is the offer. If the buyer's pile is worth the same or more than the merchant's pile, the merchant gives the buyer the article and keeps all the coins in the offer. (If the offer is worth more than the price, then the buyer is giving the merchant a tip!) If the offer is worth less than the price, this is the sign for bargaining to begin.

1. You are a Zorandrian rug merchant. The pile of coins on the right below is the price you have displayed for one of your lovely rugs. The pile of coins on the left is the buyer's offer.

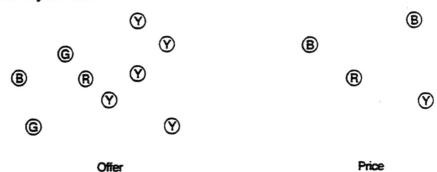

Offer   Price

You must decide which is worth more. Duplicate the two piles drawn above with Trading Chips and decide which is worth more. How you decide is up to you—there is no "right" method. But you must use only the two piles of coins; you must not use written or spoken numerals or pencil scratching.

What is your decision? _____

Describe in words and pictures how you would convince the buyer of your decision:

2. An affluent Zorandrian merchant has a cash box and allows himself (and his buyers) to trade any number of coins from a given pile for a coin or coins of equal worth from the cash box. For example, he can trade an ⓇBB in the buyer's pile for ⓖⓖ from the cash box. Or he can trade ⓇⓇⓇ in the price for ⒷBB from the cash box.

    This time you are a merchant with cash box. Allowing yourself to trade coins in the manner just described, decide which of the following piles is worth more:

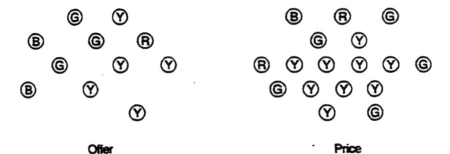

Offer   Price

Again, how you decide is up to you—but no spoken or written numbers or pencil scratching are allowed.

What is your decision? ______________________________

Describe in words and pictures a couple of ways you can make the decision:

Way #1:

Way #2:

What is the difference in worth between the offer and the price? Find the answer and draw a picture of it below as a pile of Zorandrian coins.

3. You, a merchant, have decided that a special rug is worth the following price:

Ⓑ Ⓑ Ⓖ Ⓖ Ⓖ
Ⓡ Ⓡ Ⓡ Ⓡ
Ⓨ Ⓨ Ⓨ Ⓨ Ⓨ Ⓨ Ⓨ

You have the option of displaying either this pile of coins or any other pile equal in value to it through a series of trades. Here are four such piles, each of value equal to the one just above.

Ⓑ Ⓑ Ⓡ	Ⓑ Ⓑ	Ⓑ	Ⓑ Ⓑ Ⓡ
Ⓡ Ⓡ Ⓡ	Ⓑ Ⓑ	Ⓑ Ⓡ Ⓡ	Ⓖ Ⓨ Ⓨ
Ⓖ Ⓖ Ⓖ	Ⓨ Ⓨ Ⓨ	Ⓡ Ⓡ Ⓡ	Ⓑ Ⓨ Ⓨ Ⓨ
Ⓖ Ⓨ Ⓨ Ⓨ		Ⓡ Ⓨ Ⓨ Ⓨ	Ⓡ Ⓨ Ⓨ
(a)	(b)	(c)	(d)

Which pile should you display? One pile may be best for comparing price with offer; another pile may be best for attracting a buyer. Discuss the advantages and disadvantages of displaying each of the piles above as the price.

4. A rich merchant may use a counting board (or a Spindle Board) on which to display the price and another on which to place the buyer's offer. To use the counting board, place Royal Yellows on the right-most box (or right-most spindle), Greens next, then Reds and finally Blues:

If the coins were removed from this counting board and put into a pile, they'd look like this:

Here are pictures of coins on two counting boards:

On counting boards (from pages 229 and 231 of this manual) set up real coins corresponding to those above and decide which is worth more, the offer or the price. You may trade as before; otherwise keep the coins on the counting boards.

What is your decision? _____

Describe in words and pictures how you came to your decision:

5. For the coins below, the offer is greater than the price:

Offer

Ⓑ	Ⓡ	Ⓖ	Ⓨ
Ⓑ Ⓑ Ⓑ Ⓑ	Ⓡ Ⓡ Ⓡ	Ⓖ Ⓖ	Ⓨ Ⓨ Ⓨ Ⓨ Ⓨ

Price

Ⓑ	Ⓡ	Ⓖ	Ⓨ
Ⓑ Ⓑ Ⓑ	Ⓡ Ⓡ Ⓡ	Ⓖ Ⓖ Ⓖ Ⓖ Ⓖ	

Set these coins up on your counting boards. From the offer board, remove an amount of coins equal in value to the price. You may do some trading along the way. Draw here a picture of what's left on the offer counting board:

Offer

Ⓑ	Ⓡ	Ⓖ	Ⓨ

6. You, a merchant, decide on the following price:

Price

(B)	(R)	(G)	(Y)
(B)	(R)(R)(R)(R)	(G)(G)(G)(G)(G)	(Y)(Y)(Y)(Y)(Y)(Y)

You decide to display this price using the fewest number of coins possible. Draw here what you display:

Price

(B)	(R)	(G)	(Y)

7. You now have two rugs for sale. The prices for the two rugs are

Price 1

(B)	(R)	(G)	(Y)
(B)(B)	(R)	(G)	(Y)(Y)(Y)

Price 2

(B)	(R)	(G)	(Y)
(B)(B)(B)	(R)(R)(R)(R)	(G)(G)(G)(G)(G)(G)	

A buyer wishes to buy both rugs and asks you your price for the pair. You combine the coins from the two Spindle Boards and say, "This is the price for the pair."

Price for pair

(B)	(R)	(G)	(Y)

The buyer responds, "Please give me the price using the fewest number of coins?" Here is your price for the two using the fewest number of coins:

Price for pair

B	R	G	Y

Finally, today's big deals completed, you put away your cash box and counting boards and go home.

EXTENSIONS

1. You see two identical rugs whose prices are

Price 1

B	R	G	Y
	R R R R R	G G G G G	Y Y Y Y Y Y

Price 2

B	R	G	Y
B B			Y

Which is the best buy?

2. You see two rugs that you want to buy. The prices for the two rugs are

Price 1

Ⓑ	Ⓡ	Ⓖ	Ⓨ
Ⓑ	Ⓡ Ⓡ	Ⓖ Ⓖ Ⓖ Ⓖ	Ⓨ Ⓨ Ⓨ Ⓨ

Price 2

Ⓑ	Ⓡ	Ⓖ	Ⓨ
Ⓑ	Ⓡ Ⓡ Ⓡ	Ⓖ	Ⓨ Ⓨ

Here are the coins you have

Ⓑ Ⓑ   Ⓨ Ⓨ Ⓨ Ⓨ
  Ⓑ Ⓡ Ⓖ Ⓖ Ⓨ Ⓨ Ⓨ

Do you have enough to buy the two rugs if you were to meet the merchants' prices?

REFLECTIONS

1. Is the counting board helpful in dealing with Zorandrian coins? Discuss.

2. Compare the Zorandrian coinage system with our own system of written and spoken numerals.

3. Were you panicked or frustrated at any time while working in the Zorandrian system? Discuss.

SUMMARY OF IMPORTANT IDEAS AND TECHNIQUES

■ Use of a number system different from our own:
  □ The system did not use writing or counting.
  □ The system did allow trading "coins" of equal value.
■ Use of counting boards.

BASE 6 PLACE VALUE BLOCKS

Nowadays, most persons in the world use the numerals we use. It wasn't always so. The Hindu-Arabic numerals we now use began to be accepted in Western Europe and the New World around 450 years ago. Not everybody was enthusiastic; some found them mysterious and difficult. A child today learning to work with them may also find them a little bit magical.

To give you a sense of what such a child might feel, we take you in this lab to the Hexlander Confederation, a country whose numerals are different. To obtain the full benefits of a visit to this quaint place, you must speak its language. You must count and calculate with their coins and numerals in their fashion. You may count to six, but otherwise you may not use our numerals.

EQUIPMENT NEEDED

- A set of Base 6 Place Value Blocks obtainable from ARC or ETA. (The assembled cut-outs from pages 233–237 of this manual can also be used.)

WHEN TO USE THIS LAB

This may be used any time while studying Chapter 3 up through the beginning of Chapter 4.

THE HEXLANDER CONFEDERATION

Hexlander Confederation has coins which are blocks.

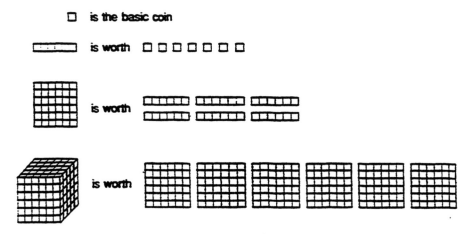

Hexlanders also count and calculate using these blocks. They shun the use of pencil and paper and, instead, push the blocks about on a table top as they carry out their daily business.

For example, to find out how much money she has, a Hexlander might empty the contents of her pockets and find these blocks:

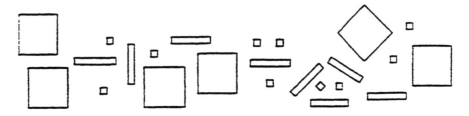

She would slide them together:

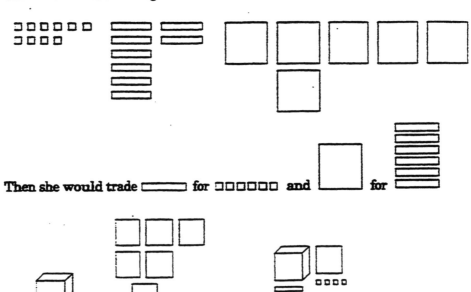

Then she would trade ▭ for ⊐⊐⊐⊐⊐⊐ and ▢ for ▤ and ▥ for ▢ and put ▥ back in her pocket.

Formerly, Hexlander merchants would display the price of a ware by drawing a picture of the correct amount of blocks and placing it in front of the object for sale, like this:

1. You are shopping for a baby buggy and notice the two items above. To decide which one is more expensive, you take out blocks corresponding to those drawn on the two price tags. Then decide by moving and trading blocks in the Hexlander way. (No use of our written and spoken numerals—except "one" through "six"—and of pencil and paper calculations allowed!)

   What is your decision? _____

   Describe in words and pictures how you made this decision:

2. A few years back, there was a craze among merchants to use price tags like this:

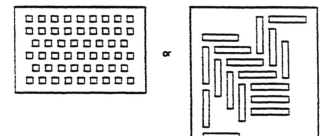

   This created such an uproar among shoppers that the Hexlander Consumer Protection Agency (HCPA) ruled that a displayed price must use the fewest number of blocks. So the tag

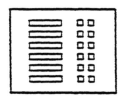

   can no longer be used but must be replaced by the tag

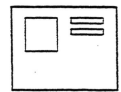

   which has coins of equal value.

You are a Hexlander merchant and have been using the now illegal price tags shown below. On the blank tag to the right of each of these, draw blocks of equal value to make price tag legal. (For each one, take out blocks and trade in the Hexlander way.)

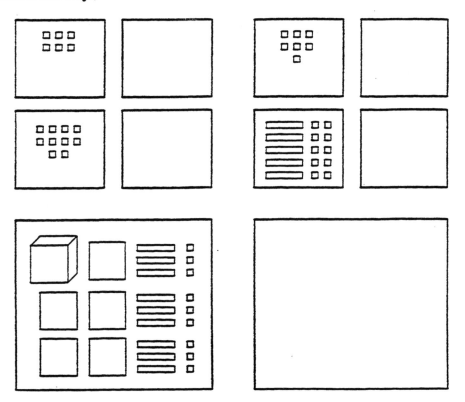

3. The Hexlander Market (known fondly as H-Mart) is having a sale on toothpaste. Here are the prices for various brands:

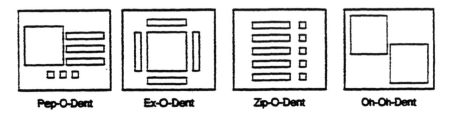

Pep-O-Dent   Ex-O-Dent   Zip-O-Dent   Oh-Oh-Dent

Rank these toothpastes according to price, most expensive first (use the blocks, please): _____

4. You are shopping in H-Mart and have this much to spend:

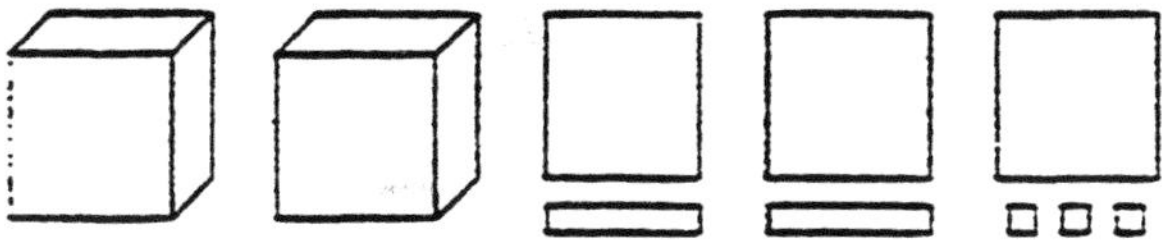

You decide to buy items having these price tags:

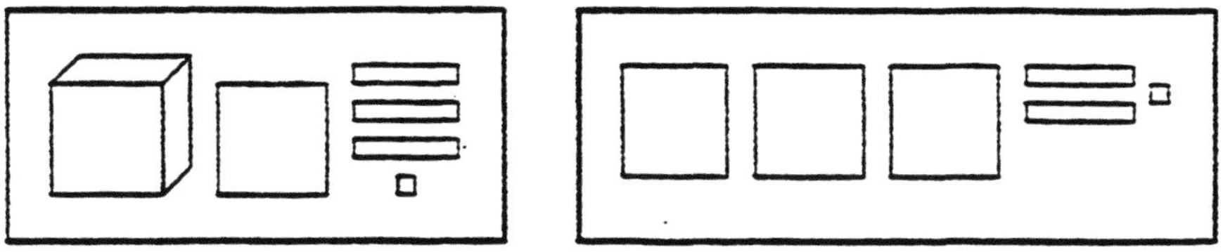

You want to know if you have enough money to pay for them. Take out blocks and figure out the total price for the items. Draw here what the total must be using the fewest number of coins:

Do you have enough to pay for the two items? _____

If you have enough and give all you have to the cashier, what will your change be using the fewest number of coins? (Use blocks to figure this out.)

If you don't have enough, how much more (in fewest number of coins) do you need? (Use blocks to figure this out.)

5. On your next shopping spree in H-Mart, you decide to buy several items whose prices are shown below:

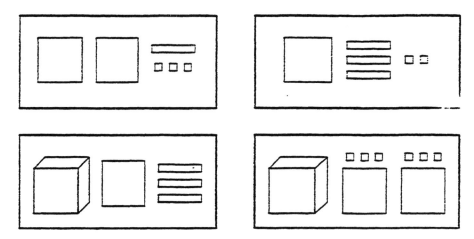

The total of these prices, in legal price tag form, is:

Looking in your wallet, you find

You give this all to the cashier. Your change, in fewest number of coins, is:

6. On the international currency exchange market, the Hexlander basic coin is worth two U.S. cents. What would be the price of each of the four items just shown in U.S. dollars? (To figure this out, you may use ordinary numerals.)

7. At the Hexlander border you have a $10 (U.S.) bill which you wish to exchange for Hexlander money. What do you get? (Fewest number of blocks, please!)

REFLECTIONS

1. What do you think of the Hexlander system of coins and price tags? Did you feel comfortable using it? How does it compare with our system of written and spoken numerals?

2. How does the Hexlander system compare with the Zorandrian system (using Trading Chips)?

3. What would be the advantages and disadvantages of young children using the Hexlander system in place of our system of written and spoken numerals?

4. Were you panicked or frustrated at any time while working in the Hexlander system? Discuss.

SUMMARY OF IMPORTANT IDEAS AND TECHNIQUES

- Introduction of base 6 place value blocks.
- Comparing, adding and subtracting entirely within the system of base 6 place value blocks.
- Converting base 6 to base 10 and base 10 to base 6.

MULTIPLICATION WITH BASE 10 PLACE VALUE BLOCKS

In this lab Hexland (first visited in Lab 3b) goes metric and replaces base 6 place value blocks, its system for representing numbers, with base 10 place value blocks. We will see how Hexland adds and multiplies using these blocks. The base 10 blocks are so close to our base 10 system of numerals that they can be used as concrete models for our numerals. They are excellent tools to use with children at all stages of learning the whole number operations.

EQUIPMENT NEEDED

- Supply of base 10 place value blocks. (These can be obtained from ARC, CP, CCA, DS or ETA.) If wood or plastic blocks are not available, use the assembled cutouts from pages 241–256 of this manual.
- Hexlander Calculating Pad from page 257 of this manual.
- Hexlander Multiplication Pad from page 259 of this manual.

WHEN TO USE THIS LAB

This lab should be used while studying Chapter 5.

HEXLAND GOES METRIC

Since the Hexlander Confederation will go metric next year, the government has decided to make the country's monetary (and numeral) system metric as well by adopting decimal currency. (Any number in Hexland is represented by a collection of blocks or by a picture of the collection.)

The old unit block ☐ will be kept and the new blocks will be made whose values are determined by the following scheme:

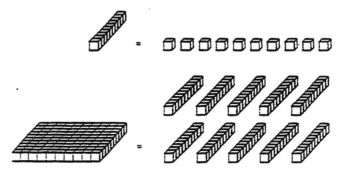

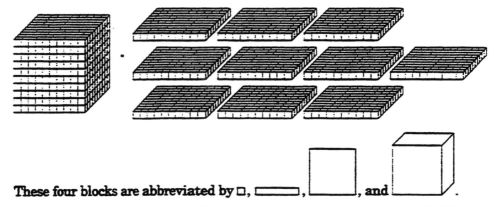

These four blocks are abbreviated by □, ⬭, ⬜, and ⬛ .

To ease the changeover, the Hexlander Currency Commission (HCC) has printed a small pamphlet to introduce the new blocks and teach Hexlanders how to cope with them. Below are some exercises from the pamphlet for you to work through. (This should be very useful to those of you who plan a trip to Hexland in the years to come.) For maximum benefit from these exercises, follow the instructions and calculate with the blocks themselves, in the Hexlander manner without use of our written and spoken numerals.

With this pamphlet comes a Hexlander Calculating Pad to help you organize the blocks when you calculate. Each vertical column of the Pad is headed by a picture of a Hexlander block; the values increase from right to left. During a calculation each block is placed in the column headed by its picture.

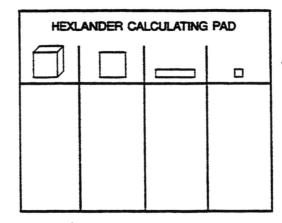

1. As with the old system, a legal price must use the fewest possible number of coins.

TO MAKE A COLLECTION OF HEXLANDER DECIMAL BLOCKS LEGAL

Place the collection of blocks on the Hexland Computer Pad. Trade any ten items in a given column for a single (appropriate) item in the column just to its left.

EXAMPLE

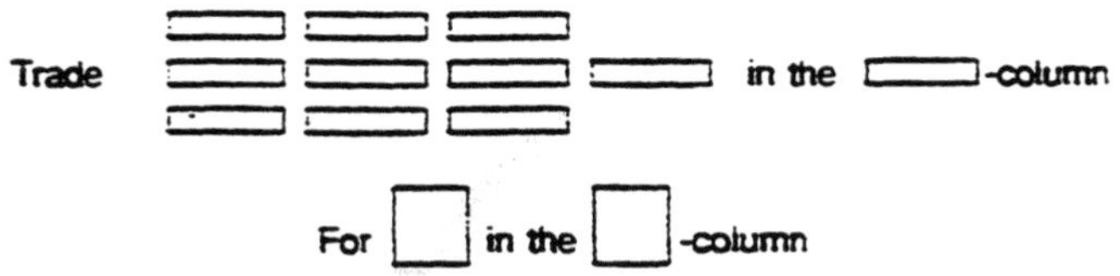

Trade

in the [____]-column

For ☐ in the ☐ -column

Keep trading until each column has fewer than ten items.

EXERCISE Try this procedure with the collection of blocks shown below left. Take out real blocks corresponding to those in the picture, place them on the Pad and trade until the collection is legal. Draw a picture of the legalized collection on the Pad at the right below.

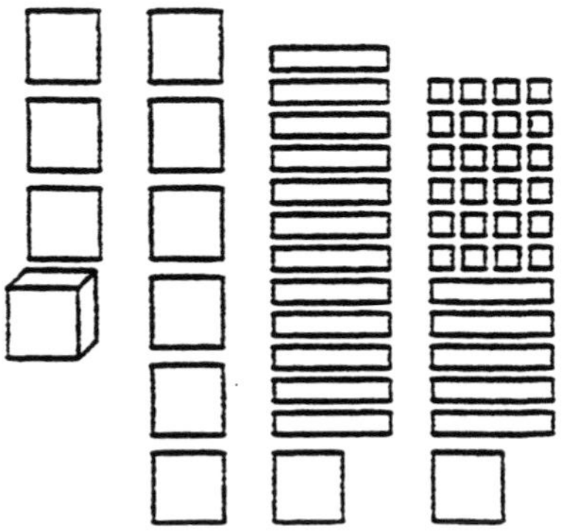

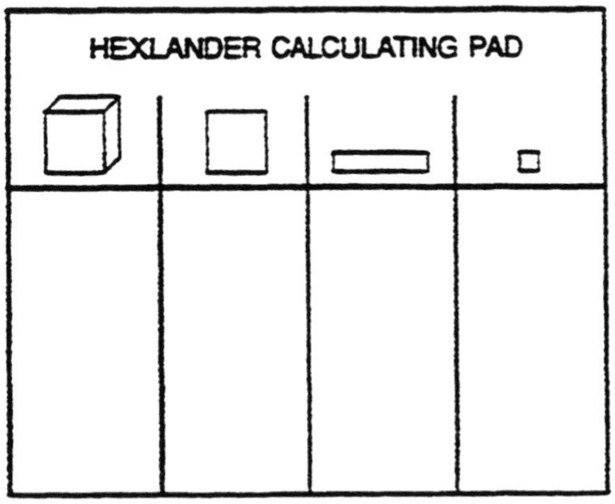

HEXLANDER CALCULATING PAD

TO ADD TWO HEXLANDER DECIMAL NUMERALS AND EXPRESS THEIR SUM LEGALLY

Place the first collection of blocks on the Pad. Do the same with the second collection. Make sure each block is in its appropriate column. Then legalize the combined collection.

EXAMPLE

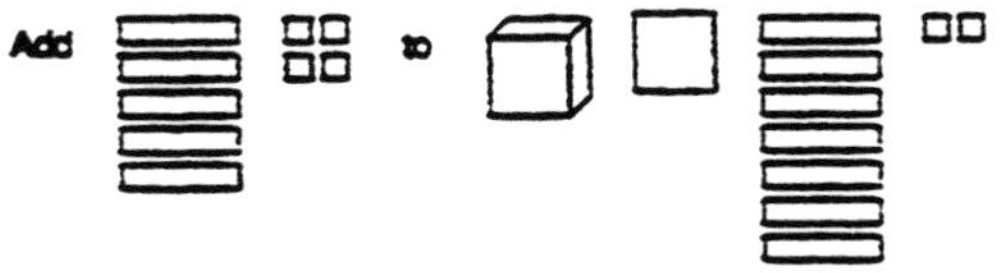

Add ▤ 🔲 to ▢ ☐ ▤ 🔲

Place blocks on Pad:

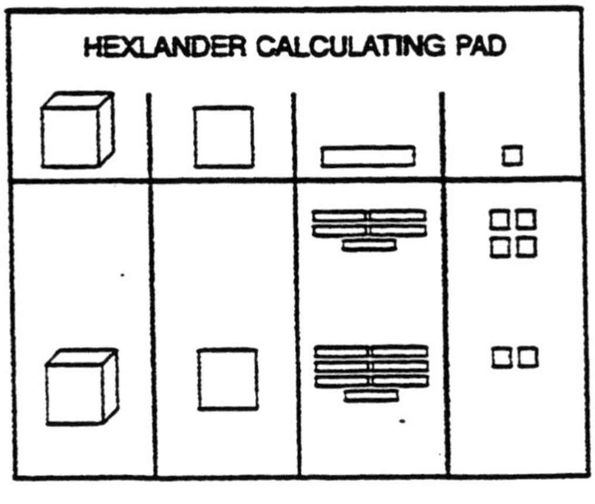

HEXLANDER CALCULATING PAD

Legalize:

HEXLANDER CALCULATING PAD

EXERCISE Try this procedure in adding the two collections of blocks shown below. (Remember to use the blocks.)

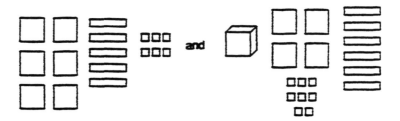

Draw a picture of the legal sum here:

HEXLANDER CALCULATING PAD

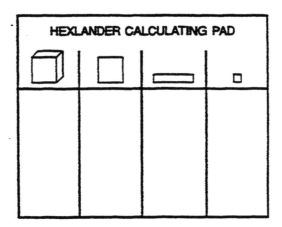

TO MULTIPLY TWO HEXLAND DECIMAL NUMBERS

In addition to a Hexlander Calculating Pad, the pamphlet comes with a Multiplication Pad:

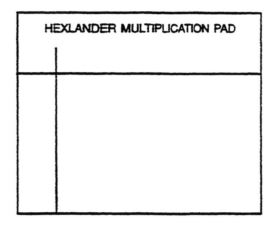

You know that to find the product of two numbers such as 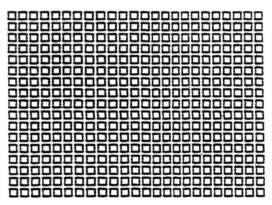 and ▭ □□ / ▭ □□, you can form an array of unit blocks having ▭ □□□□ / □□□ rows and ▭ □□ / ▭ □□ in each row:

Then to find the product you place the blocks from the array on the Computer Pad and legalize. The HCC suggests the following streamlined method.

Place the two numbers to be multiplied along the two heavy lines of the Multiplication Pad.

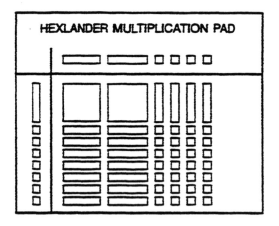

Trade the unit blocks in the array for blocks of equal value in order to transforms the original array into the following **organized array**:

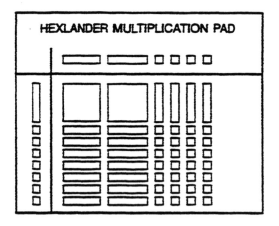

Then move the blocks in the **organized array** from the Multiplication Pad to the Calculating Pad:

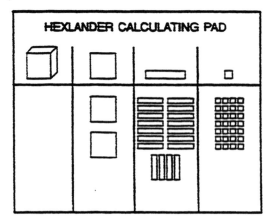

The final step in the multiplication process is to convert the blocks on the Calculating Pad to legal form. Draw the legalized blocks here:

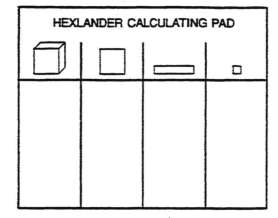

EXERCISE Following the procedure just described, find the product of the following two numbers:

Draw a picture of the **organized array** on your Multiplication Pad here:

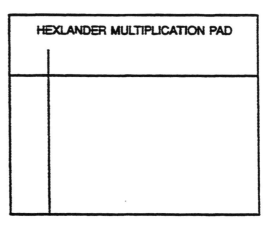

Place the blocks from the organized array onto your Calculating Pad, legalize and draw the product in legal form here:

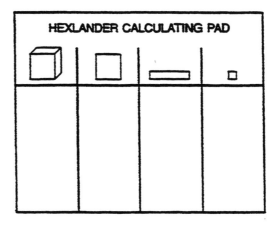

EXTENSIONS

1. Find the sum of the following pair of numbers:

Describe in pictures and words the steps you take.

2. Extend the multiplication procedure described above in order to find the product of the following pair of Hexland numbers:

Describe in pictures and words the steps you take.

3. Describe in pictures and words how you would carry out the following subtraction with Hexland blocks:

REFLECTIONS

1. Compare the method of adding using the base 10 place value blocks with the standard method for our written numerals.

2. Compare the method of multiplying using the base 10 place value blocks with the standard method for our written numerals.

3. Were you panicked or frustrated at any time while working with the Hexland decimal blocks? Discuss.

4. How do you think elementary school children would respond to using base 10 place value blocks to carry out whole number operations?

SUMMARY OF IMPORTANT IDEAS AND TECHNIQUES

■ Use of base 10 place value blocks to add and multiply whole numbers.

■ The methods for adding and multiplying with place value blocks parallel very closely the standard methods with decimal numerals.

SOLVING FRACTION PROBLEMS USING BEANS AND CUISENAIRE RODS

Real objects may help in understanding fractions and solving problems with them. Some objects may be more useful for this than another depending on the situation in which the fractions occur. In this lab we will use two types of objects: colored beans and Cuisenaire rods

EQUIPMENT NEEDED

- A jar of black beans and a jar of red beans.
- A bunch of Cuisenaire rods. (Same as for Labs 4b and 7a.)

WHEN TO USE THIS LAB

The best time for this activity is while studying Chapter 8.

COLORED BEANS AND FRACTIONS

1. Ms. Garcia's class has 35 students. Three-fifths of them are girls. To visualize this, take 35 black beans to represent the students in the class:

Then partition the class into five equal groups:

Each one of these groups is a fifth of the class. Separate three of the groups from the others to obtain three-fifths:

In each fifth there are ____ students. In three-fifths there are ____ students. There are ____ girls in the class.

2. Mr. Brown's class has 24 students. Five-eighths of them have micros at home. Take 24 black beans, partition them into eight equal groups, and draw a picture of what you get here:

With a pencil or ruler, separate five of the eight groups of beans from the others. This is five-eights of the class. Show this in the picture above.

In each eighth of the class there are ____ students.

In five-eights of the class there are ____ students.

The number of students in Mr. Brown's class with micros at home is

____.

3. Four-sixths of Mr. Brown's class ride bikes to school. To show this, partition the beans into six equal groups and separate four of them from the others with a pencil or ruler. Draw a picture of this:

Combine pairs of the six groups to get something like this:

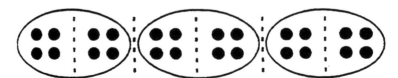

The pairs partition the class into three equal groups, two of which constitute the students who ride bikes to school. Foursixths of Mr. Brown's class is the same as two-thirds of the class. This demonstrates one instance of equivalent fractions: 4/6 = 2/3.

4. Two-eighths of Mr. Brown's class wear glasses. Show this with the beans and draw a picture of what you get here:

Starting with the beans partitioned in the picture above, pair eighths to get fourths and show how the students who wear glasses make up one-fourth of Mr. Brown's class. Draw a picture of this:

5. Mr. Brown says that the size of his class next year will be 7/6 of what it is this year. Use the beans to show this fraction. (You will need more than the 24 original beans.) Show what you get here:

One-sixth of Mr. Brown's class contains _____ students. Next year Mr. Brown's class will have _____ students.

6. From past experience you know that when you plant strawberry plants three-fourths of them will survive. In the end you want to have 24 good plants growing in your garden. You want to know how many you should plant in order for this to happen. Solve this problem by taking out the beans. You should start with 24 of them to represent the good ones that will survive. Since the 24 beans represents three-fourths of what you want to have, you will have to work backwards from what you did in solving earlier problems. (Work only with the beans!)

7. Twenty of the twenty-four students presently in Mr. Brown's class either walk or bike to school. This is what fraction of his class? Solve this using only the beans. Separate 20 beans from the rest. Partition all 24 beans into groups of the same size so that the 20 are also partitioned into groups of that same size. Draw a picture of what you do here:

(There are several answers, but all the answers should be equivalent fractions. Compare your answer with your neighbor's.)

8. Beans can also be used to visualize ratios and to solve problems associated with them. For example, in Ms. Garcia's class the ratio of girls to boys is 4 to 3. Take a bunch of red beans (to represent girls) and a bunch of black beans (to represent boys). The fact that the ratio of girls to boys is 4 to 3 means that for every four girls there are three boys. To convey this you can arrange four red and three black beans this way:

Ⓡ Ⓡ Ⓡ Ⓡ   Ⓑ Ⓑ Ⓑ
(four girls)   (three boys)

Now, you know that there are 35 students in all in Ms. Garcia's class and you have accounted for 7 of them so far. We can add another row of 7 beans (4 R and 3 B) and still keep the 4 to 3 ratio of R to B beans:

Ⓡ Ⓡ Ⓡ Ⓡ   Ⓑ Ⓑ Ⓑ
Ⓡ Ⓡ Ⓡ Ⓡ   Ⓑ Ⓑ Ⓑ

This accounts for 14 of the students in the class. Keep adding rows of 4 R and 3 B beans until you have an array of 35 beans, one bean for each student in the whole class. Show what you get here:

There are ____ girls in Ms. Garcia's class. The boys in the class constitute what fraction of the class? ____

9. Use two colors of beans to solve the following ratio problem. There are 36 pets at a pet show. You have counted the number of dogs and figured that 2/9 of all the pets are dogs. You have also noticed that there are three cats for every dog at the show. Use this information and beans to figure out how many pets in the show are neither cats nor dogs. On the other side, use pictures to explain how you figure this out.

CUISENAIRE RODS AND FRACTIONS

10. To use Cuisenaire rods to represent fractions, you first select one of the rods to represent the unit, or the Whole Thing. The other rods then represent fractions of the unit. For example, suppose that the unit is a quart of milk and that this is represented by DARKGREEN. Since a train of six WHITE rods is equal in length to a DARKGREEN, the WHITE is then one-sixth of the DARKGREEN.

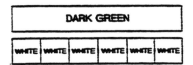

Similarly, a train of three RED rods is equal in length to a DARKGREEN so that RED then represents 1/3.

Then, since PURPLE is equal to a train of two RED rods, PURPLE represents 2/3.

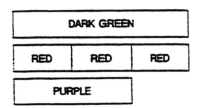

BROWN is equal to a train of four RED rods, so BROWN represents 4/3.

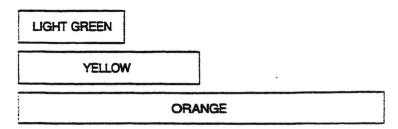

Given that DARKGREEN is the unit, figure out what fractions the rods in the picture below represent.

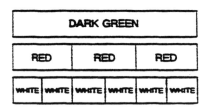

11. The RED is also equal to a train of two WHITEs. With DARKGREEN as unit, this means that RED represents the fraction 2/6 as well as 1/3. The two fractions 2/6 and 1/3 are equivalent fractions.

With DARKGREEN as unit, use the rods to show that 1/2 = 3/6. Draw a picture of how you do it here:

Similarly, show that 5/3 = 10/6. Draw a picture of how you do it here:

12. This time use BROWN as the unit and figure out what fractions each of the rods in the picture below represent:

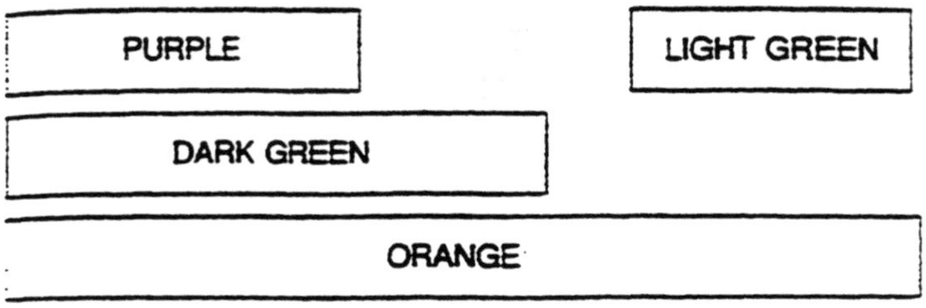

PURPLE		LIGHT GREEN
DARK GREEN		
ORANGE		

13. Suppose YELLOW is the unit. What rod represents 2/5?

What rod represents 6/10?

What rod represents 8/5?

What rod represents 2/1?

14. Suppose RED represents 1/5. What rod represents the unit? Draw a picture showing how you figure this out:

What rod represents 1/2? Draw a picture showing how you figure this out:

15. If DARKGREEN represents 3/4, what rod is 9/8? Draw pictures showing how you figure this out:

16. If YELLOW is 1/3, what is 1/5? Draw pictures to show how you answer this:

17. To add fractions represented by Cuisenaire rods, you make trains. For example, when DARKGREEN is the unit (a quart of milk), WHITE is 1/6 qt and RED is 1/3 qt. WHITE and RED together make 1/6 + 1/3 qt. The train WHITE-RED represents this sum. The train is equal in length to LIGHTGREEN, which is 1/2 qt: 1/6 + 1/3 = 1/2.

```
+-----------------------------------+
|           DARK GREEN              |
+-----------------------------------+

+-------+---------------------------+
| WHITE |           RED             |
+-------+---------------------------+

+------------------+----------------+
|   LIGHT GREEN    |  LIGHT GREEN    |
+------------------+----------------+
```

Use the rods to find the sum 2/3 + 5/6 qt. Draw a picture of how you do it here:

Similarly, find the sum 1/6 + 4/3 qt and draw the pictures here:

18. To subtract fractions represented by Cuisenaire rods, you COMPLETE trains. (Compare Making Change in the Country of Queezin.) For example, suppose that ORANGE is the unit (a mile of length). Then YELLOW is 1/2 mile and RED is 1/5 mile.

```
+-----------------+
|   LIGHT GREEN   |
+-----------------+

+-----------------------------+
|           YELLOW            |
+-----------------------------+

+---------------------------------------------+
|                   ORANGE                    |
+---------------------------------------------+
```

If you have travelled 1/5 and your goal is to travel 1/2 mile, how much farther do you have to go?

[YELLOW   ]
[RED][?]

The answer is the rod that fits [?]—that is, the rod that with RED makes a train equal in length to YELLOW. The rod that fits is _____ and represents the fraction _____ . So 1/5 mi + ? mi = 1/2 mi or 1/2 − 1/5 = _____ .

19. DARKGREEN is the unit (one quart of milk). A recipe calls for 1 1/2 qt milk. You have 2/3 qt. How much more do you need for the recipe? Solve this using the rods.

EXTENSIONS

1. You pour 3/4 of a cup of milk into a bowl to make a cake. You add a few more things to the bowl then, without thinking, you add another 1/3 of a cup of milk. To make things right, you need to know the total amount of milk you have added to the bowl. Use Cuisenaire rods to find out.

2. A recipe calls for 1 1/2 of a pound of hamburger. You have 8/10 of a pound in the refrigerator. You want to know how much more you will need. Solve this problem using Cuisenaire rods.

REFLECTIONS

You can represent fractions with beans or with Cuisenaire rods. For which situations (where fractions occur) would you prefer to use beans? For which situations would you prefer to use Cuisenaire rods? Are there situations where it doesn't matter? Discuss.

SUMMARY OF IMPORTANT IDEAS AND TECHNIQUES

- Use of beans and Cuisenaire rods to represent fractions and to visualize equivalent fractions.
- Use of beans and Cuisenaire rods to add and subtract fractions.

MODELLING FRACTIONS WITH FRACTION BARS

In Lab 8, you encountered collections of beans and Cuisenaire rods as two different devices for making fractions concrete. Another such device, which will be used in this lab, is a set of Fraction Bars. As before, these objects may help in understanding and solving problems with fractions.

EQUIPMENT NEEDED

■ Set of Fraction Bars. These are available commercially from ARC, CC or ETA. You may also use the cutouts from pages 261 through 267 of this manual.

WHEN TO USE THIS LAB

The best time for this activity is while studying Chapter 8 or 9.

FRACTION BARS

1. Take a set of the bars. The common length of all the bars represents the unit. The length of each bar is partitioned into a certain number of equal lengths; typically some of these smaller lengths have been shaded in. For example, look at the following bar:

·The bar has been partitioned into three equal lengths. Each of these smaller lengths is 1/3 of the unit and two of them have been shaded. The shaded portion is 2/3 of the unit. So this bar represents the fraction 2/3.

The bar for 2/3 is partitioned into 3 equal lengths. Gather all the bars that have been divided into 3 equal lengths. What other feature do they have?

The remaining bars in the set have been divided into different numbers of equal lengths. Make piles of the bars, one pile for each number. For each pile, describe another feature that all the bars in that pile have:

2. Turn all the fraction bars upside down. Select five of them at random, each a different color. Sketch a picture of each bar and identify the fraction associated with it:

PICTURE   FRACTION

3. The shaded part of a single bar represents a certain fraction of the unit. Two bars can be put together to represent another fraction. For example, consider these two bars:

Both bars are divided into two equal lengths. The shaded part of one represents 1/2; the shaded part of the other represents 2/2. The two shaded parts juxtaposed represent 3/2 of the unit.

For each fraction in the chart below, select the bar (or bars) whose shaded portion has length equal to that fraction of the unit. Draw a picture of what you get.

FRACTION	PICTURE
2/3	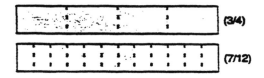
3/2	
5/6	
4/3	
3/12	
7/4	
2/4	

4. The bars can be used to compare the sizes of two fractions. For example, suppose you want to know which is larger, 3/4 of the unit or 7/12 of the unit. Take out the bars whose shaded portions correspond to these fractions and place them side by side:

(3/4)

(7/12)

The shaded portion corresponding to 3/4 is longer than the shaded portion for 7/12. So the fraction 3/4 is larger.

For the following pairs, use only the bars to figure out which is larger or whether they are the same size (in the latter case the two fractions are equal).

PAIR OF FRACTIONS		SAME?	THE LARGER FRACTION
2/3	3/4		
2/4	3/6		
2/6	3/12		
5/12	1/3		
4/3	8/6		
17/12	7/4		

5. To add fractions represented by two bars, you juxtapose the shaded portion of the two bars lengthwise. (This was suggested by the discussion in part 3.) For example, suppose that the unit corresponds to one quart, that you are cooking two items, that the recipe for one calls for 1/3 qt of milk, and that the recipe for the other calls for 1/2 qt. You want to know how much milk you will need in all: you need to know what 1/2 + 1/3 is. You take out the two bars corresponding to 1/2 and 1/3 and place their shaded portions together end-to-end:

Next, find a bar whose shaded portion has length equal to that of the shaded portion of the joined bars:

The latter bar represents the fraction 5/6: The sum of 1/2 and 1/3 is 5/6.

For each of the following addition problems, take bars representing the two addends and juxtapose the shaded portions lengthwise. Then, either find a single bar whose shaded portion has length equal to the shaded portion of the sum or find a pair of bars, both partitioned into the same number of equal lengths, one of which represents the unit (the whole bar is shaded). Sketch a picture of the juxtaposed bars and the naming bar(s).

ADDITION PROBLEM	PICTURE	SUM
1/2 + 2/3	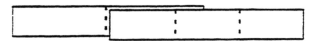	7/6
1/6 + 3/6		
1/4 + 1/6		
5/12 + 5/6		
4/3 + 1/4		

6. To subtract one fraction from another using the bars, interpret the subtraction problem as a missing addend problem. For example, to subtract 1/3 from 3/4, think: 1/3 + ? = 3/4. Take out the Bars corresponding to 1/3 and 3/4 and place them side by side:

You want to find a fraction bar whose shaded portion when joined with that of the 1/3 Bar will have a combined shaded portion equal in length to that of the 3/4 Bar:

[3/4 bar]
[1/3 bar][?]

You look through the collection of Fraction Bars and find one that fits:

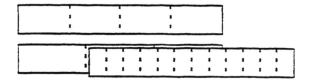

The one that works is the 5/12 bar.

Solve each of the following subtraction problems similarly with the bars. Sketch a picture of the problem and its solution.

SUBTRACTION PROBLEM	PICTURE
3/4 – 1/3 |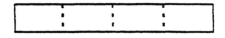

8/12 – 5/12

1/2 – 1/3

11/12 – 1/4

7/4 – 5/6

7. The bars can also be used to solve some problems which call for multiplication of fractions. For example, suppose a pancake recipe calls for 3/4 cup of flour but you want the outcome to yield 1/3 as much as the recipe would. You want to know how much flour you will need. You take out the fraction bar representing 3/4. The unit is one cup of flour and is represented by the total length of the bar.

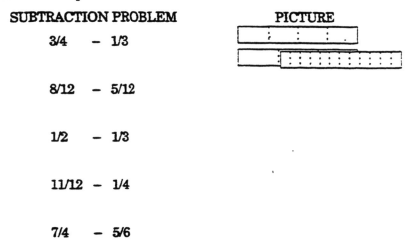

You want to divide the shaded portion of the 3/4 bar into three equal pieces and take one of them. You notice that the shaded portion of the 3/4 bar is already divided into three equal pieces: each of the pieces is 1/4. So 1/3 of 3/4 is 1/4.

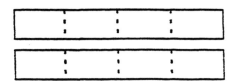

As another example you want to find 1/2 of 5/6. You take out the 5/6 bar and want to divide the shaded portion into two equal pieces and take one of them. How can you do this? The shaded portion of the 5/6 bar is divided naturally into 5 equal pieces, each one being one-sixth. But 5 is not evenly divisible by 2. Is there a bar whose shaded portion has length equal to the shaded portion of the 5/6 bar, but which is divided into an even number of pieces? (Such a Fraction Bar would represent a fraction equal to 5/6.) After a brief search you come up with this:

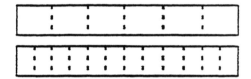

The 10/12 bar is equivalent to the 5/6 bar. The 10 equal pieces of its shaded portion can be divided into two equal pieces of 5 each:

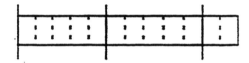

Each of the 5 pieces is 1/12. Five of them is 5/12. The answer to 1/2 of 5/6 is the same as the answer to 1/2 of 10/12, namely, 5/12.

Use the bars to find 1/3 of 5/4. Show how you do it below, using pictures and words:

8. You have 3/4 of a yard of imitation leather. You are making wallets out of the material; each wallet requires 1/6 of a yard. You want to know how many wallets you can make. To solve this problem you take out the 3/4 and 1/6 bars:

You want to know how many times you can subtract the 1/6 bar from the 3/4 bar:

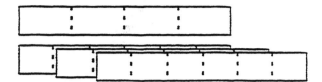

You find that you can subtract the 1/6 bar from the 3/4 bar four times with a little bit left over. The little bit is 3/4 − 4/6. The 1/12 bar solves the missing addend problem:

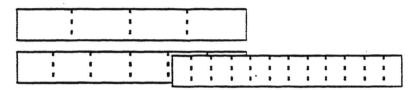

The answer to your problem is: You can make 4 wallets; 1/12 yard of the imitation leather material will be left over.

This time you have 5/6 of a yard and each wallet requires 1/3 yard of material. How many wallets can you make and how much you will have left over? Solve this with the bars and show how below:

REFLECTIONS

1. Compare subtraction of fractions using the bars with subtraction using Cuisenaire rods.

2. How do the bars compare with Cuisenaire rods for representing fractions and solving problems with them?

EXTENSIONS

1. Use the bars to find 2/3 of 5/6.

2. You are interested in finding 1/2 of 3/4 using Fraction Bars. You take out the 3/4 Bar and you search for a bar representing a fraction equivalent to 3/4 and whose numerator is even. You are not successful—in fact none exist with that property. With a piece of paper create your own bar that will do the job. The length and width of the bar should be the same as a bar in the original set. Then solve the problem using old and new bars.

3. You are making wallets again. Now you have 2 2/3 yards of material and each wallet requires 3/4 yard of material. Use the bars to find out how many of these wallets you can make and how much material you will have left over.

SUMMARY OF IMPORTANT IDEAS AND TECHNIQUES

- Use of bars to represent fractions.
- Use of bars to add, subtract, multiply and divide fractions.

SCALE DRAWING

The purpose of this activity is to make a scale drawing of a real, three-dimensional object. This activity will involve the coordination of a number of expected skills, including the use of metric tapes or sticks, transferring measurements to graph paper, making flattened patterns of three dimensional objects, . . . But, since it is a **real** object, you may come across unexpected difficulties for which, to overcome them, you will have to muster all the problem solving strategies at your command.

EQUIPMENT NEEDED

- Meter stick or metric tape measure. (A metric trundle wheel might come in handy, if available.)
- Four sheets of graph paper. (Pages 275 through 281 of this manual.)
- Transparent tape.

WHEN TO USE THIS LAB

The best time to use this lab is while studying Chapter 13.

THE SCALE DRAWING

You are planning to redecorate the room in which you typically carry out these lab activities. To do this, you have decided that it would be helpful to have a scale model. So you decide to make one that will include the floor and the walls, but not the ceiling. You want to include in your scale model as many built-in physical features as possible, such as windows, doors, chalkboards, and closets. You have decided not to include moveable furniture, such as chairs, desks, and tables.

To accomplish this task, form a team with a couple of friends in your lab section.

Start with the floor. Make measurements of the floor using metric units with meter sticks, metric tape measures, a metric trundle wheel, and whatever other devices you think will be helpful to make the measurements. Use one piece of the graph paper for the scale model of the floor and decide what length on the graph paper will represent a meter. Since you want it to be useful, you will want the scale drawing of the floor to be as large as possible and therefore take up as much of the sheet of graph paper as it can.

In the space below, describe the steps you used to make the scale drawing of the floor. Mention any difficulties or problems you encountered in doing this and discuss how you resolved them.

Next, turn to the walls. Use the other pieces of graph paper to make scale drawings of the walls. On the scale drawing be sure to mark important features such as windows, doors, and chalkboards. Since you will eventually attach the scale drawings for the walls to the scale drawing for the floor to make the complete scale model, you will want to use the same scale for the walls that you used for the floor.

Describe the steps you took in making the scale drawings of the walls. Again, list the problems you encountered and how you resolved them.

Now assemble all the scale drawings of the walls and the floor to make a scale model of the room. You might want to make a flattened out pattern first, which you will then fold into the three dimensional scale model. Before making the flattened out pattern, you might want to make a sketch of how the scale drawings of the walls and floor will fit together.

In the space below, describe the steps you used in assembling the final scale model. Mention any difficulties you had in doing this and how you overcame them.

SUMMARY OF IMPORTANT IDEAS AND TECHNIQUES

- Use of a variety of measuring tools for making a scale model: metric units, metric measuring tools, graph paper.
- Making a scale drawing.
- Use of flattened out patterns of three dimensional objects.
- Use of problem-solving strategies and ingenuity to deal with features special to **your** lab room.

AREAS USING GRIDS AND DISSECTION

The area of a rectangle is equal to its base times its height. The areas of many other nice shapes can determined by dissecting them and rearranging the pieces to form a rectangle or other shape whose area we already know. In the real world not all shapes are "nice" and some other method must to be used to figure out its area. In this lab we will use grids to calculate the areas of irregular shapes. We will compare this method with the dissection method in case the shapes are "nice" to make sure they both give answers that are close to each other.

EQUIPMENT NEEDED

- Scissors.
- Shapes cut out from pages 299–300 of this manual.
- A page of graph paper. (See page 283 of this manual.)

WHEN TO USE THIS LAB

The best time to use this is while you are studying Chapter 17 of the text.

BASIC AREA

1. The length of this line segment _____ is 1 centimeter. This square tile

has 1 centimeter on a side and so has area 1 square centimeter (1 cm^2). Four of these tiles assemble to make

or

each of which has area 4 cm^2.

Thus

has area = _____ .

has area = _____ .

The lines on this 1 cm^2 divide it into four congruent pieces so each piece has area 1/4 cm^2. Thus the shaded part of

has area 7/4 cm^2. Also, the shaded part of has area = _____ and

that of has area = _____ .

ESTIMATING AREA

2. Certainly if a shape is made up of little squares on a grid it is easy to calculate its area: simply count the number of little squares that make up the shape. If a shape is not made up of little squares, you can **estimate** its area by tracing the shape on a grid, counting the whole number of squares of the grid that lie entirely inside the tracing, and adding to that the number of squares you'd have to cut up to fill in the remaining space. (The latter part is where the estimating comes in.) Use this method to estimate the area of the shape below. Each square on the grid is half a centimeter on a side.

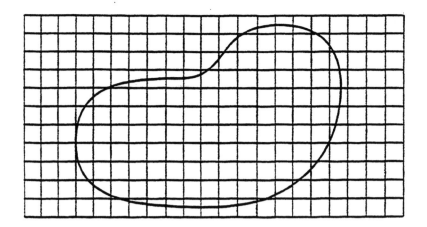

Estimated area of the shape is _____. The shape is a scale drawing of the top surface of a swimming pool in which 1 cm represents 1 m. Estimated area of real pool surface is _____.

3. Use the technique in 2 to estimate the area of the circle below.

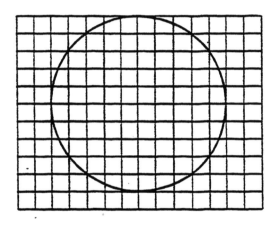

Estimated area of circle is _____.

It's likely that you know how to find the area of this circle using another method. In the space below, describe the method, calculate the area using it, and compare the answers you get from the two methods.

DISSECTIONS

4. To find the area of a rectangle there is no need to count squares in a grid, just measure two lengths—base and height—and multiply. Areas of many other shapes can be found easily by relating them to rectangles. To do this we use two principles: (1) Congruent shapes have the same area; (2) the area of a shape dissected into pieces is equal to the sum of the area of the pieces.

For example, consider the rectangle below.

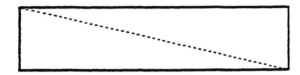

Cut the copy of it from page 299 of this manual. Then cut along the dotted diagonal. You get two triangles that are the same size and shape, i.e., they are **congruent.** (Superimpose the two triangles to check this.) Since the two triangles have the same area and the area of the rectangle is the sum of the areas of the two triangles, **the area of one of the triangles is half the area of the rectangle!**

Here is another rectangle.

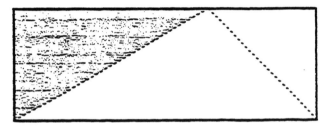

Cut out the copy of this from page 299. Dissect it into three triangles by cutting along the dotted lines. Fit the two shaded pieces together so that the pieces look like these two large triangles:

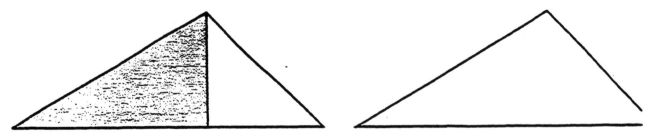

Superimpose the white triangle on the shaded one to show that the two large triangles are congruent. In the space below write a sentence or so describing the relationship between the area of the rectangle and the area of the white triangle.

5. Measure the rectangle in 4 to find its area.

      Its area is _____.

      Thus the area of the white triangle is _____.

Trace the white triangle on graph paper (where each square has side 1/2 cm) and estimate its area with the method used earlier in this activity. The estimated area is _____.

      How do the areas from the two methods compare?

6. Here is a third rectangle.

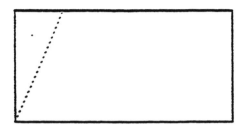

Cut out the copy of this from page 299. Dissect it into two pieces by cutting along the dotted line. Move the smaller piece on the left and attach it to the larger piece on the right to obtain a parallelogram. In the space below write a sentence describing the relationship between the area of the rectangle and the area of the parallelogram.

7. Here is a parallelogram.

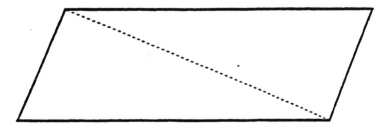

Cut out the copy of this from page 299. Dissect it into two triangles by cutting along the dotted line. Superimpose the two triangles to convince yourself that they are congruent. In the space below write a sentence describing the relationship between the area of the parallelogram and the area of one of the triangles.

8. Here is a second parallelogram.

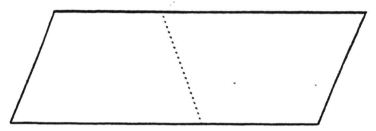

Cut out the copy of this from page 299. Dissect it into two pieces by cutting along the dotted line. Superimpose the two pieces to convince yourself that they are congruent. In the space below write a sentence describing the relationship between the area of one of the trapezoids and the area of parallelogram.

REFLECTIONS

We have discussed two methods for finding areas: grids and dissections. Which method is more useful? With a shape on which both methods can be used, do both methods give the same answer? If the answers are different, which method gives the correct answer?

EXTENSIONS

1. Starting with the formula for the area of a rectangle, show how each of the dissections described above leads to an area formula for some other shape.

2. Consider the right triangle below. The two legs of this triangle have lengths A and B; the hypotenuse has length C.

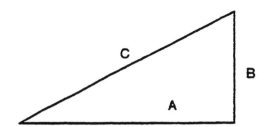

Cut out the four copies of this triangle from page 301 of this manual. Also, cut out the three squares whose sides have lengths A, B and C, respectively.

(a) Arrange the square with side C and the four triangles to fit snugly in the big square below.

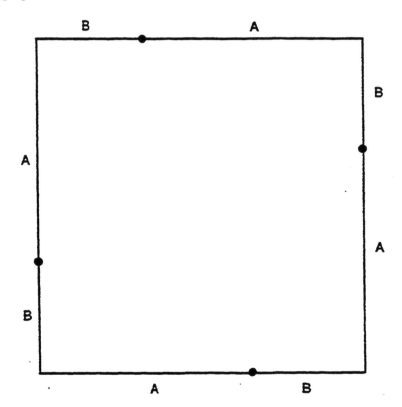

In the space below, sketch how you arranged the five items to fit.

(b) Next, remove all the pieces from the big square. Then take the square of side A, the square of side B and the four triangles and arrange these six items to fit snugly in the big square above (of side A + B).

In the space below, sketch how you arranged the six items to fit.

(c) Finally, based on what you were able to do in parts (a) and (b) write a sentence describing the relationship (and explaining it) between the areas of the three squares: the square with side A, the square with side B and the square with side C.

(d) What do (a), (b) and (c) have to do with the Pythagorean Theorem?

SUMMARY OF IMPORTANT IDEAS AND TECHNIQUES

- Use of grids for finding areas, following directly from the definition of area as the number of unit squares that fit in the shape.
- Use of dissection for finding areas, following from basic area principles. These dissections lead to familiar formulas for area.

L A B

APPENDIXES

	B
	R
	G
	Y

(B)

(R)

(G)

(Y)

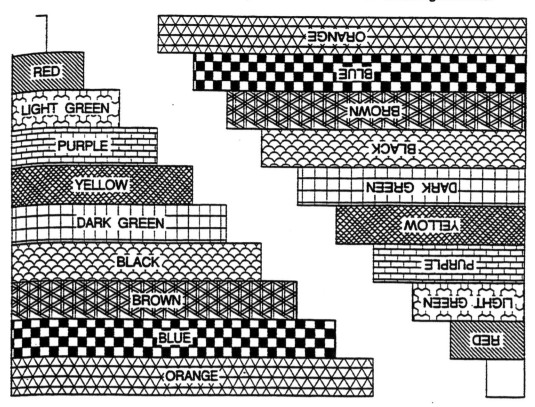

HEXLANDER CALCULATING PAD

HEXLANDER MULTIPLICATION PAD

APPENDIX LAB 9: A set of cut-outs to use in place of fraction bars.

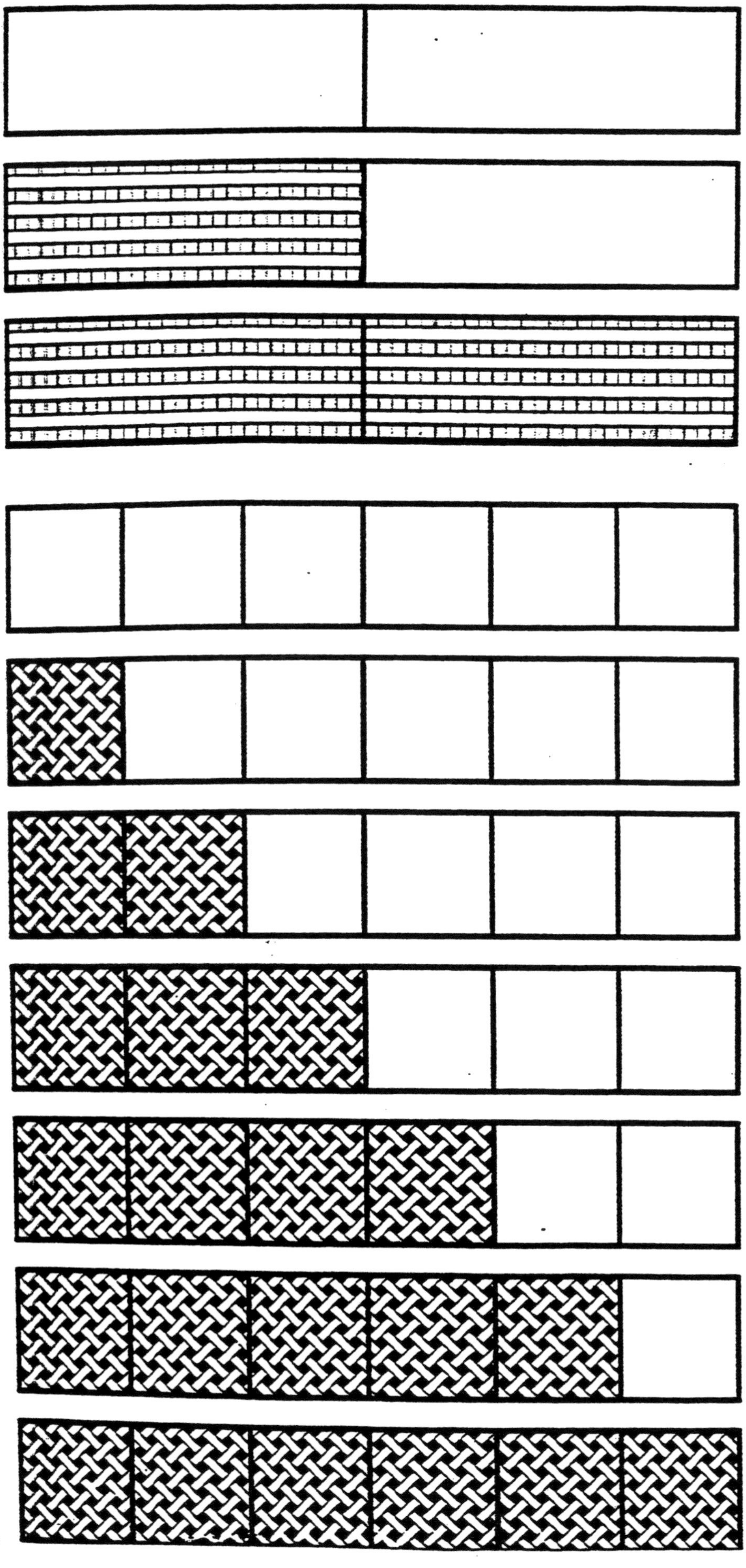

APPENDIX LAB 9: A set of cut-outs to use in place of fraction bars.

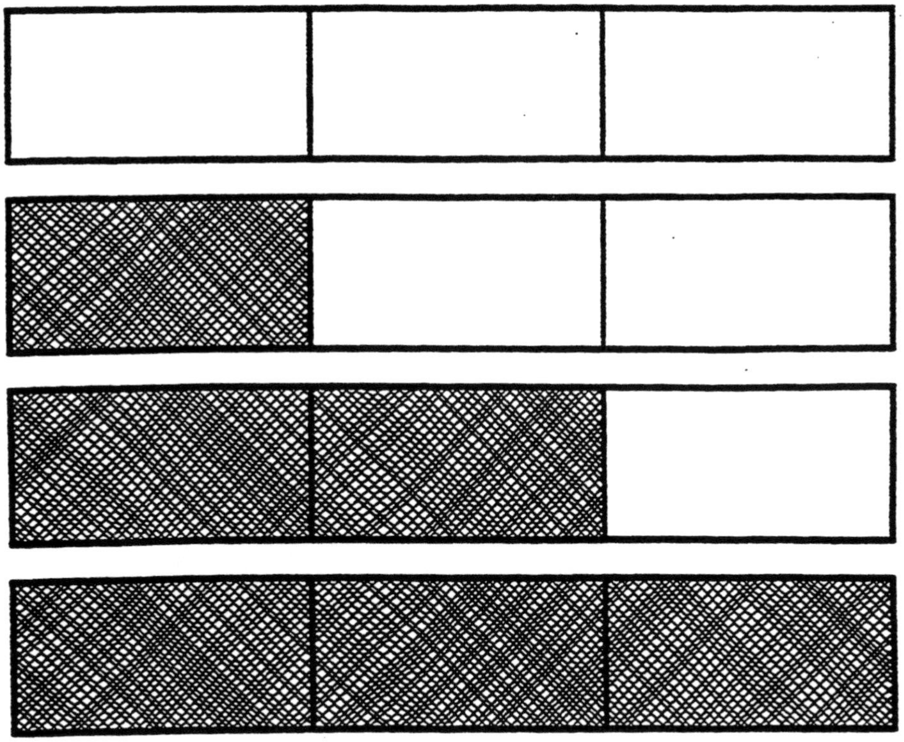

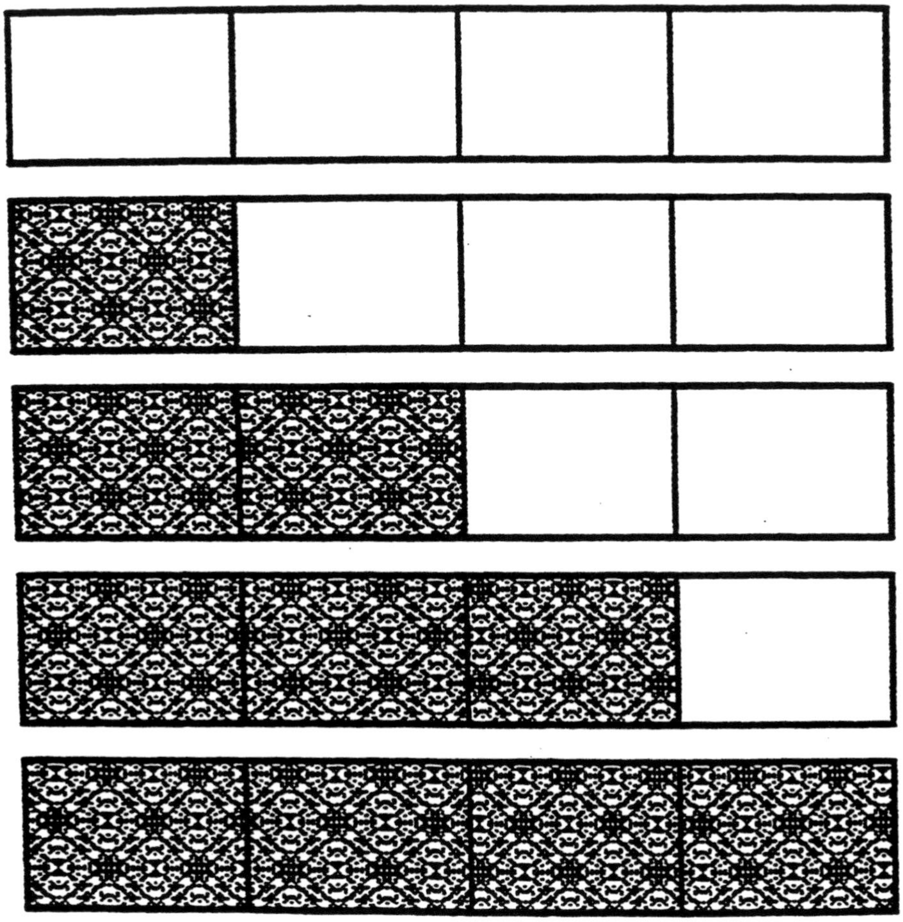

 A set of cut-outs to use in place of fraction bars.

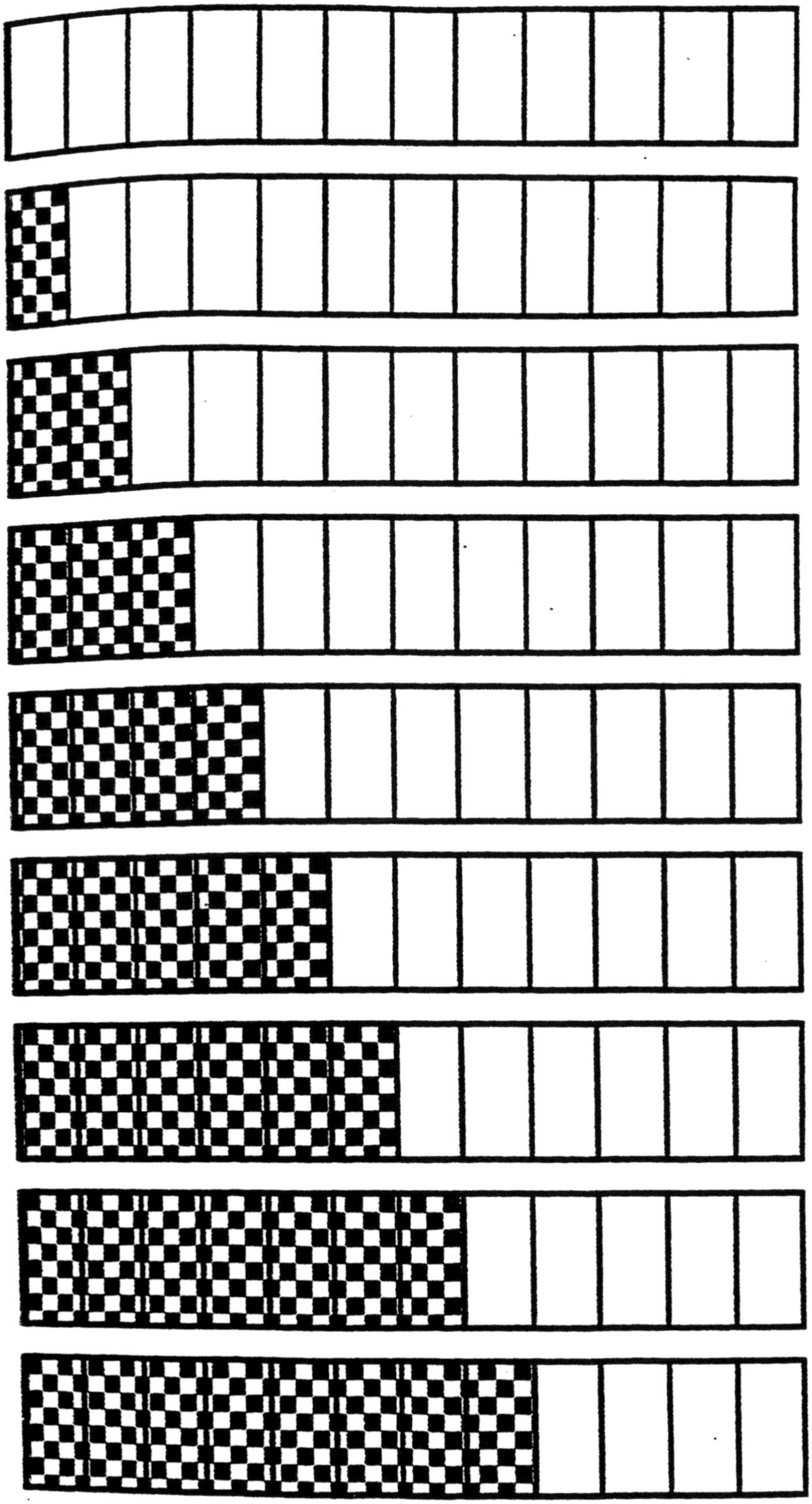

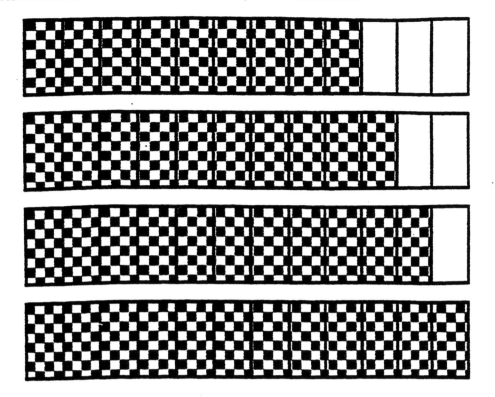

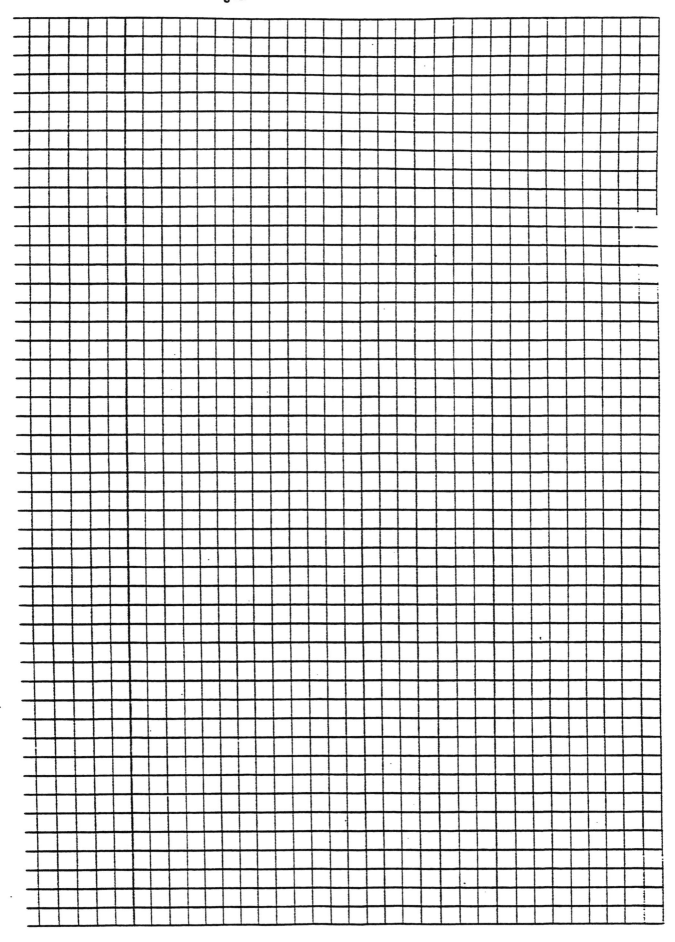

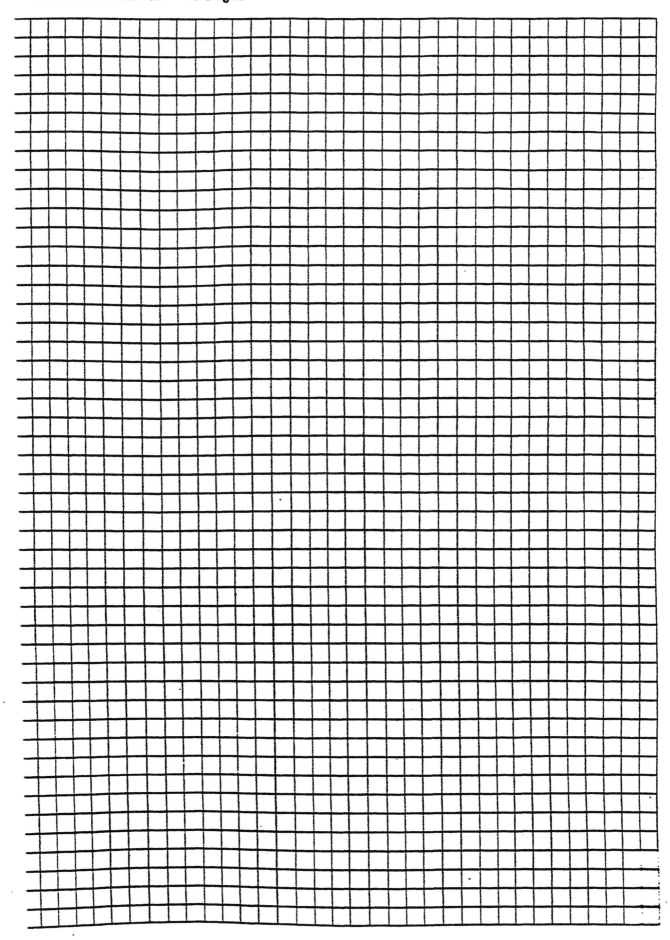

279

279

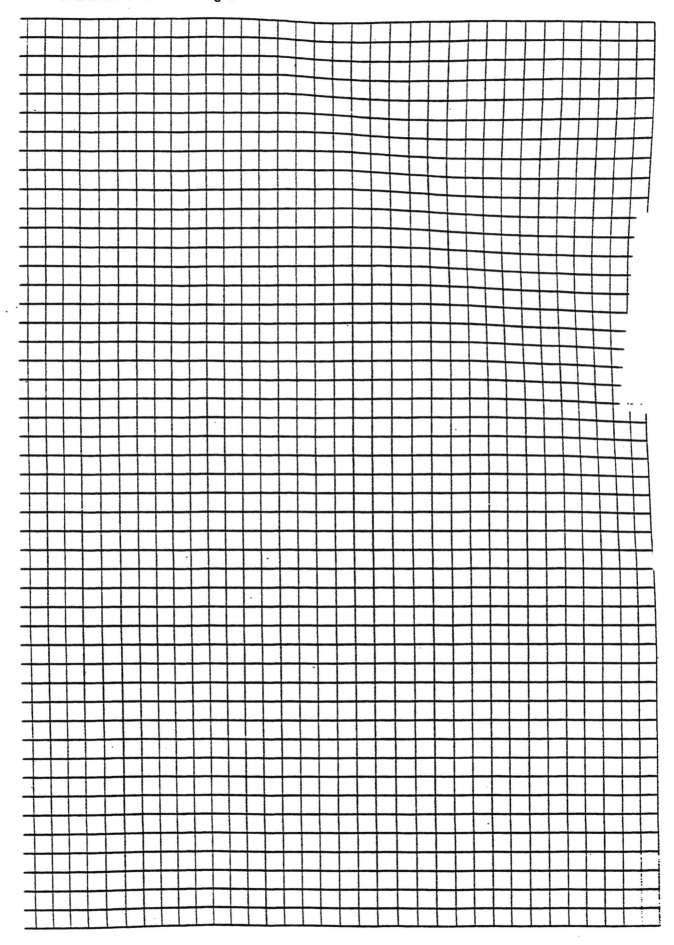

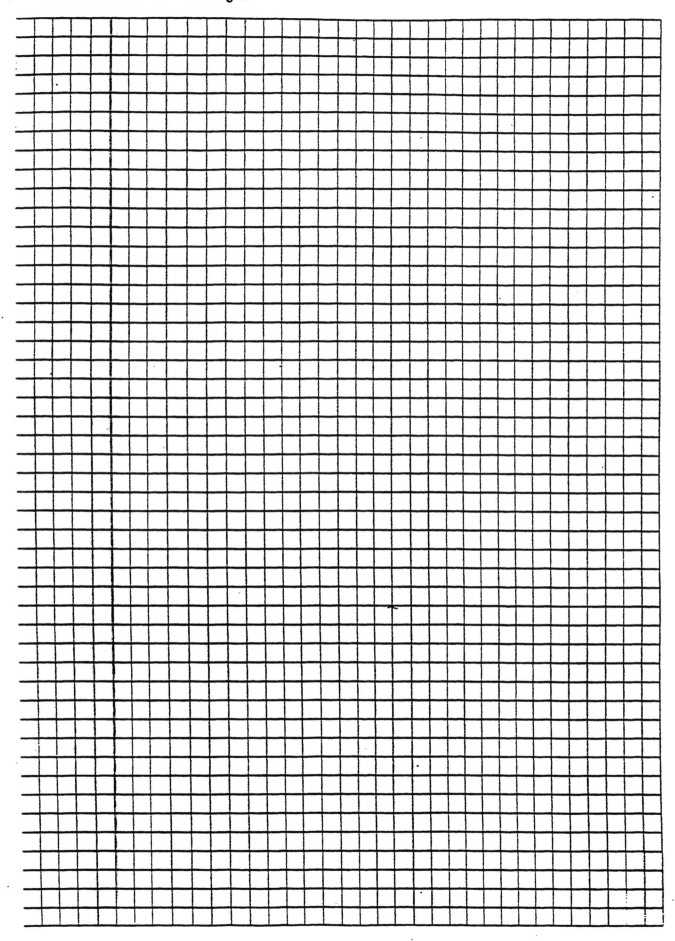

APPENDIX LAB 15: To make a portable triangle, trace a copy of this triangle on a piece of heavy cardboard. Cut out the traced triangle from the cardboard.

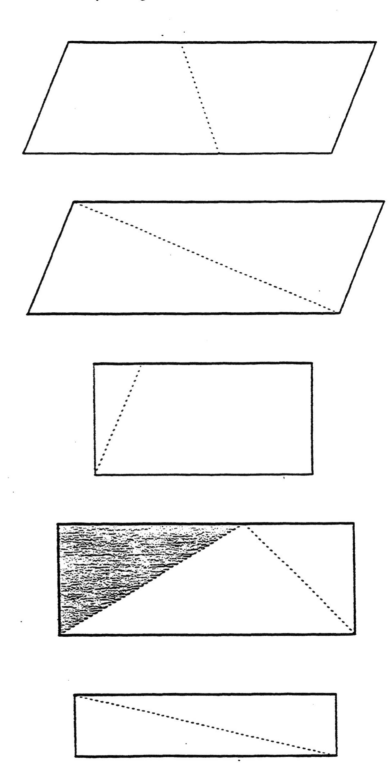

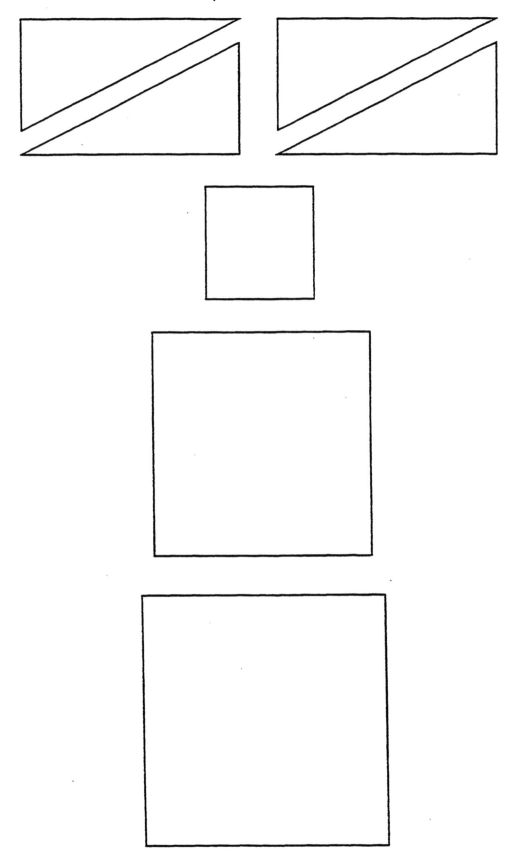

APPENDIX LAB 19:   Cut out and assemble.

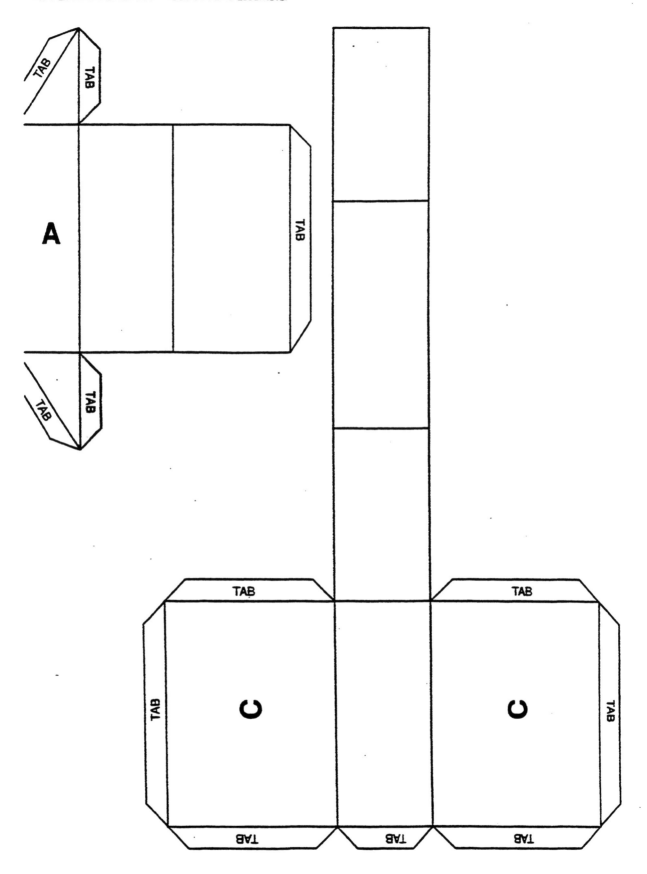

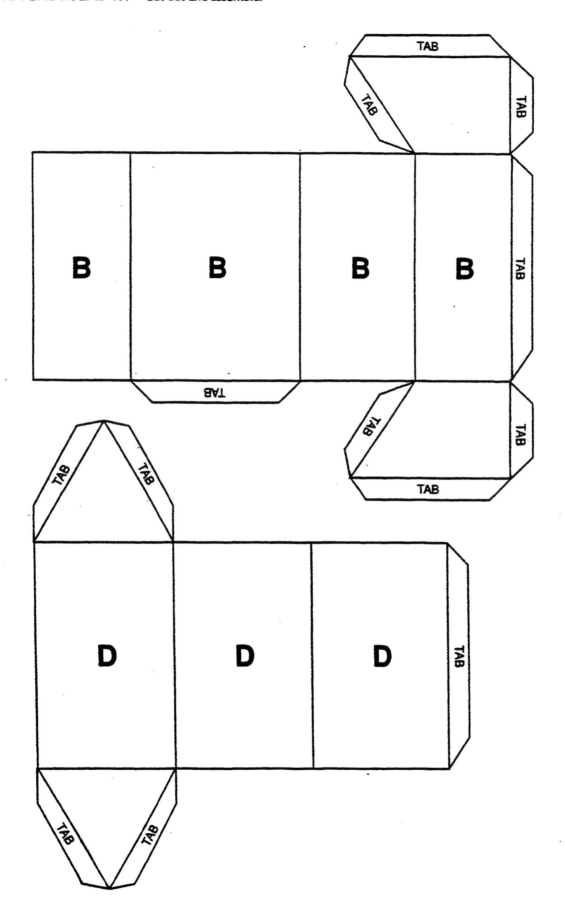

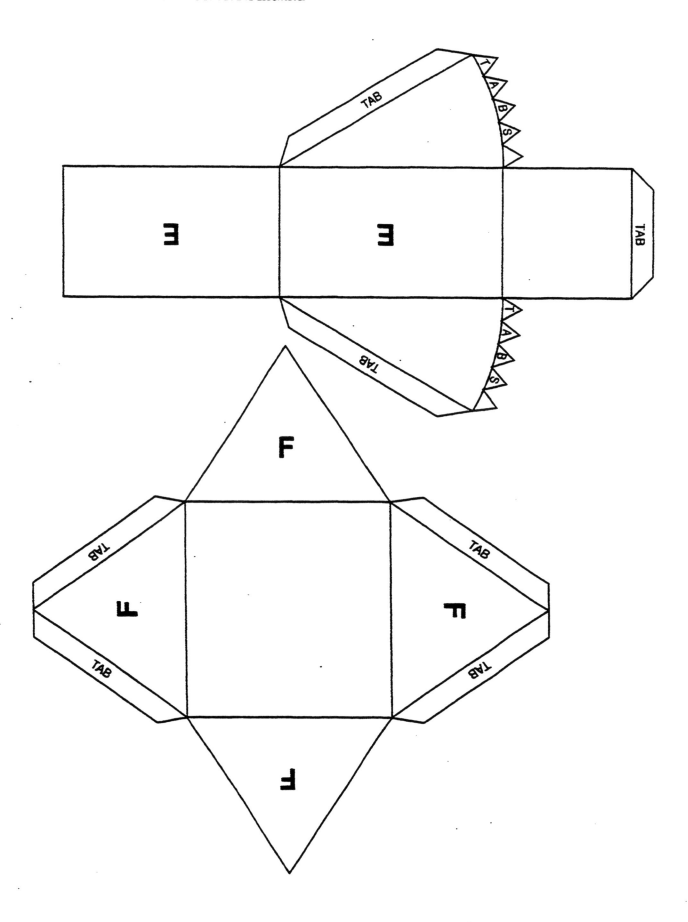

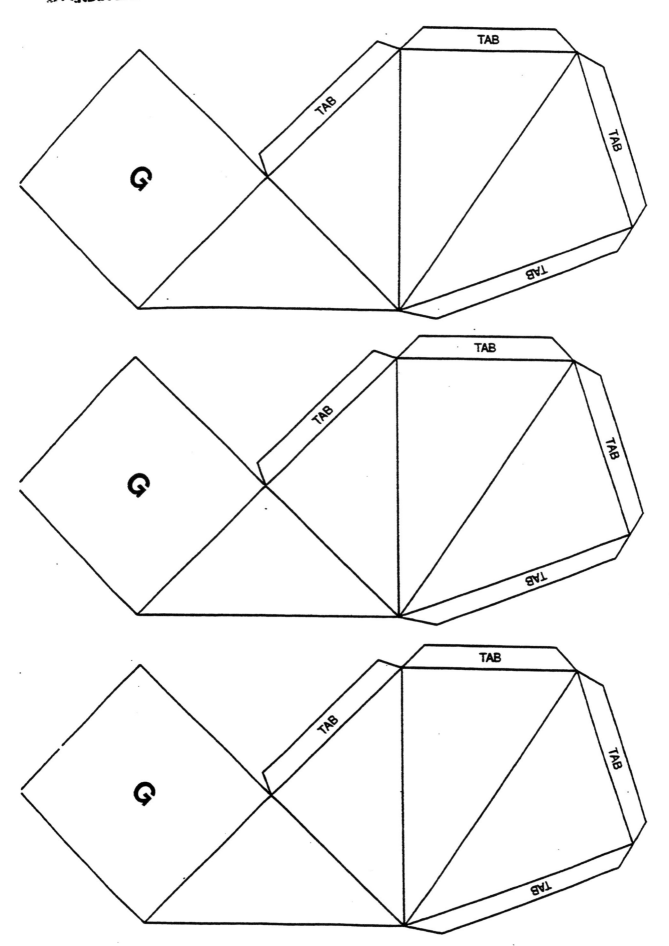

1	2	3	4	5	6	7	8	9	10
11	12	13	14	15	16	17	18	19	20
21	22	23	24	25	26	27	28	29	30
31	32	33	34	35	36	37	38	39	40
41	42	43	44	45	46	47	48	49	50
51	52	53	54	55	56	57	58	59	60
61	62	63	64	65	66	67	68	69	70
71	72	73	74	75	76	77	78	79	80
81	82	83	84	85	86	87	88	89	90
91	92	93	94	95	96	97	98	99	100

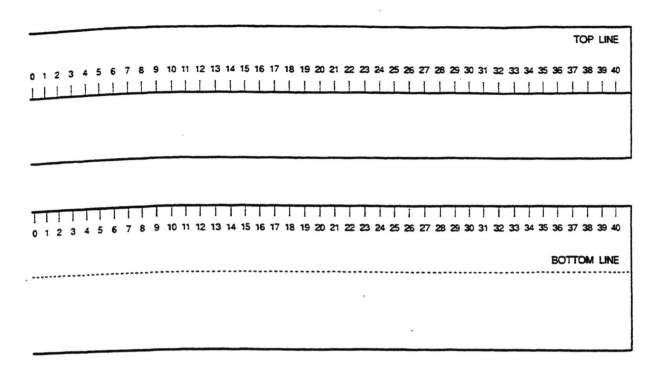

FIRST: Cut out slides for Top Line and Bottom Line.

SECOND: Fold back slide for Bottom Line on the dotted line.

THIRD: Place the slide for the Top Line inside the slide for the Bottom Line.
The Top Line will appear above the Bottom Line.

APPENDIX: Protractor to cut out and use.

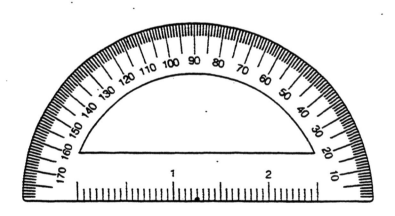

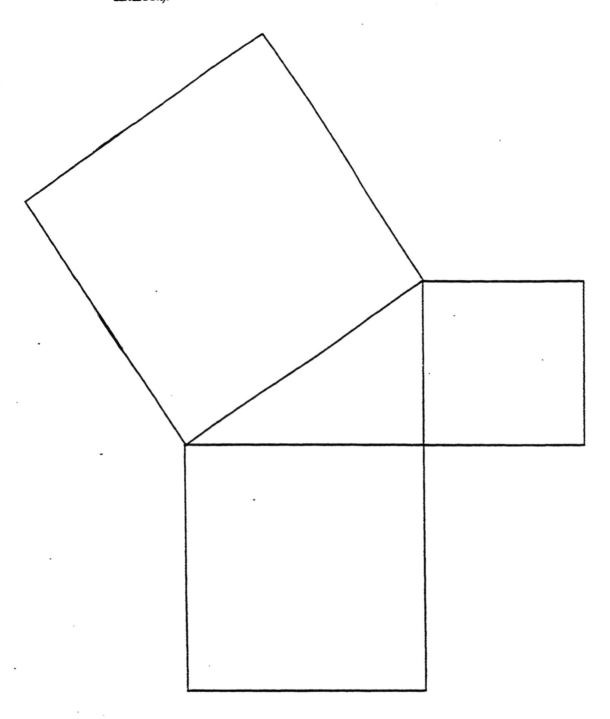

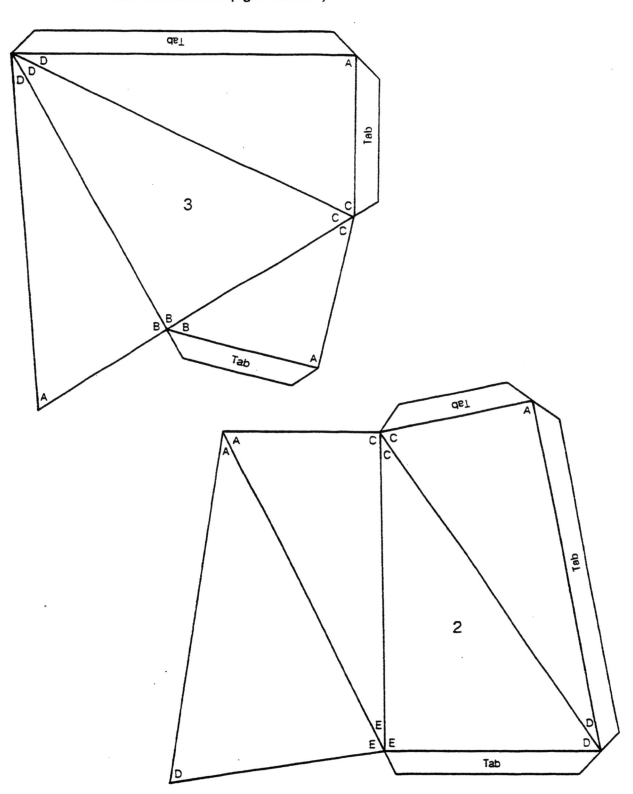

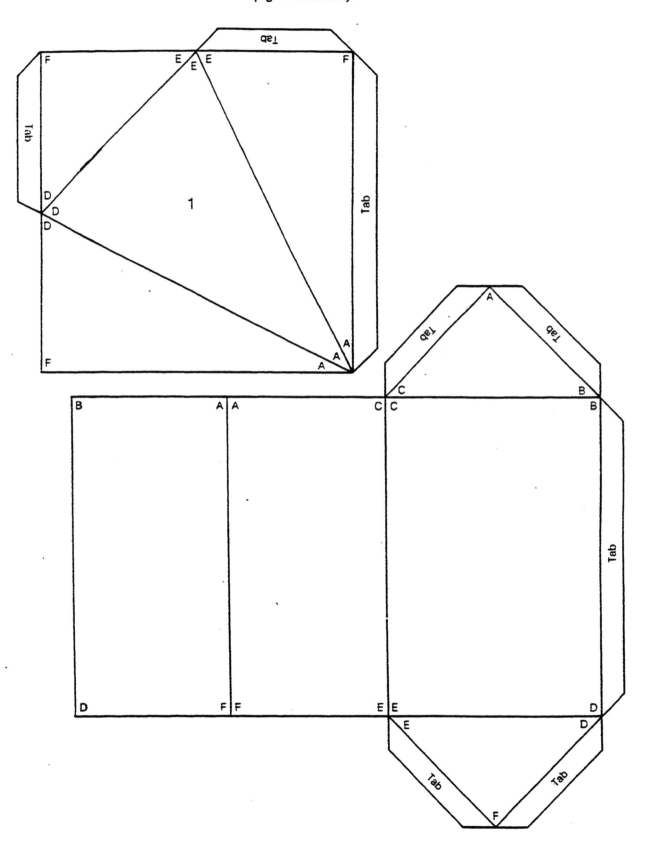

USING A SPREADSHEET TO SOLVE PROBLEMS

In this lab we will use a computer spreadsheet to solve problems. A spreadsheet is commonly used to keep track of business and personal finances. You can "give instructions to" a spreadsheet to get the computer to carry out several calculations in sequence. In this activity we will find out what some of the rules are for doing this, at the same time as we solve problems for which organizing data in a chart is a good strategy.

EQUIPMENT NEEDED

☐ Microcomputer.

☐ Spreadsheet software. This activity is designed to be used with the *ClarisWorks* spreadsheet. By altering the sequences of key-strokes, it could be used with another spreadsheet as well. (For example, the key strokes for *Microsoft EXCEL* are almost identical to those for *ClarisWorks*. We will point out where they are different.)

GETTING STARTED

After turning on the microcomputer and calling up the spreadsheet, something like the following will appear on the screen:

FILE   EDIT FORMAT CALCULATE OPTIONS VIEW   ✎[Menu Bar]

→ A1

Name of outlined cell appears here.

	A	B	C	D	E	F
1						
2						
3						
4						
5						
6						
7						
8						
9						
10						
11						
12						
13						
14						
15						
16						
17						
18						

What you see is evidence that a spreadsheet is basically an array with a large number of ROWS and COLUMNS. The rows are named by the numbers 1, 2, 3,... starting near the top of the screen and going to the bottom, and beyond; the columns are named by the letters A, B, C,... going from left to right. A box, called a CELL, of the array occurs at the intersection of a row and a column. The name of a cell is determined by the row and column to which it belongs; for example, cell C2 is the cell in row 2 and column C. By following a couple of simple steps you can fill a cell with a number or a word. At the moment, all cells are EMPTY; they are waiting for you to fill them. Cell A1 in the upper left-hand corner is particularly ready: it is outlined and should stand out. You can change the outlined cell by moving the arrow keys on your key board. Do this now. *Use your arrows keys to make C3 the outlined cell.*

There is another way to outline a cell. Near your keyboard you will notice a device called a MOUSE. You will also notice an arrow or a cross somewhere on the screen — an arrow if it appears above the array of rows and columns, a cross otherwise. You can change the position of the arrow/cross by moving the mouse around on the foam rubber mat (called a MOUSE PAD) lying under it. Use the mouse to move the arrow/cross to cell B6. (This is called POINTING THE MOUSE at cell B6.) Then press the button on top of the mouse. (This is called *clicking* the mouse.) What happens?

You will also notice a row of words printed at the very top of the screen. This is called the MENU BAR. You can access an item on the menu bar using the mouse. Point the mouse at item CALCULATE on the menu bar. Click the mouse and hold the button down. What do you see?

NEW CAR COST COMPARISONS ON A SPREADSHEET

1. You are shopping for a new car. You have identified five cars you might buy. You know the dealer's price for each. You also know that there will be sales tax and license fees to add to that. Let's get the spreadsheet to calculate the total cost of buying these new cars. The cars and their dealer costs are shown in the chart below.

	A	B	C	D	E	F
1		Nissan	Ford	Chevy	Toyota	Jeep
2	Cost	13223	14550	10588	12200	14585
3	Tax 7%					
4	License					
5						
6	Total					

The cells where we want to enter this information is suggested by the labels on the chart. Let's enter the makes of the cars in row 1. To do this:

- Outline cell B1 (row 1, column B).
- Type Nissan. (Notice where this word appears.)
- Then press RETURN (or TAB or an arrow key).

What do you see now in cell B1?

(If you don't see anything, check with your spreadsheet expert.) Follow the same procedure in cells C1, D1, E1 and F1 to get the remaining car makes to appear in the first row. Similarly, enter the items in the second row:
- Cost in cell A2,
- 13223 in cell B2, and so on.

Finally, enter
- Tax 7% in cell A3,
- License in cell A4 and
- Total in cell A6.

Your spread sheet should look a lot like the chart above. (If it doesn't, check with your expert.)

Now let's have the spreadsheet calculate the sales tax on the Nissan and enter this just below its cost in cell B3. To do this,
- outline cell B3.
- Type =. (Don't press RETURN yet!)
- Point and click the mouse at cell B2.

What appears at the top of the screen, just above the array?

Now type * followed by .07. What appears now at the top of your screen?

The sequence of symbols =B2*.07 instructs the spreadsheet to take the number in cell B2 and multiply it by .07. Next, press RETURN. The result of the calculation should appear in cell B3. Does it jibe with what you get with your calculator?

2. Now let's calculate the sales tax for the other cars and enter them on the spreadsheet. We could replicate the steps we just took for the Nissan, doing them in column C for the Ford and column D for the Chevy, etc. With a spreadsheet there is no need to duplicate all this, one column at a time. We can do all the columns at once! Here's how.

3

Point the mouse at cell B3, press the button, hold it down while moving the cross to the right along row 3 until the cross reaches column F. (This procedure is called CLICK AND DRAG the cross.) You should see row 3 darkened from cell B3 through cell F3. Then point the mouse at the word CALCULATE on the menu bar [for *Microsoft EXCEL*, you want to point the mouse at EDIT on the menu bar], click and drag to option FILL RIGHT on the drop-down menu that appears below CALCULATE. Release the button. You should see numbers appear in all the cells of row 3, from column C through F. In one fell swoop, the sales tax for all cars have been calculated and entered! The procedure just described,

- point mouse at B3
- click and drag from B3 to F3
- point mouse at CALCULATE
- click and drag down to FILL RIGHT

copies the instructions for cell B3 onto cells C3 through F3.

3. Next, let's enter the license fees for all the cars. The fee is $100 for each car. Outline cell B4, type 100 (no $ sign, please!), then RETURN. What happens?

This enters the license fee for the Nissan. We could do the same for the other cars. But, again, the spreadsheet will do it for us. Use the following steps:

- point mouse at B4
- click and drag from B4 to F4
- point mouse at CALCULATE
- click and drag down to FILL RIGHT
- release clicker

What happens?

The license fees for all the cars should now be entered in row 4.

4. Finally, let's calculate the total amount of money you actually have to pay when you buy each car. This total is Cost plus Tax plus License. Let's do it for the Nissan first, then copy the instructions for the other cars. Use the following steps:

- outline B6
- type =
- point and click mouse at B2; type +

4

- point and click mouse at B3; type +
- point and click mouse at B4

What appears at the top of the screen between the array and the menu bar?

Finally,

- press RETURN

What happens?

Next copy the instructions for cell B6 onto cells C6 through F6:

- point mouse at B6
- click and drag from B6 to F6
- point mouse at CALCULATE
- click and drag down to FILL RIGHT
- release clicker

What happens?

(If your computer has access to a printer, make it print out a copy of what's on your screen to attach to this lab.)

SOLVING THE COFFEE BLEND PROBLEM WITH A SPREADSHEET

Let's utilize the power of a spreadsheet to solve a problem. Recall the following problem from chapter 1:

Max's Coffee Mill sells coffee by the pound. At the moment, Max sells inexpensive Costa Rican coffee for $4.50/lb and expensive mocha coffee for $7.00/lb. ..." Max wants to make a blend of the two costing $5.20/lb; he wants to have 50 lb of the blend to sell; he wants to know how many pounds of each he will need in order to do this.

To solve the problem, Max made some guesses and organized them in a chart which began in the following way:

5

Pounds Costa Rican	Pounds Mocha	Cost Costa Rican	Cost Mocha	Cost Blend	Target Cost
30	20	135	140	275	260

(Target cost = 5.20 x 50 = 260.)

He made several guesses in an attempt to get the Cost of Blend to equal the Target Cost. What we can get the spreadsheet to do is to fill in the table for all possible (whole number) guesses for the number of pounds of Costa Rican in the blend. To begin:

- start with a clean spreadsheet: point at FILE on the menu bar, click and drag down to NEW
- in the first two rows of the array, type in the column headings from the chart above (abbreviate CR for Costa Rican so the words fit in the cells)

Next, to fill in all possible guesses in column A, take the following steps:
- enter **0** in cell A3
- outline cell A4; type =
- point and click mouse at cell A3; type **+1**
- press RETURN

What happens?

- point mouse at cell A4
- click and drag down column A to cell A53
- point mouse at CALCULATE on the menu bar
- click and drag down to option FILL DOWN on the drop-down menu
- release clicker

What happens?

- outline cell B3; type **=50-**
- point and click mouse at cell A3
- press RETURN

What happens?

- point mouse at cell B4
- click and drag down column B to cell B53
- point mouse at CALCULATE on the menu bar
- click and drag down to option FILL DOWN on the drop-down menu
- release clicker

What happens?

- point and click mouse at C3; type =
- point and click mouse at A3; type **4.50**
- press RETURN

What happens?

This time you figure out what the instructions should be for cell D3 (the cost of 50 pounds of mocha — recall that mocha costs $7 per pound). What are they? (Carry them out.)

Next, figure out the instructions for cell E3. (The result should be the sum of the values in cells C3 and D3.) What are the instructions? (Carry them out.)

Enter the target cost in cell F3.

Finally, copy the instructions for cells C3, D3 and E3 to all the cells below them — up to cells C53, D53 and E 53. Take the following steps:

- point mouse at C3
- click and drag right to E3
- without releasing clicker drag down to E53 (columns C, D, and E should be darkened from row 3 through row 53)
- point mouse at CALCULATE
- click and drag down to menu item FILL DOWN
- release clicker

What happens?

Now go back and read the original problem and use what you have created on the spreadsheet to solve it! Write your solution below.

REFLECTION

Do you think you could use a spreadsheet to help solve other problems? Explain.

PROBABILITY LAB
MATH 301

The following activities are designed to give you experiences using probability. You will be instructed to do some of these experiments or play some of these games and make conclusions. Please thoughtfully record your results and use what you see to form conclusions.

1. Get a little bag from your lab instructor. The bags contain an unknown number of colored objects. These may be marbles, tiles, counters, or cubes (one kind only; the bags do not contain a mixture of these 4 types of objects). The bags may contain all of one color, or several different colors, and different amounts of the various colors. Draw an object from the bag and record its color. Replace the object. Repeat the procedure at least 20 times. Organize your results and approximate the probabilities of drawing each color. It is okay to estimate the number of objects in the bag by holding it, but do not count them. Once you have estimated the probability of drawing each color examine the objects in the bag. How accurate were you? Are you surprised by the contents of the bag? Why or why not?

2. Play the two games described below:

game 1. Let one player be 'odd', the other 'even'. Take turns rolling a pair of dice (random number generators). For each roll calculate the difference of the two numbers. If the difference is an odd number, the 'odd' player scores a point. If the difference is an even number, the 'even' player scores a point. Remember zero is an even number. The winner is the player with the most points. Roll the dice at least 11 times. Who wins?

game 2. As above, let one player be 'odd', the other 'even'. This time, after rolling a pair of dice calculate the product of the numbers. If the product is an odd number, the 'odd' player scores a point. If the product is an even number, the 'even' player scores a point. The winner is the player with the most points. Who wins?

Which of the games above is more fair? Why?

3. Play this game with a partner. One player is designated 'A', the other 'B'. Put two red tiles and two green tiles in a bag. Without looking in the bag choose two of the four tiles. If the tiles are the same color, player A wins. If the colors are different, player B wins.

Before you play this game, do you think this is a fair game? Why or why not?

Play this game several times and record your results.

Any observations or comments?

Now play the same game but with three red tiles and one green tile in the bag. Is this version of the game fair? Why or why not?

4. To play this game you need 8 counters for each player and a pair of dice. Two or more players can play this game. Each player should make a number line having all the numbers between and including 2 and 12. Make the number line large enough so the counters will fit on each of the numbers. Each player now places her/his eight counters on their number line, wherever they want. Players take turns rolling the pair of dice. On each roll a player can remove one counter if it matches the sum of the number on the dice. (If a player has more than one counter on the number that matches the sum of the roll, only one counter may be removed.) The winner is the first player to remove all 8 counters. Play this game a few times. Record your observations below.

Why does your number line need only the numbers 2 to 12?

What do you think a winning strategy is? Explain your thinking.

5. Find a partner to play with. Decide who will be player 'A' and who will be player 'B'. You will need a pair of dice to play this game. Each player rolls one die. Divide player A's number by player B's number with a calculator. Look at the first, non-zero, digit. A player wins using the following rules:

Player A wins if the first digit is: 1, 2, or 3
Player B wins if the first digit is: 4, 5, 6, 7, 8, or 9

Play the game several times, keeping track of how many times you win.

Is this a fair game? If not, who has the advantage? Why?

6. You need three chips (two red, one blue; each with an A on one side and a B on the other) to play this game. Find a partner to play with. Decide who will be player 'A' and who will be player 'B'. Flip the three chips. Player A scores a point if both red chips show A or the blue chip shows A or both of these conditions are met. Otherwise, player B scores a point. Play 15 rounds, and keep track of the number of wins for each player.

Does each player have an equal chance to win? Is this a fair game? What is the probability that player A will win? That player B will win?

MATH 301 LOGOWRITER LAB

The lab instructor will show you how to access Logowriter.

Part I: (Almost) Free exploration
Hopefully you are all facing a computer screen with a turtle at the center. If not, please ask for assistance.

a) Familiarize yourself with the commands given on the handout "Some Turtle Commands."
For example,

    FD 50   <Return>
What happened?

(make sure you leave a space between FD and the number. You can use capital or small letters, it makes no difference. Also, you could type FORWARD instead of the short form FD)
Now type:
    LT 45   <Return>
What happened?

You may want to record here some of your explorations and findings:
Keep exploring with the commands given in the handout. Be as creative as you want. There is no right or wrong way of doing anything here, just try it! The turtle has a very nice way of informing you when it does not understand you.

b) Communicating with the Turtle

Type cg, to start with a clear screen.

                    Make the turtle draw the word HI.

You can use the space below to write the Logo commands you used to have the turtle draw the word HI. If possible (that is, if your lab instructor is not swamped assisting students all over the lab), show your screen display to your lab instructor before proceeding to the next task

Part II: Investigating regular polygons
TYPE CG (and press RETURN).

a) Make the turtle draw a square of size 50. Record the commands below

Then type the following:

cg
repeat 4 [fd 50 rt 90]

What happened?

b) Make the turtle draw an **equilateral triangle** of side 40. Record the instructions below:

Can you do the triangle task using the repeat command? Show it here:

c) Teach the turtle to draw a regular hexagon (choose the length of the side):

d) Teach the turtle to draw a regular pentagon:

e) Teach the turtle to draw a regular octagon:

f) Use you previous work to fill in the chart below:

	Number of sides	Number of repeats	Amount of turn (angle in degrees)
Regular Triangle	3	3	120
Regular Quadril. (square)			
Regular Pentagon	5		
Regular Hexagon			
Regular Octagon	8		
Regular Decagon			

e) What is the relationship between the number of sides and the number of repeats?

f) What is the relationship between the number of sides and the amount of turn?

Part III: Some more geometric designs

a) Write a procedure to draw a **square inside a square** (the two squares should not touch). Record here how you did it:

b) **Draw a rectangle** (which is not a square) of perimeter 104 (turtle steps, of course). Record below your procedure:

c) **Write** procedures to make the following designs:

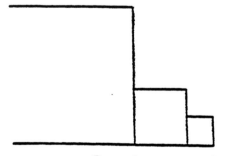

Record your procedures below:

Extension: Teaching the turtle

It would be nice to have a command called, for example, Square, so that when you type in Square, the turtle would a square. Similarly, we could have a command called triangle, which would have the turtle drawing a triangle every time you type it in.

Let's do it! Here is how:
You need to go to the flip side of logowriter (the flip side is where your teaching the turtle takes place). The flip side does not have the turtle in the middle of the screen. It is a text page where you type the procedures that you want your turtle to learn.

On the MAC: CLICK on the F/F on the upper right corner of your page.

```
to square
repeat 4 [fd 60 rt 90]
end
```

Now CLICK on the F/F again. You are back on the graphics page. Type cg if you have not done so earlier. Then type square.
What happens now?

You have just taught the turtle a new word.

Teach the turtle to draw:

a) A small square (use side 30 and call it ssqu)

    to ssqu

b) A large square (use side 100 and call it lsqu)

    to lsqu

c) A regular hexagon (use side 50)

    to hexagon

INTRODUCTION TO LOGOWRITER

Some Turtle Commands

These are just some of the very basic graphic commands that are going to allow you to do quite a few nice designs. All you need is a willingness to try different things. EXPLORE, PLAY AROUND, that's the best way to learn about logowriter.

cg   this command clears the graphics page and puts the turtle back in the center of the screen.

home   puts the turtle back to its original position (i.e., in the center of the screen, pointing up). This command does not erase anything from your graphics page.

ht   Hides the turtle.

st   Shows the turtle.

pu   Pen up. It allows you to move the turtle around without drawing.

pd   Pen down. It reverses the effect of pu.

fd   YOU NEED TO WRITE A NUMBER AFTER FD; that number will be how many steps you want the turtle to move forward. For example, FD 40 ---> means move the turtle 40 turtle steps forward. (You need a space between FD and the number) (you can also type FORWARD 40)

bk   moves the turtle backwards as many steps as you tell it to. For example, BK 30 (or BACK 30).

rt   turns the turtle to the right by as many degrees as you tell it to. For example, RT 45 (or RIGHT 45).

lt   turns the turtle to the left by as many degrees as you tell it to. For example, LT 60 (or LEFT 60).

repeat   this command repeats the commands in the brackets as many times as specified. For example, repeat 5 [fd 20 rt 15].

label: this command allows you to label your designs on the graphics page. It will put it wherever you place the turtle. For example, label [this is a square]

setsh: sets the turtle shape. Children seem to really like this feature. You have a whole set of different shapes that you can change the turtle into and you can also define your own shapes. For example, try typing setsh 15, or setsh 20, setsh 4. (some of these may give you a dot on the screen or even nothing ---> this means that this space is available for you to define your own shape). Setsh 0 returns you to the turtle.

Why I don't recommend changing shapes: The turtle is the only one that you see turning when you type rt or lt. From a geometric point of view, I think that you loose a lot in the learning experience if you cannot see the turtle turn.

Using color

setc   sets the color of the turtle and its pen. There are several colors available depending on the type of computer you have. Each color is designated by a number. Thus, to change the pen color, you would type something like: setc 5, or setc 15, or setc 100. To go back to the original color: setc 1. Be careful with setc 0 --> the turtle becomes transparent, and well, go ahead and try it out.

setbg   sets the color for the background. It works the same way as setc. For example, setbg 5, setbg 10. To go back to original background it is either setbg 0.

fill   this commands allows you to fill in a shape with the turtle color. It is somewhat tricky to use. First you must make sure that the shape you are trying to fill is really a closed shapes. Then you have to move the turtle inside the shape but by lifting the pen. So, first you do pu, then you move the turtle inside, and then you put the pen down (pd), change the turtle color (if you have not yet done so) to the color you want, and then type fill.

Using Cartesian Coordinates

Yes, you can place the turtle as if you were on a grid. The X axis goes from (-140, 0) to (139, 0). The Y axis goes from (0, -89) to (0, 90). When you type cg or home, the turtle gets back to (0, 0).

setpos [x y]   will place the turtle at the point (x, y) on the screen.
For example, setpos [100 20].

setx   sets the turtle's x-coordinate. For example, setx -100

sety   sets the turtle's y-coordinate.

print pos   will give you the coordinates of the turtle's position.

seth   sets the turtle's heading to the specified direction (degrees). For example, seth 30. (We will see an application of this command later on, under recursion.)